SKULL SHAPES AND THE MAP

PAPERS OF THE PEABODY MUSEUM OF ARCHAEOLOGY AND ETHNOLOGY
HARVARD UNIVERSITY, CAMBRIDGE, MASSACHUSETTS, U.S.A.
VOLUME 79

SKULL SHAPES AND THE MAP

Craniometric Analyses
In the Dispersion of Modern Homo

W. W. Howells

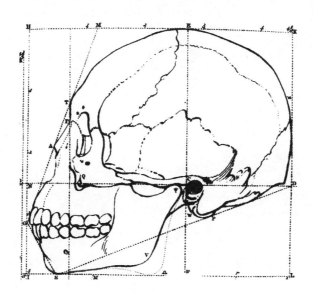

PEABODY MUSEUM OF ARCHAEOLOGY AND ETHNOLOGY
HARVARD UNIVERSITY, CAMBRIDGE, MASSACHUSETTS
1989
DISTRIBUTED BY HARVARD UNIVERSITY PRESS

© 1989 BY THE PRESIDENT AND FELLOWS OF HARVARD COLLEGE

ISBN 0-87365-205-3

LIBRARY OF CONGRESS CATALOG CARD NUMBER 89-63741

PRINTED IN THE UNITED STATES OF AMERICA

Preface

This is a survey of present-day regional skull shapes, viewed in a special way. From 28 good-sized cranial samples (26 in the female series), 18 were selected in order to represent six main geographic areas by using 3 independent series from each area. Fifty-seven measurements, taken on all individuals, were standardized to control size within each sex and to make shape comparisons easier. Inspection at this point showed some special shape trends for each area: for example, Europeans expectedly show relative retraction of the alveolar region together with a prominent nasion and a face that is narrow and pulled back at the sides. Q-mode factor analysis and cluster analysis confirmed these limited regional distinctions.

Analysis also suggested that recent humanity is relatively homogeneous in cranial shape. Within the limits of the evidence no support is apparent for tracing the perceived distinctions any considerable distance into the past (i.e., to a *Homo erectus* level), and no distinctions of sub-Saharan Africans suggest that they are parental to other modern populations.

I hope that in my previous report, *Cranial Variation in Man* (1973), and in appendix A in this volume, I will have expressed the depth of my gratitude to all those who gave me access to their collections and were generous with help and hospitality. The visits my wife and I made on five continents and in the Pacific have been outstanding pleasures of my life.

I have tried before to give adequate thanks to my wife, as recorder and companion; for my earlier report Shakespeare failed me and I had to go to the Old Testament. I can only say that she wrote down something like a hundred and seventy thousand numbers with accuracy, patience, fortitude, and plain good humor. As I have said before, she disproved the theorem that dull jobs are best done by dull minds by somehow discovering how to read French novels with one half of her mind, while catching my slips and errors of order, as well as another person could have done it, with the other half. If she had not found such a palliative, while I was shifting a skull around and fussing over a difficult measurement, through work days which often ran well over eight hours, I do not see how she could have emerged with her sanity. No other kind of help could have made the task possible, let alone pleasant. Her work was the equal of mine, although only time has made clear to me how essential she has been, in a task spanning more than twenty years.

Mary Hyde did the programming, not only skillfully but prophetically: she saw clearly what I was attempting, and on occasion prevented missteps before I had even missed the step. Together we did much work which does not appear herein, but which shed light on the whole. She has been endlessly obliging, and has given me great confidence in the results presented here.

The collection of data was made possible by National Science Foundation grants GS-664 and GS-2465. The original records and correspondence are in the Peabody Museum. The basic numerical data are also kept on magnetic files, and copies may be requested from myself or the Publications Department of the Peabody Museum.

SKULL SHAPES AND THE MAP

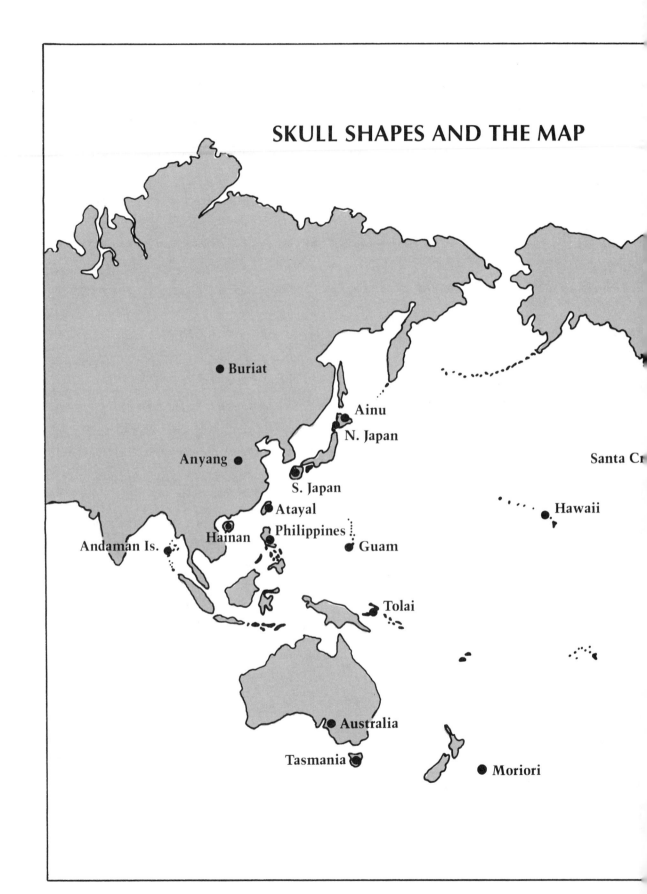

Contents

Figures

Tables

1

Introduction

This report extends my 1973 study, *Cranial Variation in Man*. It also analyzes the material with a different method and point of view. The earlier study was based on 17 cranial series, chosen worldwide but not ideally covering recent humanity (Asia in particular was hardly represented). The analysis was addressed to the general question of loci of variation in the skull, as expressed in measurements and as elicited by multiple discriminant functions and by factor analysis. In these terms the general kinds of variation between populations seemed to be extensions of those within populations.

The present work is addressed instead to a search for specific distinctions between the populations of different major regions. This is of course analogous to the idea of "racial" differences of past anthropology, but on an objective and systematic basis, not on one of typology. The hope is to arrive at valid comparative descriptions of the several populations, such as might be useful in problems of the origins of recent humanity in general.

Carleton Coon, in *The Origin of Races* (1962), postulated five Old World geographic human subspecies, becoming mutually distinct at the level of *Homo erectus*, and all evolving in parallel to the present: Caucasoid, Congoid, Capoid (the Khoisan stem), Mongoloid, and Australoid. In *The Living Races of Man* (Coon 1965) he inventoried modern variation. Throughout, Coon presented a large amount of descriptive data, metric and non-metric. He did not—would

not have been able to from the published material then available—arrive at an overarching systematic comparison, stating how like or unlike his various divisions were, in terms common to all. That, within the limited sphere of cranial measurements, is what I attempt here.

Included in the present total of 28 series (26 in the females) are six sets of 3 each which were chosen to represent main geographic regions. Four correspond with Coon's areas: Europeans, Africans (sub-Saharan), Far Easterners (Japanese, Chinese), and Australo-Melanesians. I add two New World regions: Polynesia and the Americas. I do not want to prejudge the coherence of these population groupings by referring to them as "Caucasoid," and so on.

Nevertheless, such possible cohesion is the central question. Is each of these six geographic population complexes marked by any characteristics or emphases which distinguish it from the others? Are such characters likely to reflect very ancient separations among the regional groups? Is there evidence of recent microevolution within and between them? We know that the three peoples of the Polynesian group herein have been mutually separated only within the last 2 millennia, the American groups for anything up to 12 to 15 millennia, and the Australo-Melanesians for about twice as long. But Coon was dealing with a time span of 100 millennia and beyond. What are we thinking of when we consider existing cranial distinctions?

MATERIAL

The 18 series just referred to were meant to form a sort of central core to establish a range of modern cranial variation; unfortunately there are lacunae like India and much of Western Asia. There are 10 additional series (8 female) which I might call "non-core," meaning that they are quite local, like Ainu or Guam, or that they have unusual morphology and so are less suitable to represent the main regions above, such as Eskimos or Bushmen.

In the total of 28 series, the additions to the original 17 have been drawn primarily from the Far East and the Pacific, areas in which the earlier study was deficient.

The new data were gathered from 1968 to 1980, particularly during late 1969 on a trip supported by the National Science Foundation, grant GS-2465. Despite the overlap in years with the 1973 publication there was none in work; the earlier study was complete before the new collection began, and was published as it stood. The total body of data has already been used in a number of studies, by others as well as myself. This report is intended to present the basic material as now completed, with emphasis on comparative description and on assessment of the total intergroup variation.

LIST OF POPULATIONS

Europe

Norse of medieval Oslo. 55 males, 55 females.

Zalavár, Hungary, cemeteries of 9th to 11th centuries A.D. 53 males, 45 females.

Berg, mountain village in Carinthia, Austria. 56 males, 53 females.

Sub-Saharan Africa

Teita, tribe of Kenya, East Africa. 33 males, 50 females.

Dogon, tribe of Mali, West Africa. 47 males, 52 females.

Zulu, South Africa. 55 males, 46 females.

Australia, Melanesia

Australia, Lower Murray River. 52 males, 49 females.

Tasmania, general. 45 males, 42 females.

Tolai, tribe of north New Britain. 56 males, 54 females.

Polynesia

Hawaii, Mokapu Peninsula, Oahu. 51 males, 49 females.

Easter Island, general. 49 males, 37 females.

Moriori, Chatham Islands. 57 males, 51 females.

Americas

Arikara, Sully village site, South Dakota. 42 males, 27 females.

Santa Cruz Island, California. 51 males, 51 females.

Peru, Yauyos District. 55 Males, 55 females.

Far East

North Japan, Hokkaido. 55 males, 32 females.

South Japan, northern Kyushu. 50 males, 41 females.

Hainan Island, South Chinese. 45 males, 38 females.

For the **western Pacific**, a set less coherent than the areas above but all Austronesian-speaking:

Atayal, Taiwan aboriginals. 29 males, 18 females.

Philippine Islands, general. 50 males, no females.

Guam, Marianas, Latte period. 30 males, 27 females.

Additional local series:

Egypt, Gizeh, 26th–30th dynasties. 58 males, 53 females.

Bushmen, South Africa, general. 41 males, 49 females.

Andaman Islands, general. 35 males, 35 females.

Ainu, south central Hokkaido. 48 males, 38 females.

Buriats, Siberia. 55 males, 54 females.

Eskimo, Inugsuk culture, Greenland. 53 males, 55 females.

Shang Dynasty Chinese, Anyang. 42 males, no females.

These series, and the present locations of the specimens, are described in detail in appendix A. In addition, a total of just 600 "test" specimens were measured in our progress; these included rejects or leftovers from the above series, one or more crania from many other populations, and various Pleistocene hominids such as Neanderthals and Broken Hill as well as later protomoderns. A few of these will be put into play following the main analyses.

As I said earlier, the first 18 populations are meant to serve as a sort of core of modern humanity, distributed 3 to a region, to give some kind of central estimate of means and of intrapopulation variation. That is one way these samples are used here. This should not create an Adam-and-Eve illusion of modern "man" and "woman"; nothing more is meant than an ad hoc set of statistical figures. These 18 are used so that each major area has an equal number of series. The populations were also presumed to be non-extreme in size or shape; thus San (Bushmen) or Eskimos were excluded as representatives of their areas. Polynesians, however, do turn out to be consistently large, and some other populations also deviate from their area coinhabitants.

These choices bear little relation to the population numbers of the present world: India and Latin America are absent, while the extinct Tasmanians and Moriori are present. This is partly due to the availability of crania in museums and to the history of collection, these being major determinants of the whole study. But it is not due, despite appearances, to a penchant for exotica; rather, it stems from an attempt to cover the pattern of human variation reached by local differentiation before the European explosion after 1492, and before such populations as those of the modern North and South Americans had come to exist.

It also satisfies one aim of selection, that of using closely defined populations. At the outset, a primary consideration was that a series should represent a real population unit and time span, and not "Polynesia" or even "Greenland Eskimo." This was sought in order to give biological reality to the units of study, that is, to limit possible within-group variation due to environmental effects and to give plausible estimates of population means and internal variance. The effort has probably been successful, though varying as to closeness of origin. Many groups are tribal in nature, and geographical isolation must have played a role also, as in the cases of Berg and of island populations like the Polynesians. On the other hand, the Tasmanian and Bushman series had to be assembled from wide areas, as the detailed descriptions show.

CONSIDERATIONS OF SAMPLING

For the reasons given above, I decided in 1965 that samples of fairly large and comparable size should be used. (Knussman [1967], comparing Penrose and Mahalanobis distances, found them to be highly correlated only when using "large" series of 27 or more individuals.) In addition, I decided that the study should include both sexes, in order to allow replication of all analyses, and to protect myself against bias in selecting specimens of one sex only, when sex had to be estimated, as was the case with most series. I must say here, and not for the last time, that having the two sets of series, male and female, for parallel analyses is of the utmost importance in judging the reliability of results.

Primarily for multivariate work, it was necessary to use calvariums that were either complete or not so damaged that close estimates of a few missing measurements could not be made. (Mandibles and teeth could not be included, being associated with the calvarium in very few series.) Figures in the literature on a given collection may convey a false idea of the number of complete calvariums included. Accordingly, in making original plans and corresponding with colleagues over projected work, I took care to ascertain that specimens were known to be complete, or that the total numbers in a series were generous (about 2½ to 3 times the number actually needed).

From experience I settled on 50 to 55 crania of each sex as the desired and practical number. This was a fortunate choice, since these numbers could be met or approximated in the case of most of the populations, as the respective descriptions testify. The Peruvian series was ample, and an extra number was measured for testing purposes; in the Norse and Egyptian series the numbers could have gone higher. Tolais could have been extended from other collections, and the Berg series afforded a very small surplus. Beyond this, 23 additional series either provided just about the numbers desired or fell clearly short of them.

PROBLEMS OF SEXING

The problems of sexing are discussed at some length in my 1973 publication, and it does not seem necessary to repeat these or the standards of assessment used. Individual sex is known for three series (Zulu, North Japan, South Japan) from the dissecting rooms of three medical schools and can be inferred for the majority of Ainu skulls on other grounds. There are no female series for Anyang or the Philippines, due to special reasons. I assigned sex by inspection in the remaining 22 series (and in the test group). This seemed easy in some series and very difficult in others. In sexing cranial series, the certainty of overlapping cases and of misassignment is well known, and this was especially evident from working with the Zulu series, in which several crania would certainly have been wrongly assigned without the records of the actual individual. In other series, an accompanying skeleton sometimes made it clear that the sex was the opposite of that indicated by the skull.

For the present work, this is more of a statistical problem than one of individual cases, since the composition of the samples must reflect the problem of overlap. If anything, assignment of sex by inspection may increase the apparent arithmetical distinctions, if skulls of "male" or "female" appearance are segregated accordingly, since this would act to reduce the actual morphological overlap. This is probably not important: the limits of available specimens obliged me to assign "doubtful" cases one way or the other, regardless of overlap, thus approximating the natural situation. The older practice of forming samples of "male," "female," and "unknown" surely gave improper results. So even where numbers of specimens were ample I assigned sex, difficult or not, as I went along up to the desired total, giving way only in a couple of series to the luxury of picking two or three of what seemed to be obvious males and females to finish up the job.

G. N. van Vark and Willem Schaafsma at the University of Groningen used the series of known sex to develop a discriminant function, and applied it separately to all the series (the original 17 and the 9 new ones). As might be expected, this gave comparable degrees of overlap in each population, including those of known sex. I made a very few changes in my previous sex assignments as a result, in cases where the discriminant showed a very positive allocation and I had also indicated on the original record sheet my own grave doubts as to my original opposite assessment.

A still smaller number of corrections or changes was made for other reasons. Also, some additional cases could be added to increase the original published samples. Accordingly, slight changes from the 1973 publication may be noticed in appendix A, in the detailed descriptions, with respect to the number of cases in some populations of the original samples, as well as small differences in population means and standard deviations. All this currying and grooming may seem excessive, but I have felt that the purposes of the investigation deserved such care.

2
Measurements

Fifty-seven measurements were recorded on each specimen, and these are the material analyzed. The measurements are defined below, together with four additional measurements not taken in the earliest data collection and so not used. A number of angles not used in this study are defined and included in appendices B and C (tables B-1, B-2, C-1, C-2), which also list all means and standard deviations. All such basic data are present in magnetic files.

The following are minimum definitions, for purposes of reading the present study. They are insufficient directions for measuring, which requires landmark definitions and technical discussion, as noted.

GOL Glabello-occipital length
Greatest length, from the glabellar region, in the median sagittal plane.

NOL Nasio-occipital length
Greatest cranial length in the median sagittal plane, measured from nasion.

BNL Basion-nasion length
Direct length between basion and nasion.

BBH Basion-bregma height
Distance from basion to bregma, as defined.

XCB Maximum cranial breadth
The maximum cranial breadth perpendicular to the median sagittal plane (above the supramastoid crests).

XFB Maximum frontal breadth
The maximum breadth at the coronal suture, perpendicular to the medial plane.

STB Bistephanic breadth
Breadth between the intersections, on either side, of the coronal suture and the inferior temporal line marking the origin of the temporal muscle (the stephanion points).

ZYB Bizygomatic breadth
The maximum breadth across the zygomatic arches, wherever found, perpendicular to the median plane.

AUB Biauricular breadth
The least exterior breadth across the roots of the zygomatic processes, wherever found.

WCB Minimum cranial breadth
The breadth across the spheniod at the base of the temporal fossa, at the infratemporal crests.

ASB Biasterionic breadth
Direct measurement from one asterion to the other.

BPL Basion-prosthion length
The facial length from basion to prosthion, as defined.

NPH Nasion-prosthion height
Upper facial height from nasion to prosthion, as defined.

NLH Nasal height
The average height from nasion to the lowest point on the border of the nasal aperture on either side.

OBH Orbit height, left
The height between the upper and lower borders of the left orbit, perpendicular to the long axis of the orbit and bisecting it.

OBB Orbit breadth, left
Breadth from ectoconchion to dacryon, as defined, approximating the longitudinal axis which bisects the orbit into equal upper and lower parts.

JUB Bijugal breadth
The external breadth across the malars at the jugalia, i.e., at the deepest points in the curvature between the frontal and temporal process of the malars.

NLB Nasal breadth
The distance between the anterior edges of the nasal aperture at its widest extent.

MAB Palate breadth, external
The greatest breadth across the alveolar borders, wherever found, perpendicular to the median plane.

MDH   Mastoid height
The length of the mastoid process below, and perpendicular to, the eye-ear plane, in the vertical plane.

MDB   Mastoid breadth
Width of the mastoid process at its base, through its transverse axis.

ZMB   Bimaxillary breadth
The breadth across the maxillae, from one zygomaxillare to the other.

SSS   Zygomaxillary subtense
The projection or subtense from subspinale to the bimaxillary width.

FMB   Bifrontal breadth
The breadth across the frontal bone between frontomalare anterior on each side, i.e., the most anterior point on the fronto-malar suture.

NAS   Nasio-frontal subtense
The subtense from nasion to the bifrontal breadth.

EKB   Biorbital breadth
The breadth across the orbits from ectoconchion to ectoconchion.

DKS   Dacryon subtense
The mean subtense from dacryon (average of two sides) to the biorbital breadth.

DKB   Interorbital breadth
The breadth across the nasal space from dacryon to dacryon.

NDS   Naso-dacryal subtense
The subtense from the deepest point in the profile of the nasal bones to the interorbital breadth.

WNB   Simotic chord (least nasal breadth)
The minimum transverse breadth across the two nasal bones, or chord between the naso-maxillary sutures at their closest approach.

SIS   Simotic subtense
   The subtense from the nasal bridge to the simotic chord, i.e., from the highest point in the transverse section which is at the deepest point in the nasal profile.

IML   Malar length, inferior
The direct distance from zygomaxillare anterior to the lowest point of the zygotemporal suture on the external surface, on the left side.

XML   Malar length, maximum
Total direct length of the malar in a diagonal direction, from the lower end of the zygotemporal suture on the lateral face of the bone, to zygoorbitale, the junction of the zygomaxillary suture with the lower border of the orbit, on the left side.

MLS   Malar subtense
The maximum subtense from the convexity of the malar angle to the maximum length of the bone, at the level of the zygomaticofacial foramen, on the left side.

WMH   Cheek height
The minimum distance, in any direction, from the lower border of the orbit to the lower margin of the maxilla, mesial to the masseter attachment, on the left side.

SOS   Supraorbital projection
The maximum projection of the left supraorbital arch between the midline, in the region of glabella or above, and the frontal bone just anterior to the temporal line in its forward part, measured as a subtense to the line defined.

GLS   Glabella projection
The maximum projection of the midline profile between nasion and supraglabellare (or the point at which the convex profile of the frontal bone changes to join the prominence of the glabellar region), measured as a subtense.

FOL   Foramen magnum length
The length from basion to opisthion, as defined.

FRC   Nasion-bregma chord (Frontal chord)
The frontal chord, or direct distance from nasion to bregma, taken in the midplane and at the external surface.

FRS   Nasion-bregma subtense
                                          (Frontal subtense)
The maximum subtense, at the highest point on the convexity of the frontal bone in the midplane, to the nasion-bregma chord.

FRF   Nasion-subtense fraction
The distance along the nasion-bregma chord, recorded from nasion, at which the nasion-bregma, or frontal, subtense falls.

PAC Bregma-lambda chord (Parietal chord)
The external parietal chord, or direct distance from bregma to lambda, taken in the midplane and at the external surface.

PAS Bregma-lambda subtense
(Parietal subtense)
The maximum subtense, at the highest point on the convexity of the parietal bones in the midplane, to the bregma-lambda chord.

PAF Bregma-subtense fraction
The distance along the bregma-lambda chord, recorded from bregma, at which the bregma-lambda, or parietal, subtense falls.

OCC Lambda-opisthion chord
(Occipital chord)
The external occipital chord, or direct distance from lambda to opisthion, taken in the midplane and at the external surface.

OCS Lambda-opisthion subtense
(Occipital subtense)
The maximum subtense, at the most prominent point on the basic contour of the occipital bone in the midplane.

OCF Lambda-subtense fraction
The distance along the lambda-opisthion chord, recorded from lambda, at which the lambda-opisthion, or occipital, subtense falls.

VRR Vertex radius
The perpendicular to the transmeatal axis from the most distant point on the parietals (including bregma or lambda), wherever found.

NAR Nasion radius
The perpendicular to the transmeatal axis from nasion.

SSR Subspinale radius
The perpendicular to the transmeatal axis from subspinale.

PRR Prosthion radius
The perpendicular to the transmeatal axis from prosthion.

DKR Dacryon radius
The perpendicular to the transmeatal axis from the left dacryon.

ZOR Zygoorbitale radius
The perpendicular to the transmeatal axis from the left zygoorbitale.

FMR Frontomalare radius
The perpendicular to the transmeatal axis from the left frontomalare anterior.

EKR Ectoconchion radius
The perpendicular to the transmeatal axis from the left ectoconchion.

ZMR Zygomaxillare radius
The perpendicular to the transmeatal axis from the left zygomaxillare anterior.

AVR Molar alveolus radius
The perpendicular to the transmeatal axis from the most anterior point on the alveolus of the left first molar.

The following measurements, and relevant angles, are not used in analyses in this study.

BRR Bregma radius
The perpendicular to the transmeatal axis from bregma.

LAR Lambda radius
The perpendicular to the transmeatal axis from lambda.

OSR Opisthion radius
The perpendicular to the transmeatal axis from opisthion.

BAR Basion radius
The perpendicular to the transmeatal axis from basion.

The above definitions, accompanied by full discussion of instruments used, comparison with other measurements and definitions, rationale of usage, technique of measuring and difficulties involved, all appear (with the exception of the last four above) in appendix B of my 1973 report, *Cranial Variation in Man*. Much of the same may be found in the recent fourth edition of Rudolf Martin's *Lehrbuch der Anthropologie* (Bräuer 1988).

Several writers have made use of some or all of the above set of measurements and designations. Some have supplemented it with new ones, clearly useful in most cases; unfortunately, I am limited to the set I started with.

My 1973 report contains sections discussing at length my reasons for the choice and formulation of measurements, and other matters of approach and of handling the data. This was largely before the fact. G. M. Heathcote (1986) has produced an important monograph dealing with many such problems of practice and theory by direct testing (on a set of Eskimo-Aleut samples). He has introduced a number of further measurements and demonstrated their value (such as the fronto-nasal breadth, at the fronto-nasal suture). Like myself and others he had difficulty with the points where greatest convexity of the vault bones may lie (e.g., PAF, bregma-subtense fraction, and PAS, parietal subtense); he has substituted subtenses at specified subdivisions of the chords involved, as giving a better profile and a more definite location of points.

These are details. Heathcote also investigated the behavior of different subsets of measurements in distancing and discrimination, pointing to such influencing factors as redundancy, noise, response to masticatory function, age, and so on. He tested some opinions of others, such as the undesirability of using indices in multivariate work (I am one of the "others" here), and found that such use may in fact elicit valuable information. (My suggestion that accidental occipital deformation would tend to increase variability in curvature he finds to be contradicted in his own data.) I do not mean to review his admirable treatise here, but anyone starting a craniometric project will profit from it.

3

Size and Shape

In my earlier study (Howells 1973) multiple discriminants and factor analysis were used to compare and relate groups, giving only indirect evidence as to the nature of morphological differences. Other papers published by myself and others since then have also used these axes of transformation to plot or cluster the populations. But in such work much remains tied to the input of raw measurements: those selected, and the factors they determine. The populations are seen through the prism of combinations of transformed measurements.

In this section the main effort will be to see measurements through the prism of combinations of populations. This may sound bizarre, because of course the ultimate aim is always to describe the population differences metrically. But along the way (1) the populations will be used to modify the measurements in terms of size and shape, and (2) the correlations among populations will be used to discern the shape differences involved.

The earliest craniometrists tried to see shape differences directly from measurements, but the method became unwieldy because of poor control of the relations among measures (placing much reliance on the cranial index) and, in general, of the samples being compared. Inspection of means of measurements is still unwieldy, and, important though they are, these tables, together with the sample standard deviations, are relegated to appendix B (tables B-1 and B-2).

Instead, I attempt here to enhance comparability of both size and shape by double-centering the measurements of all individuals based on the means and standard deviations of the 18 core populations already specified. This uses, for each measurement, not the grand mean but the mean of the 18 population means (to avoid weighting by different sample numbers), and a standard deviation based on the pooled variances of the same populations. These are shown in table 1; corresponding tables were also displayed in the 1973 report (tables 45 and 47).

Z-SCORES. Using these base figures, in a familiar device all individual raw scores (measurements) are rendered into standard form, or Z-scores: the deviation of each score from the general mean is divided by the general standard deviation, so that over all specimens the mean is zero and the standard deviation is 1.0. (For ease in reading, all Z-scores have been multiplied by 10.0.) Thus, if an individual skull were an exact representation of the average of all the members of all the series, it would have Z-scores which were uniformly zero.

PENSIZE. A second skull, in shape exactly like the first but slightly larger, would have Z-scores which were all positive but otherwise identical among themselves. I have approached the size distinction simply by finding the mean of each individual's Z-scores and calling this mean figure PENSIZE. (This is in honor of Lionel Penrose, who first [1954] attempted to separate size and shape computationally. His "size" figure, however, is quite different from the one below, being based on the several measurement differences between two populations, not on the summed standardized measurements of individuals, as here.)

$$\text{PENSIZE} = (Z_1 + Z_2 + \ldots + Z_g)/G$$
(G being the number of measurements)

C-SCORES. The Z-scores are centered once again by subtracting from each of them that individual's PENSIZE, so that the sum of these deviated scores is zero. These newly centered figures I call C-scores.

$$\text{C-scores: } C_1 = (Z_1 - P), C_2 = (Z_2 - P), \text{ etc.}$$
$$\text{and } (C_1 + C_2 + \ldots + C_g) = 0$$

Now, in the case of the two skulls just imagined, there will be a difference in PENSIZE but none in the individual C-scores. (This whole procedure is not particularly original; Corruccini [1973] used a related device.)

The hope, of course, is to achieve a separation of size and shape, and to have an individual's C-scores reflect, not the absolute height of its face, let us say, but the relative prominence, or the reverse, of face height in the total configuration of that skull. Viewed another way, instead of having an index of two measurements (the original avoidance of size problems), each diameter or measurement is indexed relative to all the others.

TABLE 1
Generalized Means and Standard Deviations (Based on Groups 1–18)

		Mean of Means		S.D. on Pooled Within-Group Variances	
		Males	*Females*	*Males*	*Females*
Glab-Occip Length	(GOL)	183.60	174.71	5.69	5.61
Nasio-Occip Length	(NOL)	180.75	172.86	5.52	5.49
Bas-Nasion Length	(BNL)	101.70	96.44	3.90	3.66
Bas-Bregma Height	(BBH)	134.33	128.43	4.88	4.43
Max Cranial Breadth	(XCB)	138.47	133.64	4.72	4.53
Max Frontal Breadth	(XFB)	115.13	110.79	4.59	4.38
Bistephanic Breadth	(STB)	110.42	107.47	6.02	5.39
Bizygomatic Breadth	(ZYB)	135.19	125.72	4.36	4.24
Biauricular Breadth	(AUB)	123.42	116.98	4.21	4.11
Min Cranial Breadth	(WCB)	72.17	68.75	3.58	3.29
Biasterionic Breadth	(ASB)	108.58	104.20	4.30	4.17
Bas-Prosth Length	(BPL)	100.46	95.96	4.94	4.42
Nas-Prosth Height	(NPH)	68.13	63.70	3.93	3.80
Nasal Height	(NLH)	51.41	48.28	2.74	2.56
Orbit Height	(OBH)	33.90	33.31	1.87	1.74
Orbit Breadth	(OBB)	40.16	38.64	1.53	1.48
Bijugal Breadth	(JUB)	118.49	111.40	3.97	3.77
Nasal Breadth	(NLB)	26.95	25.89	1.78	1.73
Palate Breadth	(MAB)	65.45	61.66	3.30	2.97
Mastoid Height	(MDH)	29.44	25.37	3.06	2.78
Mastoid Breadth	(MDB)	13.29	11.30	1.70	1.53
Bimaxillary Breadth	(ZMB)	97.38	91.89	4.49	4.05
Zygomaxill Subtense	(SSS)	24.22	22.79	2.66	2.58
Bifrontal Breadth	(FMB)	99.48	94.74	3.30	3.18
Nasio-Front Subtense	(NAS)	17.08	15.88	2.19	2.09
Biorbital Breadth	(EKB)	99.34	95.32	3.22	3.05
Dacryon Subtense	(DKS)	10.07	9.77	1.84	1.86
Interorbital Breadth	(DKB)	22.19	21.06	2.14	2.00
Naso-Dacryal Subtense	(NDS)	10.27	9.24	1.37	1.29
Simotic Chord	(WNB)	8.48	8.45	1.95	1.87
Simotic Subtense	(SIS)	3.42	2.88	1.03	0.87
Infer Malar Length	(IML)	37.70	34.81	3.13	3.02
Max Malar Length	(XML)	54.62	50.48	3.23	3.13
Malar Subtense	(MLS)	11.58	10.71	1.55	1.43
Cheek Height	(WMH)	23.37	21.55	2.22	2.08
Supraorbital Projection	(SOS)	6.54	5.20	1.18	0.98
Glabella Projection	(GLS)	3.76	2.49	1.06	0.87
Foramen Mag Length	(FOL)	36.58	34.75	2.33	2.21
Frontal Chord	(FRC)	111.52	106.75	4.27	4.24
Frontal Subtense	(FRS)	25.05	25.12	2.54	2.35
Nas-Subtense Fraction	(FRF)	49.97	46.46	3.95	3.48
Parietal Chord	(PAC)	112.90	108.11	5.45	5.43
Parietal Subtense	(PAS)	24.12	23.03	2.76	2.63
Breg-Subtense Fraction	(PAF)	58.32	55.82	4.59	4.15
Occipital Chord	(OCC)	96.97	94.44	5.12	4.79
Occipital Subtense	(OCS)	28.47	27.42	3.31	3.08
Lam-Subtense Fraction	(OCF)	47.48	45.29	5.49	4.87
Vertex Radius	(VRR)	122.99	118.19	3.99	3.60
Nasion Radius	(NAR)	95.00	89.94	3.54	3.38
Subspinale Radius	(SSR)	97.07	91.85	4.20	3.73
Prosthion Radius	(PRR)	103.54	98.42	4.56	4.21
Dacryon Radius	(DKR)	83.47	79.50	3.36	3.12
Zygoorbitale Radius	(ZOR)	81.34	77.65	3.47	3.13
Frontomalare Radius	(FMR)	78.44	74.86	3.36	3.04
Ectoconchion Radius	(EKR)	73.02	69.61	3.16	2.78
Zygomaxill Radius	(ZMR)	73.58	69.81	3.60	3.39
M1 Alveolus Radius	(AVR)	82.67	77.79	4.16	3.83

PENSIZE

The problem of such control of size is an old one, frequently discussed (see Corruccini 1973 and 1987 for reviews). Rao (1971) offered the following "intuitive" definitions:

> A size factor is a function of a set of measurements such that an increase in its value results on the average in an increase in each of the individual measurements. Similarly a shape factor is a function such that an increase in its value results on the average in an increase in each of a given subset of the measurements and a decrease in the rest.

The problem has actually never been solved in satisfactory fashion, and the use of PENSIZE is simply the cutting of a Gordian knot. Nevertheless it has a logic, without necessarily meeting the criterion of Rao's definition, as the figures in table 2 show.

The first pair of columns in table 2 gives the coefficient of correlation of PENSIZE with the raw scores, across the pooled individuals of the 18 core populations. This finds the highest association with "size" in major diameters of the "skeletal" structure: lengths, especially basion-nasion, and radii from the ear to facial points. Breadths are another matter. Those of the upper face appear to be involved with general size. But measures of the membranous cranium, including those expressing rounding of the bones constituting the vault profile, are poorly correlated with PENSIZE. This is not surprising: older craniometry often measured size via the "cranial module," using length, breadth, and height, but more recent factor analyses have separated size of the cranial skeleton from that determined by relative size of the brain (e.g., Howells 1957). Small measurements of the nasal region have low correlations with PENSIZE.

More important, the second pair of columns in table 2 gives the loadings for the first factor found in a principal components analysis of the raw scores of the same individuals, i.e., groups 1–18, pooled. (This analysis is not otherwise shown herein.) Such a first component or factor is commonly believed to be essentially one of size, and the high degree of correspondence of these loadings with the coefficients in the first column supports this belief and, conversely, supports the validity of PENSIZE as a size measure, not as a mere statistical device. (Where there is some disagreement, the high loadings can be ascribed to especially high correlation among a group of closely related measurements, e.g., the last eight listed.)

PENSIZE could be expected to be highly correlated with every raw measurement only if there were very little shape variation among crania, a case in which this investigation would not have been undertaken. That is to say, the mutual correlations among the raw measurements would all have to be high. In fact, in any table of such correlations some, like those between small nose measures and cranial length, are insignificantly different from zero.

Mean PENSIZE for all populations appears in table 3, which also gives the means of all the population C-scores. As the basis for computing PENSIZE and C-scores, the first 18, the core populations, were selected for world coverage but also in the hope that they would be roughly central for size in modern humanity. This turns out to be the case, except for the Polynesians, who are uniformly large. Within this set of 18 populations, Dogon are smallish, as are the Peruvians. Outside it, Guamanians and Buriats are large, and Atayals, Bushmen, and Andamanese are small to very small, as would be expected.

TABLE 2
PENSIZE as Size Factor (in All Individuals of Groups 1–18)

		Correlations, PENSIZE With Raw Scores		PCA[a] Factor 1 on Raw Scores	
		Males	Females	Males	Females
Glab-Occip Length	(GOL)	0.73	0.73	0.73	0.70
Nasio-Occip Length	(NOL)	0.72	0.73	0.70	0.69
Bas-Nasion Length	(BNL)	0.77	0.74	0.82	0.79
Bas-Bregma Height	(BBH)	0.56	0.52	0.53	0.50
Max Cranial Breadth	(XCB)	0.28	0.31	0.10	0.14
Max Frontal Breadth	(XFB)	0.24	0.28	0.04	0.09
Bistephanic Breadth	(STB)	0.15	0.19	-0.05	0.00
Bizygomatic Breadth	(ZYB)	0.65	0.62	0.62	0.57
Biauricular Breadth	(AUB)	0.51	0.48	0.42	0.38
Min Cranial Breadth	(WCB)	0.28	0.30	0.19	0.18
Biasterionic Breadth	(ASB)	0.39	0.29	0.27	0.15
Bas-Prosth Length	(BPL)	0.59	0.62	0.72	0.74
Nas-Prosth Height	(NPH)	0.46	0.43	0.40	0.37
Nasal Height	(NLH)	0.52	0.47	0.46	0.41
Orbit Height	(OBH)	0.24	0.24	0.20	0.21
Orbit Breadth	(OBB)	0.53	0.55	0.54	0.58
Bijugal Breadth	(JUB)	0.70	0.70	0.70	0.71
Nasal Breadth	(NLB)	0.34	0.31	0.40	0.37
Palate Breadth	(MAB)	0.45	0.43	0.45	0.42
Mastoid Height	(MDH)	0.29	0.23	0.25	0.15
Mastoid Breadth	(MDB)	0.45	0.36	0.45	0.32
Bimaxillary Breadth	(ZMB)	0.47	0.41	0.48	0.41
Zygomaxill Subtense	(SSS)	0.40	0.29	0.44	0.30
Bifrontal Breadth	(FMB)	0.61	0.64	0.60	0.64
Nasio-Front Subtense	(NAS)	0.31	0.38	0.27	0.35
Biorbital Breadth	(EKB)	0.64	0.68	0.64	0.69
Dacryon Subtense	(DKS)	0.27	0.32	0.26	0.32
Interorbital Breadth	(DKB)	0.27	0.28	0.24	0.26
Naso-Dacryal Subtense	(NDS)	0.18	0.21	0.11	0.11
Simotic Chord	(WNB)	0.11	0.14	0.04	0.07
Simotic Subtense	(SIS)	0.15	0.13	0.05	-0.00
Infer Malar Length	(IML)	0.44	0.47	0.52	0.56
Max Malar Length	(XML)	0.56	0.59	0.59	0.64
Malar Subtense	(MLS)	0.23	0.33	0.27	0.39
Cheek Height	(WMH)	0.45	0.36	0.42	0.32
Supraorbital Projection	(SOS)	0.32	0.29	0.31	0.28
Glabella Projection	(GLS)	0.36	0.28	0.40	0.31
Foramen Mag Length	(FOL)	0.26	0.27	0.20	0.22
Frontal Chord	(FRC)	0.56	0.58	0.48	0.50
Frontal Subtense	(FRS)	0.02	0.14	-0.05	0.07
Nas-Subtense Fraction	(FRF)	0.34	0.37	0.29	0.32
Parietal Chord	(PAC)	0.37	0.33	0.34	0.29
Parietal Subtense	(PAS)	0.11	0.08	0.06	0.06
Breg-Subtense Fraction	(PAF)	0.06	0.14	0.00	0.11
Occipital Chord	(OCC)	0.36	0.29	0.32	0.23
Occipital Subtense	(OCS)	0.19	0.16	0.16	0.09
Lam-Subtense Fraction	(OCF)	0.27	0.21	0.22	0.15
Vertex Radius	(VRR)	0.50	0.48	0.43	0.42
Nasion Radius	(NAR)	0.82	0.84	0.86	0.88
Subspinale Radius	(SSR)	0.75	0.73	0.85	0.84
Prosthion Radius	(PRR)	0.68	0.68	0.80	0.79
Dacryon Radius	(DKR)	0.78	0.78	0.84	0.86
Zygoorbitale Radius	(ZOR)	0.76	0.76	0.85	0.86
Frontomalare Radius	(FMR)	0.73	0.70	0.80	0.77
Ectoconchion Radius	(EKR)	0.71	0.70	0.80	0.79
Zygomaxill Radius	(ZMR)	0.68	0.68	0.79	0.80
M1 Alveolus Radius	(AVR)	0.69	0.71	0.80	0.81

[a] PCA - Principal components analysis.

ANALYSIS BY COMPARISON OF C-SCORES

It is possible to make simple descriptions of populations by inspection of the C-scores. These scores do not change relations that might be seen in raw measurements. But reading such tables of raw score means is stultifying, and the relations may be hidden. The C-scores do make a size correction, they do reveal shape, and they make the two sexes comparable. A few illustrations will help to demonstrate.

Mean male raw scores and C-scores

	Nasal breadth		Bifrontal breadth	
	Raw	*C-score*	*Raw*	*C-score*
Norse	25.42	−9.29	99.02	−2.10
N Japan	25.93	−5.65	98.00	−4.40
Dogon	28.43	+13.76	99.34	+5.05

Here the nasal breadth differences are highlighted in the C-scores, and although the differences in the bifrontal width seem minor in the means, the C-scores show that width here contrasts between Africans and both Europeans and Far Easterners (as will be seen later). The mean parietal subtense (PAS) in the small Andaman Islanders is about the same in absolute size as in the large Polynesians; but the C-scores in the latter are negative while in the Andamanese the value is +14.85, correcting for size and showing that PAS is prominent in the Andamanese conformation and not in the Polynesian.

Thus, scanning the mean figures for all the measurements, as presented in table 3, allows easier detection of those diameters in which a population, or a group of populations, is distinguished from the generality of others. The following is my own brief summation of such inspection, which may be checked from the table.

The **Europeans** here are of average size, and are not uniform in vault shape. The "brachycranial" or round-skulled Berg Austrians would once have been typed as "Alpines," distinct from the longer-skulled "Nordic" Norse; this is apparent at once in the C-scores for glabello-occipital length. Let us ask, rather, what are the traits that the European series have in common?

European crania are if anything rather low in the vault, but uniformly above the norm in breadth expansion of the membranous skull (maximum, frontal, stephanic, and asterionic breadths), although only moderately broad at the base (biauricular breadth). The Berg population is special in this lateral expansion, but it is clearly a general European trait.

European orthognathy—a generally retracted and on the whole a small face—is seen in many measures. Although the skull base, basion-nasion, is around average, basion-prosthion and the prosthion radius (PRR) are low, as are radii to most points on the face. The malar lengths and projection (MLS) are small. The facial breadths (bijugal, maxillary, nasal, palatal) are low, but the nose is prominent in general (SIS, NDS, the highest C-scores of all populations except Peruvians!), as it is also at nasion relative to the sides of the frontal (NAS).

In a word, Europeans share vaults which are relatively expanded in breadth above the eyes and ears. Contrariwise, faces are rather small, especially as to breadth, and the face is retracted, especially at the sides and in the mouth; but the nasal region is decidedly projecting. All this is familiar enough, but it is being stated here in a more precise numerical context of all populations.

Sub-Saharan **Africans**, by a similar reading, have a focal character at the frontal and the upper face. The forehead is convex (FRS), and supraorbital development (GLS) is small. The upper nose is very flat, with a wide interorbital space (DKB); the face is broad across the nose and eyes, where the sides are also swept back relative to the midline (e.g., FMR vs. ZOR). The face is somewhat short; the dental region is only modestly projecting (BPL) and is in fact rather flat across the muzzle (SSS), while radii to lower facial points are low; the supposed skeletal prognathism of Africans is not present. Elsewhere, the base is very narrow (AUB) by comparison with other main populations.

Two other African samples are Egypt and Bushman. **Egyptians** are generally like Europeans, with retracted faces and a low prosthion projection (BPL, PRR), with a narrow upper face, nose, and palate, and with particularly prominent upper noses. There seems to be no likeness to Sub-Saharans except a very low bizygomatic breadth and a somewhat narrow base (AUB).

Bushman skulls are very small, as PENSIZE reveals, and some of their features (e.g., basion-nasion) might be allometric effects relative to other Africans, although the low heights (BBH, VRR) are not obviously so. Although the San peoples have sometimes been viewed (Coon 1962) as a phyletic line separate from other Africans, here they clearly seem to share a general African pattern: very low faces and noses, but with the interorbital region (evidently not something that shrinks in proportion) maintaining its importance in breadth and prominence (though this does not hold for the nasalia themselves). In the cranial vault profile, frontal and occipital bones are decidedly convex.

Australoids, or Australo-Melanesians, comprise a single Australian tribal area, the somewhat dissimilar Tasmanians, and one Melanesian tribe, the Tolai. Here frontal and upper face differ from Africans: supraorbital development is marked and the frontal is strongly constricted at the usual points of greatest breadth (XFB, STB). The upper face is broad, as in Africans, but not the upper nose or interorbital space, and the prominence of this same region is lacking. The whole face is short—positively squat in Tasmanians (NPH, NLH, OBH). The projecting lower face is another difference from Africans (PRR, SSR, AVR, BPL, IML).

The **Andamanese**, dark-skinned, woolly-haired, steatopygeous, and very small-skulled, do not obviously relate themselves in these cranial descriptions to either Africans or Australoids, though they probably favor the former. They contrast in various ways with the similarly small-skulled Bushmen: they are not so broad in the nasal aperture nor low in the vault, where they have an especially convex parietal. They have wide interorbital and nasal bone widths as well as a prominence of the interorbital region (as in Africans) but lack flatness of the nasalia or of the subnasal maxillary region seen in Bushmen and Africans. Altogether the face is rather retracted, with relatively prominent malar angles, certainly not like Australoids.

All the remaining populations, from Siberian Buriats to Peruvian Indians and Greenland Eskimos, are grouped by usual consent under the rubric of "Mongoloids." But the heterogeneity among them is obvious from the outset, and the meaning of such a possible "family" is one object of this study.

We may begin with the traditionally "classic" Mongoloids (a concept I here abjure) of the Far East, represented among the core populations by North Japan, South Japan, and Hainan Island Chinese. For the last I would have substituted the Anyang Shang Dynasty had there been a female series, and I would have liked a Korean sample had one been available to me at the right time.

To these **Far East** series may be appended the Bronze Age Anyang males, who conform in every essential detail. The primary character is again found in the upper face, where there is a concentrated flatness. The lower margin of the frontal (FMB) is narrow and rather straight across (low NAS). In particular, the nasal saddle is very flat and depressed relative to the eyes (DKS, dacryon subtense), giving rise to the familiar sight, in the living, in which the eyelashes of both eyes are often visible in a side view. This is a general character of the crania of all the Mongoloid series herein, with the exception of American Indians. It is also a character of contrast with Europeans.

In other traits, the Far East series are high in the vault and high in the face, which is also somewhat retracted in the subnasal and mouth region but broad at the spheroid (WCB). The facial height seems to be the most important among these features.

The obvious candidates for immediate comparison are the **Atayals** and the **Philippines**. These do not depart from the above series in significant ways, and the Philippines especially appear to be a good match for the Hainan Chinese: in upper and minimum cranial breadths, and in facial flatness (especially in the very low naso-dacryal subtense characteristic of the mainland Mongoloids), as indicated by the generally low facial radii.

Farther afield the major populations are those of Polynesia and the Americas. In the past it has been suggested that both of these were composites of several "races," particularly including Caucasoids; it is now realized from population genetics and from the constraints of archaeology that these populations necessarily derive from East Asia, and should be studied as "Mongoloids."

The **American Indians** are not strikingly uniform, which is hardly surprising given the area and the time depth these few samples are required to represent. They share with Far Easterners a relatively broad sphenoid (minimum cranial) and palatal breadth. Also like the Asians, facial heights are marked, here including orbital. Otherwise the vault appears to be low; the base is broad, especially in the auricular region, where the zygomatic breadth is particularly prominent but the bijugal is not. The frontal profile is especially flat (FRS, something others have long noted among Indians), and the parietal is long, with the point of greatest curvature relatively far forward. As in Asiatic Mongoloids, the face seems relatively flat, or at least retracted, judging by the radii to facial points. However, the subnasal region is less flat, and the upper nose is prominent (SIS, NDS), in marked contrast to the Far Easterners. The Peruvians surpass Europeans in upper nasal prominence.

The Inugsuk **Eskimo**, being North Americans, can be considered here. They are emphatic in their particularity, which is doubtless not unrepresentative for Eskimos generally. There is no evident special likeness in conformation to American Indians as described above. In some ways they seem, so to speak, like Super-Mongoloids. Facial, nasal, orbital, and cheek heights are high. The nasal aperture is extremely narrow, as are the nasalia. Glabellar and supraorbital development is very low, as is height of the mastoids. All these things have been considered by numerous students in the context of cold adaptation.

A general extreme character in these Eskimos is that of facial flatness and forward extension. All the subtenses across the face are very low: NAS, DKS, NDS, SSS. The facial mask is produced forward (IML, XML), especially at the sides, as witnessed by the order of high positive C-scores: ZMR, EKR (the sides of the malars and orbits), FMR, ZOR, DKR, NAR (progressively less nearer the midline). The prosthion and subspinale radii, however, are distinctly lower, according with the general facial flatness which is combined with the forwardness.

The large-skulled **Polynesians** are diverse in some characters, notably in the very long skulls of Easter Islanders (longest GOL of any sample, and much the longest BNL). This diversity is important, since these marginal Polynesians are currently believed (by the authorities, not by the romantics) to have a common genetic origin within the last two millennia, showing us a time-controlled degree of cranial evolution.

There are uniformities nonetheless. A major one is conformation of the forward part as a whole. The moderately high face is forwardly placed relative to the skull (as seen in the radii), although the individual features are unprojecting (subtenses across nose and face). Rather, the whole face projects, but much more so above (BNL, NAR) than below (BPL, PRR, AVR). Also in the lower part, the palatal and spheniod (WCB) breadths are low. Thus the lower face is relatively retracted and contracted. The vault is decidedly high but not convex in the parietal region; this is less true of the Moriori, in whom frontal and parietal flatness is extreme (a Moriori divergence as marked as is Easter Island long-headedness). Polynesians differ from East Asiatics in narrowness in the least cranial breadth and palate but agree in marked flatness across the interorbital space and flatness and narrowness across the upper margin of the orbit.

Guam in Micronesia naturally invites comparison with Polynesia. The skulls are large and have the pronounced flatness across the upper face in all aspects, but these are also general "Mongoloid" traits seen in the Far Eastern populations. The lower face is quite different from that of Polynesians. The Polynesian character, of prominence of the nasion region relative to prosthion, is not seen; instead the special feature is a very marked flatness of the subnasal region, but above all the lateral extension of the malars, from the front (XML, ZMB) all the way to the rear (JUB, ZYB) and including breadth of skull base (AUB), which is exceeded only by Buriats and Arikara Indians. In fact, this malar ebullience strikes the viewer of the cranium. The Polynesian glabellar prominence and frontal flatness are not present. So Guamanians appear to have no particularly close relations to Polynesians and instead share mainly features seen in Far Easterners generally.

Two Mongoloid populations remain: Siberian Buriats and the Ainu of Hokkaido, Japan. Morphologically, the **Buriats** are extreme and isolated, like the Eskimos, in various ways, in some of which they resemble the latter and in some the American Indians, but in all being characteristically "Mongoloid." Their large skulls are somewhat short and low and are extremely broad, especially in maximum and basal breadths. Like Eskimos they are extremely flat across the upper orbital margin and the middle face; though the facial mask is not produced forward to an Eskimo degree, the radius to the orbital margin (EKR) is especially high, signifying flatness.

The **Ainu** exhibit no such distinctions, with vaults that in total configuration are somewhat long, broad, and high, and especially broad in the forward base (WCB). Face and nose are somewhat low, but broad all across the upper part (EKB, JUB) though not in the nasals or the interorbital space. There is a general though muted Mongoloid flatness registered by the subtenses here (NAS, DKS, NDS), and the malars are short from front to back (IML). The supraorbital frontal is especially flat. In many figures Ainus clearly depart from Europeans and Australoids, further nails in the coffins of two hypotheses of Ainu affiliations.

SUMMARY

From looking over the descriptions above it would be hard to say how many different significant patterns might be seen, and impossible to conjecture what a complete world inventory might be like if representation were fuller. There seems to be some coherence among populations within areas as here defined. This holds for some features which might therefore be seen as characters of those areas, but there is also distinct within-area divergence in other traits.

Is there any discernible "Mongoloid" character? There is a general facial flatness, most consistently in the upper part and across the interorbital region, and above all in the lower border of the frontal. Faces and noses are also on the high side, and the cheek height is uniformly positive in C-scores. Eskimos and Buriats are extreme in flatness, and extreme in some other ways which they do not share. If they seem like Super-Mongoloids, the Ainu are Sub-Mongoloids, being extreme in no ways but apparently not departing from Mongoloids generally in a reading of C-scores.

American Indians exhibit the facial height and broad skull base (including palatal and sphenoid breadths) of Mongoloids generally, but not the flatness across the upper nose or subnasally. Polynesians, on the other hand, do share the marked flatness across the upper face and orbital margin, but have a face that is pulled in below and narrow across the palate and spheriod region. Thus, Americans and Polynesians have quite different patterns, both of which seem to have "Mongoloid" affiliations. This illustrates the difficulty of trying to discern such patterns by a descriptive approach.

Europeans and Egyptians have a relatively expanded breadth of vault and a retracted and narrow face and palate, but with a prominence of the nose and of the glabella region relative to the sides of the face. Supposedly this is a general "Caucasoid" pattern probably reaching across into South Asia. Sub-Saharan Africans (Bush included) have narrow-based skulls but faces that are broad and flat across the interorbital region; this region is nevertheless relatively prominent with respect to the sides of the frontal. Australoids, finally, do not share these last traits, of flattish nasal region but curved-back upper orbital margin; however, they do share a very low face which is also more prominent in the lower part.

From this actually rather limited data base, it might be thought that Europe, Africa, and Australo-Melanesia each has a degree of special cranial character (one can hear the shrieks of "typology!"). "Mongoloids," however, would be harder to delineate as such: Polynesians and American Indians would appear to differ mutually as much as do Africans and Australo-Melanesians. From the above descriptions, would one dare to make comparisons of these recent populations with antecedents in the same area? Long-faced East Asian Mongoloids with short-faced Upper and Middle Pleistocene forerunners?

In fact, the recent populations included here seem, on another look, to be cranially rather homogeneous, with a limited dispersion of character into which some early Upper Pleistocene specimens like Dali, Ngaloba, Qafzeh, or Border Cave—or later ones like Afalou or Mladeč—might be introduced only with trepidation. This, I think, is a feeling my colleagues would share. What we have lacked is a measure of the degree of likeness among all the moderns, and a measure of the distinctness of the patterns considered above. The search for such things calls for more rigorous numerical treatment, which follows.

TABLE 3
Population Means of C-Scores

	PENSIZE		Glab-Occip Length GOL		Nasio-Occip Length NOL		Bas-Nasion Length BNL	
	Male	*Female*	*Male*	*Female*	*Male*	*Female*	*Male*	*Female*
Norse	0.70	1.21	7.86	8.18	9.14	9.41	-0.44	1.17
Zalavár	-0.30	-0.01	2.99	3.10	3.04	3.02	-0.77	0.21
Berg	-0.40	-0.53	-5.35	-6.92	-5.87	-7.32	-7.56	-9.08
Teita	-1.64	-1.46	2.34	1.48	4.78	2.70	2.95	1.41
Dogon	-5.47	-4.10	-4.88	-4.60	-3.59	-2.89	-2.75	-0.20
Zulu	-1.13	1.66	3.81	5.90	5.86	7.53	1.90	0.64
Australia	1.41	0.99	10.37	10.40	7.06	7.07	-0.69	-1.74
Tasmania	-0.19	-0.45	3.28	5.97	-1.04	1.44	-4.84	-4.08
Tolai	0.72	0.86	-0.86	-1.07	-3.82	-2.59	-1.23	-3.18
Hawaii	5.15	3.58	-0.39	-2.38	-0.54	-1.92	8.42	10.12
Easter I	6.78	4.26	8.22	6.51	5.95	3.52	17.77	17.67
Moriori	4.47	4.96	3.97	1.15	4.95	1.76	5.65	8.32
Arikara	1.43	1.42	-8.67	-7.83	-6.97	-6.22	1.47	1.53
Santa Cruz	-1.75	-2.17	-4.89	-2.34	-4.98	-1.64	-9.49	-7.83
Peru	-5.58	-6.02	-4.32	-4.15	-2.69	-2.60	-9.02	-10.00
N Japan	-0.08	-2.02	-0.81	-4.42	-1.08	-4.04	-0.45	-0.21
S Japan	-1.24	-1.66	-2.80	-2.30	-1.61	-1.29	1.85	-0.55
Hainan	-2.84	-0.51	-9.85	-6.75	-8.74	-5.80	-2.88	-4.14
Atayal	-6.19	-5.09	-5.34	-6.66	-5.35	-7.19	-3.46	-1.88
Philippines	-2.63	–	-9.10	–	-8.11	–	-5.62	–
Guam	5.44	5.05	-1.93	-4.07	-2.03	-3.51	2.92	4.79
Egypt	-2.55	-2.82	6.10	4.38	7.65	6.78	2.03	1.30
Bushman	-10.48	-8.64	1.29	3.30	2.05	4.06	-7.30	-4.40
Andaman Is	-12.28	-11.12	-13.61	-14.88	-11.64	-13.33	-7.81	-8.05
Ainu	3.90	2.85	7.31	4.33	7.50	4.69	8.66	6.67
Buriat	5.88	5.60	-9.33	-10.72	-8.99	-9.56	-5.49	-4.88
Eskimo	3.91	4.68	4.34	6.43	2.83	5.70	8.35	5.75
Anyang	-0.16	–	-4.41	–	-3.27	–	-0.91	–

TABLE 3. Continued.
Population Means of C-Scores

	Bas-Bregma Height BBH		Max Cranial Breadth XCB		Max Frontal Breadth XFB		Bistephanic Breadth STB	
	Male	Female	Male	Female	Male	Female	Male	Female
Norse	-6.03	-6.77	6.50	4.64	8.01	6.83	7.80	6.65
Zalavár	1.37	0.75	6.50	7.18	9.39	11.16	11.28	11.30
Berg	-7.95	-8.39	19.75	15.35	21.09	18.69	20.84	19.44
Teita	-9.16	-6.00	-16.68	-14.37	-6.64	-4.77	-6.25	-6.12
Dogon	0.96	3.35	3.35	0.70	3.75	0.19	5.87	2.52
Zulu	-0.21	-0.97	-8.10	-5.90	2.67	4.98	6.89	7.26
Australia	-11.07	-12.03	-15.23	-14.51	-12.38	-11.42	-16.47	-14.43
Tasmania	-4.44	-4.23	0.05	-1.49	-4.40	-8.65	-6.74	-8.42
Tolai	0.40	-3.62	-17.63	-13.42	-12.48	-10.15	-15.67	-13.58
Hawaii	14.74	14.77	5.98	7.52	-0.61	-0.86	2.61	0.35
Easter I	14.70	15.24	-14.08	-15.57	-12.71	-14.34	-8.53	-11.30
Moriori	-1.04	2.25	4.64	3.92	-8.53	-6.81	-11.05	-9.79
Arikara	-3.42	-5.06	5.09	4.84	1.40	3.20	-4.73	-0.58
Santa Cruz	-9.13	-7.95	4.78	5.21	-1.10	-2.55	-1.00	-3.76
Peru	-2.21	-1.92	4.47	8.86	5.81	8.95	5.00	9.30
N Japan	5.22	4.50	6.75	1.64	3.37	1.57	2.31	3.81
S Japan	9.45	7.12	0.88	1.80	1.21	1.13	4.19	2.10
Hainan	7.71	8.86	2.78	3.45	1.97	2.92	3.61	5.11
Atayal	4.52	7.13	0.45	1.23	2.15	1.13	4.69	2.88
Philippines	3.59	–	5.44	–	2.69	–	5.95	–
Guam	13.82	14.02	-0.51	0.97	-5.07	-2.20	-2.16	0.75
Egypt	1.34	0.53	4.14	7.07	3.28	4.16	6.66	7.13
Bushman	-13.68	-11.47	0.14	-2.54	-0.54	-0.77	5.73	2.24
Andaman Is	2.18	0.04	6.32	5.49	2.28	0.44	8.21	3.78
Ainu	4.77	6.27	5.61	4.79	5.94	6.53	3.84	5.41
Buriat	-9.54	-8.44	28.92	26.85	18.83	19.64	9.44	15.01
Eskimo	5.77	5.30	-13.30	-10.54	-10.24	-9.31	-17.98	-16.99
Anyang	12.31	–	0.82	–	-0.54	–	-0.19	–

TABLE 3. Continued.
Population Means of C-Scores

	Bizygomatic Breadth ZYB		Biauricular Breadth AUB		Min Cranial Breadth WCB		Biasterionic Breadth ASB	
	Male	Female	Male	Female	Male	Female	Male	Female
Norse	-2.43	-4.24	2.27	0.43	-2.80	-3.21	6.99	4.80
Zalavár	-4.72	-0.64	1.05	4.00	4.63	9.33	5.88	8.58
Berg	1.24	2.08	10.13	8.65	7.87	7.53	12.08	10.09
Teita	-7.84	-2.03	-12.59	-9.61	-10.87	-11.50	-7.81	-6.49
Dogon	-7.41	-6.95	-13.74	-14.26	-5.35	-5.00	-6.80	-4.67
Zulu	-10.90	-8.60	-15.91	-11.76	0.60	-0.84	-6.47	-3.81
Australia	2.21	-0.86	-9.20	-10.06	-3.82	-1.66	1.31	-0.29
Tasmania	1.64	-0.19	0.52	-0.72	-0.47	-1.83	1.79	2.36
Tolai	1.10	0.37	-8.75	-5.71	-4.39	-3.75	-6.84	-3.24
Hawaii	3.19	-0.85	5.95	1.38	-3.49	-4.43	-4.26	-7.29
Easter I	-3.47	-4.69	-5.64	-6.90	-15.93	-17.53	-6.94	-10.63
Moriori	6.21	7.13	8.65	8.72	-8.43	-8.96	-1.45	-3.32
Arikara	11.63	10.25	17.35	15.37	4.82	6.19	-0.39	1.47
Santa Cruz	5.76	4.36	8.38	7.89	10.81	8.40	9.01	7.56
Peru	4.98	5.74	5.79	7.44	3.99	2.69	4.61	8.55
N Japan	1.32	-0.71	2.58	1.16	10.64	11.69	2.29	1.76
S Japan	-2.50	-0.50	-0.09	2.42	4.62	4.71	0.12	0.42
Hainan	0.00	0.12	3.32	1.65	7.58	8.38	-3.26	-5.64
Atayal	1.32	1.56	5.11	4.20	11.79	11.42	5.80	7.94
Philippines	-2.03	–	1.54	–	9.59	–	-0.30	–
Guam	11.40	9.86	10.96	8.68	-0.51	4.03	-1.99	-2.33
Egypt	-12.05	-10.55	-8.84	-7.95	-7.33	-5.24	0.16	3.33
Bushman	-16.20	-13.05	-13.84	-14.07	4.41	1.10	6.30	3.47
Andaman Is	-13.79	-8.04	-11.63	-9.45	3.89	2.08	-7.06	-9.14
Ainu	4.70	3.09	1.63	0.72	5.94	6.38	5.11	3.17
Buriat	15.13	14.77	24.74	24.02	15.96	17.92	13.68	13.40
Eskimo	6.52	5.89	3.15	3.85	1.68	1.93	-1.40	-1.50
Anyang	1.90	–	5.54	–	5.81	–	-0.64	–

TABLE 3. Continued.
Population Means of C-Scores

	Bas-Prosth Length BPL		Nas-Prosth Height NPH		Nasal Height NLH		Orbit Height OBH	
	Male	Female	Male	Female	Male	Female	Male	Female
Norse	-7.78	-5.60	1.33	0.25	1.32	2.24	-1.53	-1.74
Zalavár	-6.59	-8.64	1.12	-1.36	0.39	0.83	-6.24	-6.99
Berg	-13.18	-13.16	-0.20	-0.02	1.51	0.32	-0.40	-2.65
Teita	5.67	2.19	-3.24	-5.79	-2.74	-5.79	-2.05	-4.56
Dogon	4.50	4.37	-3.19	-1.48	-7.99	-4.12	4.64	1.11
Zulu	5.02	4.57	-0.91	-2.42	-4.02	-5.47	0.40	-4.19
Australia	8.79	9.16	-9.96	-7.71	-7.68	-7.89	-3.76	-2.18
Tasmania	5.83	5.54	-14.10	-13.92	-9.09	-11.52	-15.35	-14.58
Tolai	12.59	11.75	-6.00	-3.33	-11.48	-7.44	-9.37	-6.99
Hawaii	2.73	6.02	-3.93	-3.44	1.80	0.74	1.06	1.08
Easter I	5.34	7.56	-5.71	-8.73	1.19	-1.14	-5.04	-3.10
Moriori	0.82	1.25	10.96	7.59	12.10	11.93	10.54	9.23
Arikara	-5.20	-3.26	7.63	8.91	9.68	7.31	4.21	6.14
Santa Cruz	-1.45	0.40	3.76	4.66	-0.83	-3.97	8.58	7.70
Peru	-6.94	-10.01	4.69	5.90	1.69	3.58	7.58	10.81
N Japan	-3.97	-5.45	7.29	8.48	5.16	9.83	3.64	8.30
S Japan	-1.07	-1.51	3.50	7.32	2.51	5.89	1.99	5.19
Hainan	-5.07	-5.23	6.80	4.97	6.29	4.55	1.23	-2.17
Atayal	-6.19	-5.49	-1.42	-3.76	2.05	-0.12	3.95	2.36
Philippines	-2.59	–	-0.81	–	2.81	–	-1.01	–
Guam	-3.34	-3.95	-0.86	2.56	5.23	5.71	3.13	3.16
Egypt	-5.43	-7.84	3.31	3.76	3.76	5.48	-2.55	0.07
Bushman	-3.29	-3.46	-16.54	-11.29	-17.47	-12.52	-5.98	-4.84
Andaman Is	-3.17	-0.42	-6.67	-7.47	-4.35	-6.69	5.92	4.76
Ainu	4.41	0.46	-5.50	-2.06	-5.55	-3.22	-2.58	2.47
Buriat	-9.10	-8.69	10.35	9.27	14.20	14.12	4.69	3.46
Eskimo	1.34	3.26	5.26	4.29	6.03	3.73	8.55	5.64
Anyang	-5.84	–	3.46	–	4.05	–	-5.81	–

TABLE 3. Continued.
Population Means of C-Scores

	Orbit Breadth OBB		Bijugal Breadth JUB		Nasal Breadth NLB		Palate Breadth MAB	
	Male	Female	Male	Female	Male	Female	Male	Female
Norse	0.75	2.58	-4.13	-4.87	-9.29	-11.06	-6.25	-6.44
Zalavár	-0.99	0.19	-7.15	-4.82	-8.63	-7.04	-3.63	-3.19
Berg	0.29	-1.25	-2.99	-0.38	-7.93	-5.25	-4.37	-3.03
Teita	-2.37	-3.82	-1.58	4.64	6.51	9.36	-6.51	-6.56
Dogon	1.52	0.68	-2.02	-0.57	13.76	14.49	2.44	2.53
Zulu	2.93	2.10	-2.89	-0.48	10.70	10.37	0.81	1.68
Australia	9.72	7.95	4.62	-0.16	3.83	1.06	2.93	2.29
Tasmania	4.22	6.43	-1.04	-2.00	10.95	10.00	5.15	7.37
Tolai	5.92	1.83	-0.42	-2.46	3.97	3.72	1.00	0.66
Hawaii	-1.72	1.76	0.57	-0.21	-2.67	-2.83	-4.14	-3.33
Easter I	-8.75	-8.78	-3.64	-3.10	1.63	0.42	-8.45	-11.68
Morori	6.74	5.98	6.66	7.08	-3.79	-6.58	-2.75	-2.42
Arikara	1.10	2.52	8.25	8.12	-0.61	-1.86	2.90	-0.03
Santa Cruz	2.36	-0.31	2.63	0.07	-10.30	-10.87	7.74	5.43
Peru	-6.85	-6.32	-0.41	-1.50	-4.03	-5.08	3.01	4.10
N Japan	-3.33	-0.84	1.00	-2.44	-5.65	0.85	5.43	6.11
S Japan	-4.37	-4.66	-1.21	-0.24	-3.53	-1.08	3.87	3.95
Hainan	-6.90	-6.50	3.84	3.29	4.86	1.30	0.87	2.81
Atayal	-6.10	-6.02	1.74	-2.44	4.15	5.09	1.07	0.43
Philippines	-4.68	–	1.80	–	9.98	–	0.84	–
Guam	2.86	2.41	10.02	11.36	-0.86	-1.42	0.56	2.09
Egypt	-1.76	-2.41	-14.09	-11.14	-9.36	-7.97	-5.44	-3.86
Bushman	4.66	2.09	-8.00	-6.05	11.72	8.80	-5.87	-3.84
Andaman Is	-4.61	-4.05	-4.49	-2.35	-0.27	1.05	-1.80	-0.83
Ainu	6.48	6.01	6.82	5.72	0.47	0.36	0.10	-0.81
Buriat	3.04	1.86	10.23	3.94	2.15	0.16	4.47	4.60
Eskimo	7.97	7.74	2.78	0.09	-22.27	-19.45	-2.42	-4.02
Anyang	-7.10	–	7.01	–	7.65	–	3.91	–

TABLE 3. Continued.
Population Means of C-Scores

	Mastoid Height MDH		Mastoid Breadth MDB		Bimaxillary Breadth ZMB		Zygomaxill Subtense SSS	
	Male	Female	Male	Female	Male	Female	Male	Female
Norse	-0.35	1.12	-1.66	1.58	-8.19	-5.52	-5.43	-4.06
Zalavár	0.53	3.40	1.81	2.99	-5.54	-4.44	-2.23	-4.25
Berg	-3.19	1.31	-0.67	2.15	-8.71	-5.30	-5.33	-2.81
Teita	0.79	-2.67	0.29	-5.07	6.19	5.74	-5.92	-7.86
Dogon	4.11	3.53	-1.37	-1.75	2.78	7.18	-5.36	-2.67
Zulu	-2.21	-0.81	-7.74	-3.77	-2.22	-3.54	-0.04	-4.89
Australia	-0.02	-3.27	-4.81	-4.55	0.74	-1.62	-1.73	0.69
Tasmania	-9.16	-9.97	-0.60	-0.74	-5.85	-6.99	11.16	12.22
Tolai	-3.09	1.94	2.72	1.17	-0.45	-3.15	8.00	6.76
Hawaii	-0.31	-2.93	7.22	3.12	-1.37	-1.70	-2.58	-1.90
Easter I	-4.68	-8.12	5.45	5.25	-4.90	-6.66	0.15	-2.09
Moriori	4.93	1.40	6.01	0.77	-1.09	-2.46	10.55	7.61
Arikara	-5.35	-3.15	-3.97	-2.66	7.06	5.81	4.73	1.83
Santa Cruz	0.05	1.33	4.88	8.15	8.10	4.04	4.46	5.49
Peru	7.29	9.40	1.52	2.28	4.53	5.80	-0.52	2.26
N Japan	4.29	6.42	-5.47	-1.57	1.83	1.75	-3.96	1.26
S Japan	3.33	1.11	-3.65	-2.85	2.53	1.93	-1.77	-2.44
Hainan	3.00	0.03	0.48	-4.02	4.66	9.04	-4.01	-5.09
Atayal	-2.68	-0.64	-0.59	-1.58	2.50	-2.46	-5.80	-3.98
Philippines	3.22	–	3.86	–	4.45	–	-3.84	–
Guam	-0.56	1.08	-4.40	-2.89	6.25	6.76	-10.41	-11.97
Egypt	5.00	2.30	1.55	-0.25	-5.36	-3.39	2.69	3.34
Bushman	-3.23	-4.88	0.73	-5.32	-1.07	0.94	-7.33	-2.71
Andaman Is	-0.45	1.88	0.65	4.69	2.97	6.45	11.56	10.17
Ainu	-2.27	-5.03	-0.09	-2.92	0.08	1.65	-9.82	-6.82
Buriat	-4.47	-4.86	-5.77	-5.86	9.59	5.89	-23.48	-21.26
Eskimo	-10.04	-13.14	-2.29	-3.08	1.54	-2.52	-18.24	-18.99
Anyang	3.93	–	3.91	–	7.84	–	-6.77	–

TABLE 3. Continued.
Population Means of C-Scores

	Bifrontal Breadth FMB		Nasio-Front Subtense NAS		Biorbital Breadth EKB		Dacryon Subtense DKS	
	Male	Female	Male	Female	Male	Female	Male	Female
Norse	-2.10	-1.65	7.14	7.09	-2.09	-2.73	4.24	5.48
Zalavár	-4.01	0.13	6.13	2.92	-4.79	-0.31	-0.18	-1.38
Berg	0.73	1.47	5.74	4.80	-1.59	0.10	2.25	1.46
Teita	3.21	4.05	9.01	7.86	3.12	3.89	9.63	4.95
Dogon	5.05	3.04	2.11	2.10	5.34	3.56	3.83	2.66
Zulu	8.71	7.78	4.58	1.19	6.12	6.05	3.21	0.27
Australia	7.51	8.18	0.68	5.53	6.79	6.26	-0.33	1.67
Tasmania	7.23	6.29	0.54	5.22	4.45	3.22	-0.07	1.81
Tolai	5.78	3.98	-1.98	-2.85	5.04	2.16	-2.16	-2.11
Hawaii	-2.44	-2.25	-9.54	-8.56	-2.74	-2.02	-7.97	-7.27
Easter I	-6.44	-5.23	-2.86	-4.21	-5.24	-3.80	-4.28	-4.77
Moriori	-2.62	-1.55	-0.11	-1.67	-0.56	0.03	2.85	1.43
Arikara	-2.73	-1.30	0.49	0.57	-1.96	0.69	0.13	1.20
Santa Cruz	2.31	0.46	1.20	3.31	2.03	-0.16	2.11	5.09
Peru	-4.58	-5.41	0.41	-1.39	-6.48	-8.85	-0.81	-1.03
N Japan	-4.40	-4.64	-12.21	-7.11	-1.37	-0.77	-8.57	-1.44
S Japan	-6.70	-7.97	-6.33	-7.67	-4.60	-3.71	-1.96	-3.13
Hainan	-4.27	-5.46	-4.62	-7.08	-1.67	-3.55	-1.64	-4.60
Atayal	-4.88	-5.63	-7.53	-2.82	-1.29	-4.51	-3.72	0.37
Philippines	-1.49	–	-3.93	–	-0.41	–	-2.41	–
Guam	-0.13	1.83	-4.90	-6.77	0.23	3.13	-6.37	-6.40
Egypt	-7.84	-6.76	10.20	9.07	-8.41	-7.82	10.67	11.13
Bushman	3.78	5.99	6.45	6.38	3.29	3.98	10.23	9.22
Andaman Is	-9.18	-6.23	6.18	6.38	-6.87	-4.53	13.60	10.67
Ainu	0.14	0.13	-7.02	-3.53	5.91	4.81	-4.39	-1.76
Buriat	0.43	-3.03	-14.70	-13.16	3.73	-1.30	-17.69	-15.58
Eskimo	-5.42	-3.92	-14.17	-12.09	-0.69	-0.72	-10.43	-13.39
Anyang	-6.20	–	-12.58	–	-1.56	–	-8.35	–

TABLE 3. Continued.
Population Means of C-Scores

	Interorbital Breadth DKB		Naso-Dacryal Subtense NDS		Simotic Chord WNB		Simotic Subtense SIS	
	Male	Female	Male	Female	Male	Female	Male	Female
Norse	0.03	-3.33	14.03	12.33	2.31	1.79	8.09	10.17
Zalavár	-3.32	-1.96	11.67	12.32	4.26	4.82	10.26	11.25
Berg	3.61	5.61	9.50	11.58	5.17	4.00	12.58	12.27
Teita	11.23	16.07	5.63	3.49	5.54	9.03	-11.55	-12.14
Dogon	11.65	9.96	2.26	2.68	11.14	10.71	-0.86	-0.06
Zulu	7.38	4.34	-2.56	-4.54	4.18	1.86	-4.01	-6.23
Australia	-3.74	-1.80	7.84	6.19	8.04	8.26	4.88	5.79
Tasmania	1.07	-2.12	4.22	6.91	-0.93	-1.33	0.02	1.88
Tolai	-1.44	-0.14	-1.91	-3.01	0.42	-1.10	-0.18	-2.00
Hawaii	-7.69	-9.19	-10.12	-11.64	-10.33	-9.32	-9.68	-9.31
Easter I	-0.99	1.25	-5.03	-6.13	-9.47	-5.60	-7.75	-7.06
Moriori	-11.59	-9.87	-4.65	-4.38	-11.62	-10.61	-6.76	-3.53
Arikara	-6.43	-5.98	1.12	0.46	-0.99	-0.86	6.64	5.39
Santa Cruz	0.86	0.79	4.78	0.76	-2.93	-5.95	2.01	1.25
Peru	0.61	-2.10	6.53	8.39	8.51	7.09	15.20	15.82
N Japan	-2.16	-1.57	-17.79	-11.02	-6.17	-3.27	-7.32	-7.74
S Japan	-1.99	-0.23	-15.75	-13.86	-7.83	-4.93	-8.78	-8.62
Hainan	2.68	-0.05	-10.47	-10.15	1.06	-4.61	-1.93	-7.19
Atayal	7.24	2.57	-6.34	-4.12	2.23	2.00	0.65	-0.13
Philippines	4.54	–	-10.13	–	0.82	–	-1.93	–
Guam	-7.11	-5.16	-10.09	-12.96	-7.63	-9.42	-11.71	-10.93
Egypt	-3.66	-2.30	14.15	15.62	10.01	11.59	14.50	15.03
Bushman	8.34	12.01	-7.67	-5.61	2.44	1.82	-10.40	-9.72
Andaman Is	8.05	9.97	7.81	8.37	10.90	13.76	1.69	2.98
Ainu	-5.95	-5.26	-4.04	-2.87	-2.66	-4.85	-1.66	-4.01
Buriat	-7.96	-11.55	-15.67	-13.94	-7.78	-7.48	-12.08	-11.05
Eskimo	-20.77	-23.63	-9.46	-11.07	-16.41	-19.83	-12.13	-15.95
Anyang	1.38	–	-17.43	–	-3.42	–	-10.09	–

TABLE 3. Continued.
Population Means of C-Scores

	Infer Malar Length IML		Max Malar Length XML		Malar Subtense MLS		Cheek Height WMH	
	Male	Female	Male	Female	Male	Female	Male	Female
Norse	-2.65	-3.77	1.38	-0.48	-3.86	-3.51	3.04	2.35
Zalavár	-5.68	-7.52	-4.01	-6.48	-5.65	-6.84	-0.35	-2.09
Berg	-6.01	-6.52	-2.56	-3.04	-6.35	-6.30	-0.62	-1.65
Teita	4.83	11.23	0.28	3.63	3.77	2.66	-3.31	-5.11
Dogon	5.21	2.38	1.45	-1.23	8.88	6.95	-4.25	-3.62
Zulu	2.90	2.28	-1.85	-0.28	2.32	4.64	-10.78	-8.79
Australia	9.09	6.33	0.84	-1.09	-2.80	-2.96	-11.23	-10.98
Tasmania	7.27	4.94	0.34	-0.40	-1.55	-1.03	-9.19	-9.97
Tolai	10.69	10.56	4.93	5.88	-1.12	0.66	-2.63	-3.68
Hawaii	-0.30	0.56	-3.31	0.29	-2.94	0.60	4.14	5.64
Easter I	-0.40	6.84	-0.24	4.47	-2.34	2.70	2.78	0.75
Moriori	-1.82	-1.54	-0.69	2.21	-7.08	-6.77	3.44	2.38
Arikara	0.52	-1.28	2.62	-0.83	-1.17	-1.47	3.35	1.98
Santa Cruz	-2.88	0.27	0.43	1.95	3.95	3.65	2.55	0.28
Peru	-1.31	-4.01	-0.72	-1.89	-1.93	-1.89	10.47	8.44
N Japan	-7.56	-9.87	-0.54	-2.20	5.74	-0.99	0.55	4.78
S Japan	-8.87	-7.57	-1.61	-3.53	4.86	1.81	1.91	3.93
Hainan	-3.24	-3.21	3.12	3.01	7.13	7.90	9.79	14.93
Atayal	-3.88	0.39	-1.16	0.37	9.80	8.69	-3.10	-3.68
Philippines	-2.62	–	-2.88	–	6.77	–	0.96	–
Guam	2.77	-0.13	9.65	8.31	2.88	5.82	4.31	9.57
Egypt	-4.66	-6.99	-5.45	-6.60	-2.21	-2.42	-1.22	-5.44
Bushman	-0.65	-3.50	-3.73	-4.61	10.04	7.81	-0.54	0.41
Andaman Is	6.56	7.50	1.70	3.21	11.30	8.95	-1.89	-3.18
Ainu	-10.60	-11.37	-6.46	-9.16	-1.45	-4.69	-1.53	0.20
Buriat	-6.43	-6.99	4.63	5.10	1.54	0.33	19.34	20.22
Eskimo	8.45	6.24	10.68	5.10	3.93	2.07	7.35	7.26
Anyang	-5.05	–	0.96	–	7.18	–	14.05	–

TABLE 3. Continued.
Population Means of C-Scores

	Supraorbital Projection SOS		Glabella Projection GLS		Foramen Mag Length FOL		Frontal Chord FRC	
	Male	*Female*	*Male*	*Female*	*Male*	*Female*	*Male*	*Female*
Norse	-2.80	-0.28	-5.46	-7.26	-0.93	-0.98	3.06	1.69
Zalavár	1.80	2.50	-4.19	-3.83	3.00	1.95	3.06	1.70
Berg	2.03	1.19	-1.20	-0.76	10.72	7.23	-0.69	-0.70
Teita	0.91	-0.97	-19.23	-16.81	-0.59	0.15	-4.62	-0.96
Dogon	-3.40	-7.91	-9.31	-9.93	-1.31	-2.61	2.31	1.52
Zulu	-1.89	-1.26	-13.91	-13.79	4.34	4.20	1.53	4.56
Australia	5.89	9.02	13.72	15.90	-1.09	1.07	-0.51	-3.09
Tasmania	8.59	13.91	17.54	21.63	-0.29	0.28	-2.69	-1.66
Tolai	3.62	7.66	8.61	5.86	-7.89	-8.12	-7.45	-9.70
Hawaii	-7.39	-8.11	3.95	1.11	-5.37	-5.78	9.32	7.11
Easter I	0.91	0.58	4.33	6.26	-2.69	-3.74	4.37	2.44
Moriori	-10.07	-8.59	8.71	9.92	-6.58	-4.09	2.15	-1.83
Arikara	-2.17	-6.09	-4.10	-6.20	4.06	1.73	-6.66	-4.06
Santa Cruz	3.64	0.14	9.00	7.58	1.11	1.53	-2.32	-2.28
Peru	0.25	-0.64	-0.72	0.81	-0.50	1.96	1.38	2.07
N Japan	0.44	0.94	4.57	-0.74	0.09	4.14	-0.20	-1.81
S Japan	-0.79	-3.10	-8.19	-7.06	0.46	1.02	-0.03	0.75
Hainan	0.90	0.62	-3.91	-3.30	3.59	0.22	-2.02	4.08
Atayal	-1.00	0.80	-0.65	1.38	9.33	7.74	0.94	-0.08
Philippines	0.09	–	0.37	–	-1.15	–	1.17	–
Guam	-1.84	-2.18	-5.38	-4.72	-5.07	-4.08	5.97	4.01
Egypt	-2.02	-1.52	-4.29	-10.40	-1.35	-1.01	3.47	6.08
Bushman	12.10	13.66	-2.66	-1.92	12.70	9.03	4.98	4.75
Andaman Is	6.26	7.64	-0.00	1.22	-0.28	-0.82	0.90	-1.08
Ainu	-13.39	-10.24	0.52	-0.31	0.59	-2.91	-1.75	1.83
Buriat	-10.14	-9.70	-14.42	-17.40	-3.30	0.49	-1.40	2.02
Eskimo	-11.03	-12.45	-8.23	-8.43	3.89	8.32	-0.94	2.08
Anyang	-4.21	–	-5.66	–	0.53	–	4.84	–

TABLE 3. Continued.
Population Means of C-Scores

	Frontal Subtense FRS		Nas-Bregma Subtense FRF		Parietal Chord PAC		Parietal Subtense PAS	
	Male	Female	Male	Female	Male	Female	Male	Female
Norse	-0.47	0.60	3.61	4.11	2.12	1.40	1.37	-0.84
Zalavár	7.15	6.01	0.38	1.50	4.68	4.68	3.97	2.43
Berg	8.28	6.43	1.02	1.65	-4.76	-4.81	0.29	1.64
Teita	7.87	9.45	-0.89	3.88	4.16	4.36	-1.11	4.16
Dogon	12.14	6.45	0.43	-1.20	4.10	3.41	2.96	1.14
Zulu	11.58	9.27	-5.97	-2.86	5.55	5.50	1.09	-0.87
Australia	-0.70	-0.11	-0.75	-0.90	5.45	2.98	-2.19	-2.50
Tasmania	0.17	0.64	-1.76	-3.07	5.52	6.21	2.34	2.05
Tolai	-5.34	-7.82	-2.72	-4.42	5.63	7.47	5.32	7.40
Hawaii	-6.27	-6.52	-1.40	-3.97	-5.54	-8.18	-2.38	-5.79
Easter I	-1.20	1.54	-3.86	-2.48	-0.15	-1.43	-4.62	-3.56
Moriori	-16.87	-16.29	-1.19	-3.18	-8.70	-8.01	-9.04	-6.56
Arikara	-16.13	-8.85	0.46	-0.51	-8.72	-8.86	-1.52	-3.08
Santa Cruz	-6.08	-6.58	7.88	8.35	-12.72	-9.45	-8.72	-4.50
Peru	-2.69	-1.67	1.79	2.13	-1.61	-1.42	4.75	4.32
N Japan	2.82	2.70	1.63	0.34	0.90	-0.31	-1.34	-3.79
S Japan	5.21	3.63	2.58	-1.91	2.96	4.33	1.96	3.39
Hainan	0.54	1.12	-1.19	2.37	1.14	2.15	6.59	5.10
Atayal	12.23	7.89	-2.20	1.37	5.11	6.43	7.00	9.20
Philippines	2.35	–	5.44	–	0.31	–	4.80	–
Guam	3.14	3.72	-0.39	0.45	-1.89	-2.45	-1.40	-2.07
Egypt	4.65	6.47	6.94	9.80	7.73	7.20	7.80	5.79
Bushman	23.90	21.82	4.44	4.67	4.22	3.44	2.61	1.01
Andaman Is	11.41	5.16	9.10	9.80	2.44	0.50	14.85	10.69
Ainu	3.69	3.91	-1.66	3.63	1.07	1.99	-6.22	-3.66
Buriat	-4.08	-3.12	2.15	3.63	-11.81	-15.59	-11.20	-13.16
Eskimo	1.52	1.84	4.09	7.54	-0.23	1.71	-4.49	-2.24
Anyang	3.98	–	3.91	–	1.96	–	1.01	–

TABLE 3. Continued.
Population Means of C-Scores

	Breg-Subtense Fraction PAF		Occipital Chord OCC		Occipital Subtense OCS		Lam-Subtense Fraction OCF	
	Male	Female	Male	Female	Male	Female	Male	Female
Norse	5.17	4.52	-0.14	0.64	6.40	6.63	-0.85	-1.47
Zalavár	1.00	1.89	-1.26	-0.49	3.84	4.13	0.36	-0.26
Berg	0.79	-2.26	-5.40	-5.74	0.49	2.11	1.97	1.88
Teita	9.25	12.63	-4.75	-8.01	2.60	-2.23	2.20	-4.71
Dogon	18.44	17.87	0.63	3.22	-8.87	-10.43	-2.57	2.25
Zulu	6.29	6.30	0.27	-0.45	-3.75	-2.25	0.49	-1.37
Australia	-1.23	-2.96	-10.89	-7.31	0.60	4.07	-8.63	-11.05
Tasmania	-1.47	-2.85	-7.21	-4.60	0.72	1.32	-4.89	-4.30
Tolai	-0.91	2.25	-3.24	-3.32	2.66	0.18	-2.80	-2.67
Hawaii	-14.77	-12.82	5.55	7.85	-10.96	-10.71	6.16	9.14
Easter I	-8.14	-8.51	-0.62	-0.05	-2.40	0.78	-3.26	-0.92
Moriori	-10.78	-10.28	6.35	3.25	-4.24	-9.25	-0.03	-5.15
Arikara	-9.28	-7.32	-4.99	-8.52	-4.21	-4.23	-5.04	-3.76
Santa Cruz	-9.67	-9.52	2.88	3.83	8.56	11.63	-1.13	0.77
Peru	-3.03	-3.74	7.80	8.29	10.70	12.68	5.27	7.14
N Japan	1.88	-1.08	6.18	5.79	0.86	0.05	5.77	6.10
S Japan	8.86	6.90	7.89	4.55	0.48	2.27	6.96	4.81
Hainan	7.66	8.93	0.99	1.08	-3.62	-6.57	0.06	3.43
Atayal	8.50	10.47	-0.96	-1.16	0.29	-0.96	-1.35	0.28
Philippines	6.89	–	2.53	–	-6.11	–	0.37	–
Guam	0.68	1.45	0.86	0.14	-5.25	-7.25	-4.07	-0.78
Egypt	14.35	11.33	3.55	3.08	-2.00	-0.50	0.16	2.38
Bushman	7.98	8.09	-5.94	-3.82	10.39	11.38	6.67	5.49
Andaman Is	11.02	10.18	1.96	1.03	-0.37	-4.80	5.52	4.84
Ainu	0.94	-0.13	2.83	3.04	-3.05	-2.76	-3.37	-2.15
Buriat	-11.73	-12.07	-10.47	-5.16	0.56	-1.37	-4.14	1.63
Eskimo	-5.15	-3.15	-1.46	-1.31	-0.83	-3.56	2.40	1.51
Anyang	4.38	–	4.96	–	-2.42	–	2.23	–

TABLE 3. Continued.
Population Means of C-Scores

	Vertex Radius VRR		Nasion Radius NAR		Subspinale Radius SSR		Prosthion Radius PRR	
	Male	Female	Male	Female	Male	Female	Male	Female
Norse	-3.27	-3.20	0.07	0.74	-4.29	-2.71	-7.58	-6.05
Zalavár	-2.08	-1.87	-0.76	-1.12	-3.51	-7.22	-4.89	-9.12
Berg	-5.03	-4.65	0.15	-0.07	-8.78	-7.72	-11.43	-10.33
Teita	-9.88	-7.28	5.40	3.48	3.20	1.38	4.90	3.55
Dogon	2.09	2.93	-9.43	-5.85	-7.97	-6.28	0.33	0.41
Zulu	-1.07	0.58	-0.46	-0.71	-0.29	-1.67	4.41	3.59
Australia	-18.44	-18.96	1.63	2.51	6.81	8.67	9.47	11.30
Tasmania	-4.73	-4.71	-0.43	-0.22	7.76	7.56	5.15	4.99
Tolai	-1.54	-3.75	0.74	0.69	12.69	12.57	14.15	14.07
Hawaii	16.93	15.60	5.65	6.50	4.73	6.35	2.39	3.95
Easter I	12.62	11.86	15.76	13.27	8.03	8.25	2.64	2.32
Moriori	5.45	5.62	4.20	6.83	4.60	6.65	0.73	1.22
Arikara	-6.77	-7.71	4.63	4.24	3.17	2.06	-0.47	-0.40
Santa Cruz	-8.25	-7.50	-7.61	-8.44	-0.71	-0.06	-0.73	1.36
Peru	4.28	5.09	-9.67	-10.27	-9.62	-11.88	-8.88	-11.56
N Japan	5.48	0.36	-3.56	-3.91	-5.58	-5.38	-3.57	-4.47
S Japan	8.48	6.27	-1.31	-2.64	-3.55	-3.83	-2.18	-0.85
Hainan	5.65	11.45	-5.20	-5.07	-6.75	-6.57	-4.53	-3.86
Atayal	3.63	4.57	-5.21	-4.26	-12.05	-10.31	-8.68	-8.18
Philippines	1.80	–	-5.22	–	-4.50	–	-1.06	–
Guam	4.85	5.83	-0.74	-2.90	-0.92	-5.04	0.68	-2.79
Egypt	1.36	1.40	-1.84	-1.58	-3.25	-5.44	-5.14	-7.59
Bushman	-15.65	-15.45	-3.16	-1.99	-6.71	-5.36	-5.04	-3.12
Andaman Is	4.29	2.91	-9.92	-8.74	-5.25	-4.35	-7.57	-4.26
Ainu	3.28	6.48	-0.31	0.91	-3.27	-4.71	-1.98	-3.91
Buriat	-5.08	-1.96	2.90	3.62	-7.30	-7.83	-6.75	-7.30
Eskimo	0.18	4.68	9.41	8.63	5.45	6.21	3.80	6.81
Anyang	8.65	–	-4.62	–	-6.65	–	-5.10	–

TABLE 3. Continued.
Population Means of C-Scores

	Dacryon Radius DKR		Zygoorbitale Radius ZOR		Frontomalare Radius FMR		Ectoconchion Radius EKR	
	Male	*Female*	*Male*	*Female*	*Male*	*Female*	*Male*	*Female*
Norse	-3.13	-2.00	0.94	0.43	-5.53	-4.88	-5.99	-5.17
Zalavár	-4.07	-5.08	-1.55	-4.61	-4.94	-4.06	-5.07	-6.33
Berg	-2.27	-3.07	-4.18	-3.64	-3.99	-4.47	-5.36	-5.66
Teita	5.74	4.67	9.12	6.41	1.05	0.15	2.53	2.07
Dogon	-7.82	-5.95	-3.16	-2.14	-9.14	-6.82	-7.57	-5.34
Zulu	-0.10	0.36	-0.58	-0.20	-4.35	-3.85	-3.41	-2.92
Australia	-3.09	-2.72	2.87	3.52	1.52	-1.13	-3.17	-3.47
Tasmania	-3.58	-3.98	-1.75	-2.76	-1.51	-3.56	-4.08	-5.85
Tolai	1.92	1.52	6.22	6.29	2.07	2.40	3.00	2.74
Hawaii	7.04	8.04	4.09	6.46	9.60	11.65	9.97	11.82
Easter I	15.87	14.08	11.40	12.55	16.17	15.94	17.09	18.11
Moriori	4.00	6.84	-0.14	3.35	3.63	6.79	1.63	5.11
Arikara	2.84	4.34	-2.54	-1.48	4.28	3.91	2.73	3.04
Santa Cruz	-7.99	-6.73	-7.14	-6.84	-7.22	-8.46	-7.05	-7.84
Peru	-8.75	-11.39	-12.83	-16.41	-7.59	-7.99	-7.35	-10.09
N Japan	1.93	1.02	0.05	-0.35	3.70	0.83	5.94	2.86
S Japan	3.41	2.09	1.47	0.52	3.32	3.40	6.17	4.98
Hainan	-1.93	-1.77	-2.11	-1.30	-1.05	0.37	-0.10	2.20
Atayal	-2.49	-3.10	-5.12	-6.01	2.41	-0.84	2.10	-1.69
Philippines	-3.05	–	-2.79	–	-1.07	–	-0.47	–
Guam	1.39	0.24	1.26	-0.26	0.69	0.04	2.82	1.54
Egypt	-4.08	-3.33	-2.90	-4.79	-6.88	-7.40	-8.20	-9.20
Bushman	2.77	1.34	5.43	2.86	-0.78	-4.26	2.09	-0.74
Andaman Is	-8.25	-8.90	-9.10	-8.81	-5.37	-6.18	-9.28	-9.44
Ainu	1.21	2.56	1.54	0.29	2.49	1.94	0.26	1.67
Buriat	5.70	7.06	8.58	9.17	9.00	8.94	14.22	15.43
Eskimo	12.26	12.44	15.70	15.75	16.52	17.01	18.03	20.17
Anyang	-0.04	–	-0.55	–	2.53	–	4.84	–

TABLE 3. Continued.
Population Means of C-Scores

	Zygomaxill Radius ZMR		M1 Alveolus Radius AVR	
	Male	Female	Male	Female
Norse	-2.21	-1.88	-5.32	-4.08
Zalavár	-1.68	-5.79	-3.03	-6.58
Berg	-6.47	-4.92	-9.66	-7.20
Teita	9.13	8.40	4.39	2.12
Dogon	-4.30	-3.46	-3.60	-1.88
Zulu	-1.29	-1.10	1.31	2.80
Australia	8.90	8.67	11.49	10.91
Tasmania	-0.12	-2.44	5.85	3.92
Tolai	7.30	7.25	9.30	8.59
Hawaii	4.80	5.30	-1.39	0.64
Easter I	6.93	9.87	1.17	1.86
Moriori	-3.49	-0.29	5.64	6.09
Arikara	-0.06	0.23	0.91	0.09
Santa Cruz	-2.92	-2.02	2.58	3.85
Peru	-8.72	-12.43	-8.09	-12.23
N Japan	-2.08	-3.88	-2.49	-2.98
S Japan	-0.65	0.34	-3.26	-2.06
Hainan	-3.16	-1.72	-5.77	-4.02
Atayal	-5.78	-2.55	-8.43	-7.56
Philippines	-0.99	–	-4.65	–
Guam	3.97	0.65	-3.77	-6.34
Egypt	-4.87	-6.99	-4.74	-6.93
Bushman	2.49	0.58	-1.09	-0.41
Andaman Is	-7.29	-5.61	-7.59	-4.89
Ainu	2.02	-0.73	0.70	-2.23
Buriat	7.37	6.12	-5.31	-5.68
Eskimo	21.02	23.80	9.25	12.49
Anyang	-1.85	–	-4.31	–

4

Sorting the Individuals

A review of the C-score means gives the strong impression that there are morphological cranial trends distinguishing the several geographic areas. Further on we will try to specify and measure these trends, but before this we may take an objective look at the actuality of the apparent groupings, using clustering procedures.

The first of these procedures looks for clumps among the individuals. The analysis is blind as to population identity. (I have used a similar device of clustering a more limited number of anonymous individuals [Howells 1986], but the present analysis does not form a dendrogram.) In a discriminant analysis such identification by group is known a priori, and the solution attempts to segregate the group memberships as fully as possible. The picture is of overlapping swarms of points, some nearer to centroids of populations not their own, and the final inventory is a hits/misses table, measuring the success of the segregation. In the present analysis all the individuals, unidentified as to population, are deployed in the multivariate space by their mutual Euclidean distances and are asked to aggregate into clusters which are then mutually delimited (without the element of discrimination). Only then, a posteriori, are the individuals identified by group, and the inventory is the population composition of the clusters found. In other words, do the members of actual populations tend to congregate naturally?

The program used is FASTCLUS of the SAS package, designed to cluster large numbers of units. The program locates "seeds" as first estimates of cluster centroids; the position of these is adjusted as further cases agglomerate according to their mutual distances. After all individuals have placed themselves, in this blind operation, the population composition of each cluster is tabulated, as the essential result.

At the outset, the number of clusters to be formed is specified. One can see intuitively that a small number of clusters will force the bunching of perhaps inappropriate populations; as the number increases it will tend to approximate the actual number of natural groups, and then will tend to subdivide the latter as it gets higher still. But this does not necessarily proceed smoothly: permitting a new cluster is likely to displace previous centroids, perhaps markedly changing the cluster compositions. (It is of course the centroids which move, not the individuals.) Therefore results may differ widely, depending on the number of clusters specified, material input, and so on. Since the purpose here is simply to assess the grouping of populations by region, I present only one set of tabulations bearing on the point, which strike me as the most suitable.

The data employed are the C-scores for all 57 measurements. The tabulations show the percentage of each population falling into each cluster (eliminating values under 20% for simplification). Tables 4a and 4b cover the males and females of the 18 core populations. If the six geographic areas had sharply distinct populations one would expect that six clear clusters would emerge, but that is not the case: tabulations of six clusters in each sex disperse the actual populations more than do the smaller numbers. In the males, five clusters make the clearest picture, with Polynesians and Far Easterners falling mainly in the same one. (Half the Peruvians join Europe, and half the Moriori go with American Indians, transgressions which also appear in later analyses herein.) Among the females (four clusters), American Indians and many Far Easterners join Europe; many Far Easterners also join Africans in another cluster, an affiliation not present in other analyses. In any case, the only finding of importance is that the populations of the main areas do indeed tend to gather in the same region of the space set by C-scores of the individuals.

Tables 5a and 5b include the non-core populations. The results seem satisfactory if not strikingly clear-cut. Buriats and Eskimos are each apt to be well isolated; Bushmen are either strongly African or, in some runs, also isolated. But these varying runs are not reliably instructive, and the main lesson, as before, is that geographical distinctions are real.

TABLE 4a
Clusters of Individuals of 18 Male Groups
(Percentages Lower than 20% Omitted)

	Cluster				
Population	1	2	3	4	5
Norse	67[a]				
Zalavár	75				
Berg	92				
Teita		48	45		
Dogon		89			
Zulu		72			
Australia			94		
Tasmania			77		
Tolai			92		
Hawaii				92	
Easter I				93	
Moriori				43	50
Arikara					85
Santa Cruz					88
Peru	49				47
N Japan	21			50	
S Japan		22		60	
Hainan	22			28	26

[a] All numbers are percentages of population groups concerned.

TABLE 4b
Clusters of Individuals of 18 Female Groups
(Percentages Lower than 20% Omitted)

	Cluster			
Population	1	2	3	4
Norse	72			
Zalavár	82			
Berg	94			
Teita		72		
Dogon		98		
Zulu		71		
Australia			97	
Tasmania			92	
Tolai			81	
Hawaii				93
Easter I				100
Moriori				78
Arikara	70			
Santa Cruz	68		25	
Peru	96			
N Japan	56	25		
S Japan	34	36		29
Hainan	28	50		21

TABLE 5a
Clusters of Individuals of 28 Male Groups (Percentages Lower than 20% Omitted)

Population	Cluster						
	1	2	3	4	5	6	7
Norse	65						
Zalavár	62				22		
Berg	89						
Teita		57	27				
Dogon	21	63					
Zulu		58					
Australia			90				
Tasmania		24	60				
Tolai			92				
Hawaii				64	25		
Easter I				93			
Moriori				35	40		
Arikara					38	33	
Santa Cruz					66		
Peru	43				50		
N Japan					58		
S Japan				34	38		
Hainan	24				46		
Atayal	27	20			37		
Philippines					52		
Guam				26	30	23	
Egypt	60				27		
Bushman		100					
Andaman Is	40	40					
Ainu					43		
Buriat						98	
Eskimo							96
Anyang					47	21	

TABLE 5b
Clusters of Individuals of 26 Female Groups
(Percentages Lower than 20% Omitted)

Population	Cluster						
	1	2	3	4	5	6	7
Norse	47	21					
Zalavár	60						
Berg	79						
Teita			82				
Dogon		55	36				
Zulu	23		50				
Australia				93			
Tasmania				92			
Tolai			27	59			
Hawaii					53	40	
Easter I					89		
Moriori					41	33	
Arikara						22	29
Santa Cruz	54			23			
Peru	67	23					
N Japan						59	
S Japan						63	
Hainan						68	
Atayal	22	22				55	
Guam						74	
Egypt	20	75					
Bushman	42		44				
Andaman Is		85					
Ainu	23					55	
Buriat							98
Eskimo					90		

5

Analysis by Population Distances

To this point our attempt has been to individualize the regional populations using C-scores. From here on we look for their mutual statistical relations. The 1973 study (Howells 1973) essentially worked through the correlations of measurements; here we operate on the correlations of populations. This governs most of what follows.

The populations have been correlated with one another using the 57 mean C-scores of each. Such correlations make an all-purpose measure of distance, which is scale free, especially here with size under control; the advantages are pointed out by Sokal and Sneath (1963).

Tables 6 and 7 give the group correlations of the males and females. It may be seen that the 18 core groups do in fact come together by their 6 respective areas: there are no minus coefficients within the groups, but some coefficients are so low as to be negligible (e.g., Arikara and Peru). There is also some consistency as to greatest distances: the Australoid and Far Eastern groups have high negative correlations vis-à-vis one another. Among all "Mongoloids" the coefficients are generally positive or null but there are some strong disagreements: Polynesians, especially Easter Islanders, with American Indians; Peruvians with some others, especially Eskimos.

CLUSTERING THE POPULATIONS

Now we face a question. I chose 18 populations to form six areal groupings, to see whether having several populations in each would point to traits characteristic for an area, not simply for a given population. Technically, the first question is whether restricting an analysis to these 18 groups will produce a clearer picture of area differences and relationships, or whether using the total number of populations—a bigger matrix of information—will be more revealing of the same thing. The proof of the pudding being in the eating, we will do it both ways.

The first step beyond the table of correlations is to look at a cluster analysis based on distances. The method used is K. J. Jones's NATURE'S GROUPS (Jones 1964; see also Wilmink and Uytterschaut 1984), a straightforward successive joining of individual populations, and resulting groups of these, by least remaining distance. The distances are the correlation coefficients just reviewed (with all signs reversed).

Figures 1 and 2 give the dendrograms for the 18 core groups, based on the first 18 rows and columns of tables 6 and 7. In both sexes Australoids, Africans, Europeans, and Far Easterners form immediate groups, with the first two joining at a higher level and remaining most distant from all others. American Indians and Polynesians equivocate, however: Arikara and Moriori are more similar to each other than is each to its own coregionals. On the whole, all American Indians and Polynesians

join a Mongoloid supercluster, except for the Peruvians, joined also by Santa Cruz in the males, who go to the Europeans. This kind of uncertainty on the part of American Indians and Moriori was seen in the previous section.

Dendrograms for all 28 (26 female) populations appear in figures 3 and 4. The pattern of attachments differs more between sexes; absence from the females series of Philippine Islanders and Anyang may contribute to this fluidity. In these clusterings, Polynesians and American Indians are segregated; and the former are joined by Eskimos. Among the Indians, Arikara, Santa Cruz, and Siberian Buriats fall in the same bloc, which, however, attaches itself to Europeans (and Peru) in the males but to Mongoloids in the females. Otherwise, divisions are not surprising. Bushmen go with other Africans, who are also joined by Andaman Islanders and, in the females, by Atayals of Taiwan, which *is* unexpected and is certainly a comment on this kind of analysis. Ainus, however, fall with fellow Asians and Oceanics, not with Europeans. Among Mongoloids generally the sex dendrograms are not in tight agreement. But this fluidity is typical of such clustering analyses, being affected by the input; previous analyses of these data (Howells 1973, 1986) have produced similar but not identical results.

Altogether these runs do affirm the existence of area distinctions in cranial populations. American Indians and Polynesians, as total groups, seem less discrete than other main groups, and Africans and Australoids together appear to form a main branch relatively remote from others, although further analyses (vide infra) do not insist on this.

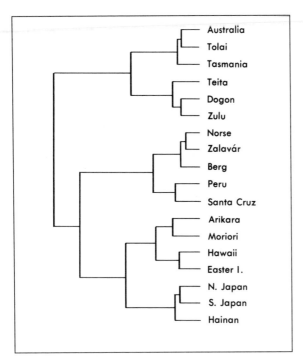

Figure 1. Cluster analysis of 18 male groups based on intergroup correlations.

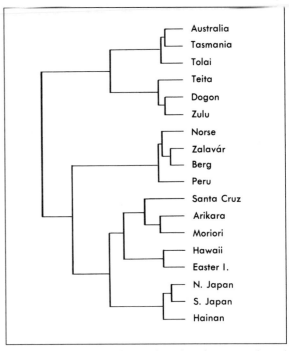

Figure 2. Cluster analysis of 18 female groups based on intergroup correlations.

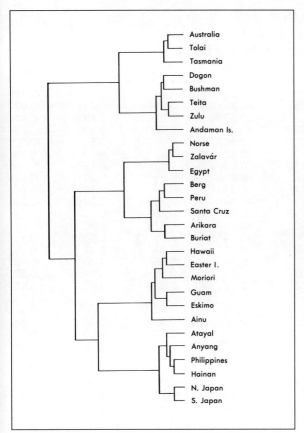

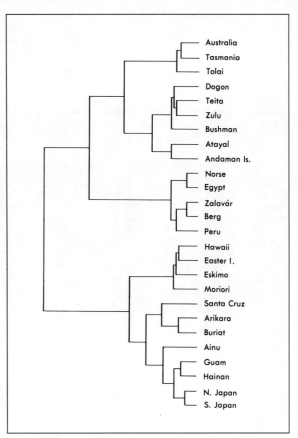

Figure 3. Cluster analysis of 28 male groups based on intergroup correlations.

Figure 4. Cluster analysis of 26 female groups based on intergroup correlations.

TABLE 6
Correlations Among 28 Male Groups
(Based on the 57 Mean C-Scores of Each)

	Nor	Zal	Ber	Tei	Dog	Zul	Aus
Norse	–	0.80	0.65	-0.05	0.04	-0.04	-0.16
Zalavár	0.80	–	0.75	-0.22	0.05	0.01	-0.27
Berg	0.65	0.75	–	-0.39	0.07	-0.12	-0.41
Teita	0.05	0.22	0.39		0.36	0.60	0.39
Dogon	0.04	0.05	0.07	0.36	–	0.67	-0.02
Zulu	-0.04	0.01	-0.12	0.60	0.67	–	0.18
Australia	-0.16	-0.27	-0.41	0.39	-0.02	0.18	–
Tasmania	-0.23	-0.16	-0.16	0.02	-0.01	0.09	0.65
Tolai	-0.54	-0.54	-0.72	0.37	-0.07	0.12	0.69
Hawaii	-0.38	-0.31	-0.28	-0.33	-0.42	-0.34	-0.36
Easter I	-0.34	-0.37	-0.59	0.25	-0.38	-0.05	0.08
Moriori	-0.19	-0.41	-0.35	-0.30	-0.57	-0.50	-0.06
Arikara	-0.12	-0.19	0.14	-0.34	-0.51	-0.56	-0.11
Santa Cruz	0.07	0.03	0.28	-0.41	-0.24	-0.47	0.01
Peru	0.43	0.47	0.52	-0.48	0.08	-0.34	-0.43
N Japan	-0.25	-0.12	0.04	-0.48	-0.18	-0.24	-0.52
S Japan	-0.22	-0.08	-0.10	-0.12	0.03	0.03	-0.65
Hainan	-0.19	-0.04	0.16	-0.26	0.27	-0.11	-0.66
Atayal	-0.02	0.19	0.38	-0.24	0.32	0.06	-0.43
Philippines	-0.26	-0.03	0.20	-0.24	0.43	0.02	-0.48
Guam	-0.34	-0.40	-0.28	-0.16	-0.13	-0.23	-0.22
Egypt	0.70	0.73	0.35	0.07	0.32	0.18	-0.16
Bushman	0.11	0.16	0.18	0.46	0.41	0.49	0.18
Andaman Is	0.15	0.30	0.29	0.04	0.60	0.23	-0.27
Ainu	0.04	0.06	0.07	-0.22	-0.06	0.03	-0.06
Buriat	-0.00	-0.05	0.34	-0.34	-0.28	-0.40	-0.40
Eskimo	-0.26	-0.38	-0.43	0.13	-0.48	-0.23	0.11
Anyang	-0.33	-0.22	-0.13	-0.22	0.06	-0.17	-0.56

	Tas	Tol	Haw	Eas	Mor	Ari	SCr
Norse	-0.23	-0.54	-0.38	-0.34	-0.19	-0.12	0.07
Zalavár	-0.16	-0.54	-0.31	-0.37	-0.41	-0.19	0.03
Berg	-0.16	-0.72	-0.28	-0.59	-0.35	0.14	0.28
Teita	0.02	0.37	-0.33	0.25	-0.30	-0.34	-0.41
Dogon	-0.01	-0.07	-0.42	-0.38	-0.57	-0.51	-0.24
Zulu	0.09	0.12	-0.34	-0.05	-0.50	-0.56	-0.47
Australia	0.65	0.69	-0.36	0.08	-0.06	-0.11	0.01
Tasmania	–	0.62	-0.23	-0.00	-0.16	-0.14	0.04
Tolai	0.62	–	-0.01	0.37	0.04	-0.14	-0.18
Hawaii	-0.23	-0.01	–	0.62	0.52	0.11	-0.26
Easter I	-0.00	0.37	0.62	–	0.32	-0.14	-0.58
Moriori	-0.16	0.04	0.52	0.32	–	0.45	0.20
Arikara	-0.14	-0.14	0.11	-0.14	0.45	–	0.41
Santa Cruz	0.04	-0.18	-0.26	-0.58	0.20	0.41	–
Peru	-0.35	-0.53	-0.27	-0.60	-0.11	0.15	0.48
N Japan	-0.43	-0.39	0.38	-0.02	0.11	0.04	0.08
S Japan	-0.56	-0.33	0.37	0.16	-0.03	-0.16	-0.25
Hainan	-0.47	-0.40	0.07	-0.24	-0.19	0.15	-0.03
Atayal	-0.24	-0.48	-0.14	-0.30	-0.49	-0.08	-0.01
Philippines	-0.19	-0.32	0.04	-0.35	-0.33	-0.04	0.05
Guam	-0.30	-0.07	0.51	0.23	0.26	0.25	-0.11
Egypt	-0.20	-0.33	-0.37	-0.20	-0.25	-0.36	-0.19
Bushman	0.22	-0.01	-0.42	-0.15	-0.64	-0.56	-0.11
Andaman Is	-0.01	-0.19	-0.39	-0.42	-0.49	-0.30	0.06
Ainu	-0.12	-0.22	0.34	0.08	0.08	-0.09	-0.14
Buriat	-0.39	-0.46	0.30	-0.17	0.15	0.53	0.24
Eskimo	-0.27	0.23	0.47	0.52	0.34	0.20	-0.17
Anyang	-0.42	-0.28	0.40	0.10	-0.01	0.01	-0.14

TABLE 6. Continued.
Correlations Among 28 Male Groups
(Based on the 57 Mean C-Scores of Each)

	Per	NJa	SJa	Hai	Ata	Phi	Gua
Norse	0.43	-0.25	-0.22	-0.19	-0.02	-0.26	-0.34
Zalavár	0.47	-0.12	-0.08	-0.04	0.19	-0.03	-0.40
Berg	0.52	0.04	-0.10	0.16	0.38	0.20	-0.28
Teita	-0.48	-0.48	-0.12	-0.26	-0.24	-0.24	-0.16
Dogon	0.08	-0.18	0.03	0.27	0.32	0.43	-0.13
Zulu	-0.34	-0.24	0.03	-0.11	0.06	0.02	-0.23
Australia	-0.43	-0.52	-0.65	-0.66	-0.43	-0.48	-0.22
Tasmania	-0.35	-0.43	-0.56	-0.47	-0.24	-0.19	-0.30
Tolai	-0.53	-0.39	-0.33	-0.40	-0.48	-0.32	-0.07
Hawaii	-0.27	0.38	0.37	0.07	-0.14	0.04	0.51
Easter I	-0.60	-0.02	0.16	-0.24	-0.30	-0.35	0.23
Moriori	-0.11	0.11	-0.03	-0.19	-0.49	-0.33	0.26
Arikara	0.15	0.04	-0.16	0.15	-0.08	-0.04	0.25
Santa Cruz	0.48	0.08	-0.25	-0.03	-0.01	0.05	-0.11
Peru	—	0.14	0.01	0.38	0.35	0.26	-0.16
N Japan	0.14	—	0.80	0.57	0.52	0.49	0.43
S Japan	0.01	0.80	—	0.60	0.48	0.48	0.43
Hainan	0.38	0.57	0.60	—	0.70	0.80	0.39
Atayal	0.35	0.52	0.48	0.70	—	0.68	0.19
Philippines	0.26	0.49	0.48	0.80	0.68	—	0.21
Guam	-0.16	0.43	0.43	0.39	0.19	0.21	—
Egypt	0.35	-0.27	-0.04	-0.07	0.00	-0.08	-0.49
Bushman	-0.18	-0.10	0.03	-0.06	0.26	0.17	-0.31
Andaman Is	0.41	-0.10	0.09	0.35	0.39	0.44	-0.33
Ainu	-0.20	0.32	0.24	-0.06	0.15	0.04	0.28
Buriat	0.11	0.51	0.27	0.38	0.25	0.31	0.49
Eskimo	-0.46	0.28	0.28	-0.09	-0.16	-0.30	0.56
Anyang	0.14	0.70	0.73	0.78	0.56	0.67	0.61

	Egy	Bus	And	Ain	Bur	Esk	Any
Norse	0.70	0.11	0.15	0.04	-0.00	-0.26	-0.33
Zalavár	0.73	0.16	0.30	0.06	-0.05	-0.38	-0.22
Berg	0.35	0.18	0.29	0.07	0.34	-0.43	-0.13
Teita	0.07	0.46	0.04	-0.22	-0.34	0.13	-0.22
Dogon	0.32	0.41	0.60	-0.06	-0.28	-0.48	0.06
Zulu	0.18	0.49	0.23	0.03	-0.40	-0.23	-0.17
Australia	-0.16	0.18	-0.27	-0.06	-0.40	0.11	-0.56
Tasmania	-0.20	0.22	-0.01	-0.12	-0.39	-0.27	-0.42
Tolai	-0.33	-0.01	-0.19	-0.22	-0.46	0.23	-0.28
Hawaii	-0.37	-0.42	-0.39	0.34	0.30	0.47	0.40
Easter I	-0.20	-0.15	-0.42	0.08	-0.17	0.52	0.10
Moriori	-0.25	-0.64	-0.49	0.08	0.15	0.34	-0.01
Arikara	-0.36	-0.56	-0.30	-0.09	0.53	0.20	0.01
Santa Cruz	-0.19	-0.11	0.06	-0.14	0.24	-0.17	-0.14
Peru	0.35	-0.18	0.41	-0.20	0.11	-0.46	0.14
N Japan	-0.27	-0.10	-0.10	0.32	0.51	0.28	0.70
S Japan	-0.04	0.03	0.09	0.24	0.27	0.28	0.73
Hainan	-0.07	-0.06	0.35	-0.06	0.38	-0.09	0.78
Atayal	0.00	0.26	0.39	0.15	0.25	-0.16	0.56
Philippines	-0.08	0.17	0.44	0.04	0.31	-0.30	0.67
Guam	-0.49	-0.31	-0.33	0.28	0.49	0.56	0.61
Egypt	—	0.10	0.51	-0.17	-0.47	-0.41	-0.29
Bushman	0.10	—	0.35	-0.04	-0.14	-0.20	-0.05
Andaman Is	0.51	0.35	—	-0.45	-0.38	-0.55	-0.01
Ainu	-0.17	-0.04	-0.45	—	0.36	0.24	0.25
Buriat	-0.47	-0.14	-0.38	0.36	—	0.33	0.47
Eskimo	-0.41	-0.20	-0.55	0.24	0.33	—	0.20
Anyang	-0.29	-0.05	-0.01	0.25	0.47	0.20	—

SKULL SHAPES AND THE MAP

TABLE 7
Correlations Among 26 Female Groups
(Based on the 57 Mean C-Scores of Each)

	Nor	Zal	Ber	Tei	Dog	Zul	Aus
Norse	–	0.73	0.53	-0.08	-0.07	0.01	-0.05
Zalavár	0.73	–	0.80	-0.31	-0.02	-0.01	-0.24
Berg	0.53	0.80	–	-0.30	-0.06	-0.14	-0.33
Teita	-0.08	-0.31	-0.30		0.49	0.58	0.34
Dogon	-0.07	-0.02	-0.06	0.49	–	0.60	-0.10
Zulu	0.01	-0.01	-0.14	0.58	0.60	–	0.15
Australia	-0.05	-0.24	-0.33	0.34	-0.10	0.15	–
Tasmania	-0.15	-0.09	-0.14	0.04	-0.10	0.06	0.69
Tolai	-0.45	-0.60	-0.63	0.35	-0.05	0.06	0.64
Hawaii	-0.41	-0.44	-0.41	-0.27	-0.24	-0.17	-0.37
Easter I	-0.33	-0.55	-0.66	0.27	-0.21	0.00	0.14
Moriori	-0.23	-0.46	-0.37	-0.36	-0.50	-0.52	-0.04
Arikara	-0.06	-0.02	0.27	-0.26	-0.40	-0.50	-0.17
Santa Cruz	0.10	0.07	0.24	-0.43	-0.35	-0.45	0.10
Peru	0.40	0.60	0.61	-0.53	0.01	-0.37	-0.46
N Japan	-0.22	0.07	0.11	-0.46	-0.08	-0.16	-0.57
S Japan	-0.26	-0.09	-0.13	-0.19	0.04	0.01	-0.66
Hainan	-0.29	-0.04	0.01	-0.15	0.21	-0.05	-0.71
Atayal	-0.08	0.34	0.34	-0.08	0.28	0.04	-0.42
Philippines	–	–	–	–	–	–	–
Guam	-0.37	-0.21	-0.18	-0.11	-0.02	-0.09	-0.51
Egypt	0.76	0.67	0.43	-0.02	0.33	0.12	-0.18
Bushman	0.13	0.10	0.11	0.49	0.30	0.55	0.29
Andaman Is	0.02	0.13	0.25	0.15	0.56	0.04	-0.12
Ainu	0.07	0.26	0.10	-0.25	-0.02	0.12	-0.33
Buriat	-0.03	0.11	0.35	-0.32	-0.32	-0.26	-0.54
Eskimo	-0.22	-0.42	-0.49	0.07	-0.42	-0.08	0.04
Anyang	–	–	–	–	–	–	–

	Tas	Tol	Haw	Eas	Mor	Ari	SCr
Norse	-0.15	-0.45	-0.41	-0.33	-0.23	-0.06	0.10
Zalavár	-0.09	-0.60	-0.44	-0.55	-0.46	-0.02	0.07
Berg	-0.14	-0.63	-0.41	-0.66	-0.37	0.27	0.24
Teita	0.04	0.35	-0.27	0.27	-0.36	-0.26	-0.43
Dogon	-0.10	-0.05	-0.24	-0.21	-0.50	-0.40	-0.35
Zulu	0.06	0.06	-0.17	0.00	-0.52	-0.50	-0.45
Australia	0.69	0.64	-0.37	0.14	-0.04	-0.17	0.10
Tasmania	–	0.54	-0.27	0.05	-0.10	-0.32	0.11
Tolai	0.54	–	0.01	0.39	0.11	-0.22	-0.09
Hawaii	-0.27	0.01	–	0.62	0.59	0.08	-0.28
Easter I	0.05	0.39	0.62	–	0.36	-0.26	-0.47
Moriori	-0.10	0.11	0.59	0.36	–	0.47	0.09
Arikara	-0.32	-0.22	0.08	-0.26	0.47	–	0.28
Santa Cruz	0.11	-0.09	-0.28	-0.47	0.09	0.28	–
Peru	-0.28	-0.60	-0.34	-0.63	-0.23	0.13	0.45
N Japan	-0.52	-0.45	0.18	-0.24	0.08	0.18	0.12
S Japan	-0.61	-0.30	0.33	0.03	0.01	0.01	-0.18
Hainan	-0.50	-0.33	0.25	-0.11	-0.13	0.02	-0.17
Atayal	-0.13	-0.34	-0.26	-0.28	-0.50	-0.12	-0.06
Philippines	–	–	–	–	–	–	–
Guam	-0.47	-0.26	0.45	0.08	0.24	0.25	-0.12
Egypt	-0.15	-0.46	-0.43	-0.34	-0.38	-0.24	-0.07
Bushman	0.26	0.00	-0.45	-0.09	-0.69	-0.49	-0.07
Andaman Is	0.09	-0.05	-0.38	-0.34	-0.51	-0.26	0.14
Ainu	-0.28	-0.50	0.34	-0.03	0.13	0.09	-0.20
Buriat	-0.55	-0.48	0.33	-0.21	0.18	0.61	0.09
Eskimo	-0.25	0.20	0.56	0.54	0.43	0.16	-0.18
Anyang	–	–	–	–	–	–	–

TABLE 7. Continued.
Correlations Among 26 Female Groups
(Based on the 57 Mean C-Scores of Each)

	Per	NJa	SJa	Hai	Ata	Phi	Gua
Norse	0.40	-0.22	-0.26	-0.29	-0.08	–	-0.37
Zalavár	0.60	0.07	-0.09	-0.04	0.34	–	-0.21
Berg	0.61	0.11	-0.13	0.01	0.34	–	-0.18
Teita	-0.53	-0.46	-0.19	-0.15	-0.08	–	-0.11
Dogon	0.01	-0.08	0.04	0.21	0.28	–	-0.02
Zulu	-0.37	-0.16	0.01	-0.05	0.04	–	-0.09
Australia	-0.46	-0.57	-0.66	-0.71	-0.42	–	-0.51
Tasmania	-0.28	-0.52	-0.61	-0.50	-0.13	–	-0.47
Tolai	-0.60	-0.45	-0.30	-0.33	-0.34	–	-0.26
Hawaii	-0.34	0.18	0.33	0.25	-0.26	–	0.45
Easter I	-0.63	-0.24	0.03	-0.11	-0.28	–	0.08
Moriori	-0.23	0.08	0.01	-0.13	-0.50	–	0.24
Arikara	0.13	0.18	0.01	0.02	-0.12	–	0.25
Santa Cruz	0.45	0.12	-0.18	-0.17	-0.06	–	-0.12
Peru	–	0.33	0.13	0.23	0.39	–	-0.02
N Japan	0.33	–	0.76	0.57	0.37	–	0.45
S Japan	0.13	0.76	–	0.73	0.43	–	0.54
Hainan	0.23	0.57	0.73	–	0.52	–	0.69
Atayal	0.39	0.37	0.43	0.52	–	–	0.25
Philippines	–	–	–	–	–	–	–
Guam	-0.02	0.45	0.54	0.69	0.25	–	–
Egypt	0.47	-0.07	-0.07	-0.09	0.21	–	-0.42
Bushman	-0.17	-0.07	-0.09	-0.10	0.19	–	-0.28
Andaman Is	0.36	-0.07	-0.14	0.19	0.44	–	-0.24
Ainu	-0.01	0.29	0.36	0.22	0.09	–	0.40
Buriat	0.18	0.49	0.43	0.44	0.11	–	0.55
Eskimo	-0.51	0.06	0.31	0.11	-0.21	–	0.41
Anyang	–	–	–	–	–	–	–

	Egy	Bus	And	Ain	Bur	Esk	Any
Norse	0.76	0.13	0.02	0.07	-0.03	-0.22	–
Zalavár	0.67	0.10	0.13	0.26	0.11	-0.42	–
Berg	0.43	0.11	0.25	0.10	0.35	-0.49	–
Teita	-0.02	0.49	0.15	-0.25	-0.32	0.07	–
Dogon	0.33	0.30	0.56	-0.02	-0.32	-0.42	–
Zulu	0.12	0.55	0.04	0.12	-0.26	-0.08	–
Australia	-0.18	0.29	-0.12	-0.33	-0.54	0.04	–
Tasmania	-0.15	0.26	0.09	-0.28	-0.55	-0.25	–
Tolai	-0.46	0.00	-0.05	-0.50	-0.48	0.20	–
Hawaii	-0.43	-0.45	-0.38	0.34	0.33	0.56	–
Easter I	-0.34	-0.09	-0.34	-0.03	-0.21	0.54	–
Moriori	-0.38	-0.69	-0.51	0.13	0.18	0.43	–
Arikara	-0.24	-0.49	-0.26	0.09	0.61	0.16	–
Santa Cruz	-0.07	-0.07	0.14	-0.20	0.09	-0.18	–
Peru	0.47	-0.17	0.36	-0.01	0.18	-0.51	–
N Japan	-0.07	-0.07	-0.07	0.29	0.49	0.06	–
S Japan	-0.07	-0.09	-0.14	0.36	0.43	0.31	–
Hainan	-0.09	-0.10	0.19	0.22	0.44	0.11	–
Atayal	0.21	0.19	0.44	0.09	0.11	-0.21	–
Philippines	–	–	–	–	–	–	–
Guam	-0.42	-0.28	-0.24	0.40	0.55	0.41	–
Egypt	–	0.16	0.42	0.00	-0.29	-0.44	–
Bushman	0.16	–	0.26	-0.10	-0.23	-0.21	–
Andaman Is	0.42	0.26	–	-0.39	-0.37	-0.61	–
Ainu	0.00	-0.10	-0.39	–	0.39	0.25	–
Buriat	-0.29	-0.23	-0.37	0.39	–	0.33	–
Eskimo	-0.44	-0.21	-0.61	0.25	0.33	–	–
Anyang	–	–	–	–	–	–	–

6
Q-Mode Analysis

The next step is to analyze the correlations and thus the configuration displayed by the dendrograms. It is clear that the correlation matrices are not one-dimensional, as they appear in the tables or the clusters. We have seen, for example, that Eskimos and Buriats seem like specialized Mongoloids, similar in some traits while differing in others, and their mutual correlation is only 0.33 in both sexes.

We proceed, therefore, to factor (by principal components analysis) the group correlations, by way of getting separate axes of population shape differences. Judging from the C-scores, for example, we might expect to find axes on one of which Eskimos and Buriats were similar and on another of which they were opposed.

This inverse of the usual procedure is known as Q-mode analysis, in which the factor pattern gives the loadings for populations, not for measurements, and in which the scoring is done on measurements, not on individuals or groups. We create a multidimensional universe of populations and find reference axes (principal components solution) through this space which are hierarchical and orthogonal. That is, the first factor places itself along the greatest general difference among populations; it does not necessarily run directly from one population at the plus end to another at the minus end, as though between absolutely polar populations, and so it does not necessarily find just the set of characters which might separate such polar opposites. By themselves the C-score means will suggest such characters, but not as integrated patterns. What is being done here is to articulate the groups into a system, while asking what characters control the system.

Especially when relating populations, Q-mode analysis avoids or alleviates various problems of the usual approach, such as what measurements or sets of measurements to enter. Of course, the route to population relations also is more direct.

18-GROUP ANALYSIS

I have asked whether we get a better statement as to regional distinctions by using all the populations at our disposal or by using the sparser and stricter set of the 18 core populations originally selected to represent those regions. We begin by trying the latter.

The full tables of factor results, even when limited to a small number of factors, are too bulky to bring into the text here. Instead, for easier comprehension and discussion, all the significant figures are abstracted below. In appendix D, table D-1 gives the factor pattern: the loadings or projections of the *populations* on the axes developed by the solution of the intergroup correlations. Table D-2 gives the corresponding scorings of the *measurements*, i.e., their relative importance in the space determined by the populations.

Throughout these analyses it will be found that the plots of the populations on the factors (figs. 5–14) give a coherence to the results that is harder to see from the values of loadings and scores. They also make clear the strong agreement between the male and female analyses. These plots should be referred to while reading what follows here.

FACTOR 1

Factor 1 opposes both Europeans and Far Easterners (and also Peruvians) to Australoids, especially Tolai (and also Easter Islanders and African Teita). This seems unfocused: clarification will follow.

	Male	Female		Male	Female
Peru	.77	.83	Tolai	-.87	-.82
Berg	.74	.73	Australia	-.76	-.71
Zalavár	.56	.67	Teita	-.60	-.58
N Japan	.49	.60	Tasmania	-.58	-.54
Hainan	.56	.44	Easter I	-.54	-.64
Norse	.48	.41			
S Japan	.36	.40			

Factor 1: Abstract from measurement scores

	Male	Female		Male	Female
XCB	2.40	2.13	BPL	-1.86	-1.88
STB	2.09	2.10	PRR	-1.75	-1.77
XFB	1.97	1.94	SSR	-1.65	-1.68
WCB	1.54	1.75	IML	-1.43	-1.69
AUB	1.68	1.57	AVR	-1.45	-1.37
ASB	1.13	1.16	NLB	-1.47	-1.26
NPH	1.38	1.37	ZMR	-1.18	-1.27
NLH	1.15	1.27	FMB	-1.03	-0.90
WMH	1.25	1.00			

It must be repeated that the analyses of males and females are parallel, but completely independent and separate, and so agreements in results give weight to their significance. The figures above are abstracted in gross order of size agreement between the sexes, giving the largest positive and negative values for population "loadings" and measurement "scores." The population figures shown are all those which seem to have any importance.

As to measurements, a high positive value, as for XCB (maximum cranial breadth), means that this measurement contributes to a positive loading for a population, like Europeans and Far Easterners, that has a positive C-score for XCB, and to a negative loading for narrow-skulled Tolais. Conversely, a projecting upper jaw (high BPL C-score), as in Tolais, will also contribute to a *negative* loading for that population, while the opposite, a low, minus C-score value for BPL (Europeans) will, by a minus-minus multiplication, enhance a positive loading.

This factor produces a simple pattern. The positive end expresses a vault that is laterally expanded at all points combined with a face that is moderately high and well retracted in its lower part. Whatever their differences (to be found on other factors), these things characterize Far Easterners and Europeans, and their opposites are traits of Australoids.

Back-scoring of outside populations. If, for a given factor, a complete vector of all the measurement scores is used to multiply the complete C-scores of a population, this will return the factor loading of that population as seen in the factor pattern. Furthermore, another population not present in the original correlation matrix may be treated in the same way, thus being given factor loading values to place it with relation to the original 18 groups, without disturbing the pattern as already found. The following are those values on factor 1, for some of these other populations, which are high enough to be of interest.

	Male	Female
Buriat	.49	.54
Atayal	.52	.44
Philippines	.43	—
Anyang	.35	—

The "Mongoloid" affiliation of these highest positive figures is obvious.

These back-scored populations are introduced among the 18 core groups plotted in figures 5b, 6b, 7b, and 8b. Their positions are instructive and logical, and conform to positions in the later analysis of all 28 (26 female) groups.

FACTOR 2

Factor 2 separates Europeans (and Africans to some degree) from Polynesians (and Far Easterners). These are the principal factor loadings (signs for the females have been reversed from tables D-1 and D-2):

	Male	Female		Male	Female
Norse	.57	.59	Hawaii	-.82	-.81
Zalavár	.56	.56	Moriori	-.67	-.58
Berg	.45	.49	N Japan	-.58	-.53
Dogon	.56	.20	S Japan	-.51	-.68
Zulu	.50	.26	Easter I	-.55	-.49
Australia	.33	.49	Hainan	-.26	-.55

Factor 2: Abstract from measurement scores

	Male	Female		Male	Female
NDS	2.71	2.85	BBH	-1.69	-2.03
SIS	1.62	2.05	VRR	-1.79	-1.92
WNB	1.97	1.57	EKR	-1.79	-1.90
NAS	1.67	1.72	FMR	-1.64	-1.61
			NLH	-1.21	-1.40
			DKR	-1.27	-1.24
			OBH	-0.72	-1.16

On the positive side the essence of this factor, apart from low heads, is in the prominence and width of the upper nasal bones (WNB, SIS) relative to the orbits (NDS) and to the sides of the face, which are somewhat drawn back (NAS, negative EKR, FMR).

This is mostly a European factor. Europeans and Africans do share some common ground here, but C- scores show that the nasal saddle (SIS) is rather low in Africans, certainly in Teita. But this seems to be overcome by other traits, and leaves in contrast the unelevated nasalia and transversely straighter upper orbital margin seen in Polynesians and other Mongoloids. Other, non-core populations register as follows (see figs. 5b and 6b):

	Male	Female		Male	Female
Egypt	.52	.50	Guam	-.59	-.65
Bushman	.52	.45	Eskimo	-.58	-.57
			Anyang	-.53	—
			Buriat	-.38	-.42

FACTOR 3

This factor seems to distinguish between Africans and some Asians on the one hand and some American Indians and Polynesians on the other, without signifying great homogeneity in such groups.

	Male	Female		Male	Female
Dogon	.60	.78	Santa Cruz	-.65	-.52
Zulu	.63	.75	Arikara	-.58	-.64
S Japan	.68	.41	Moriori	-.45	-.64
Teita	.39	.53			
*	*	*			
Anyang	.50	—			
Philippines	.45	—			
Atayal	.44	.42			
Bushman	.37	.46			

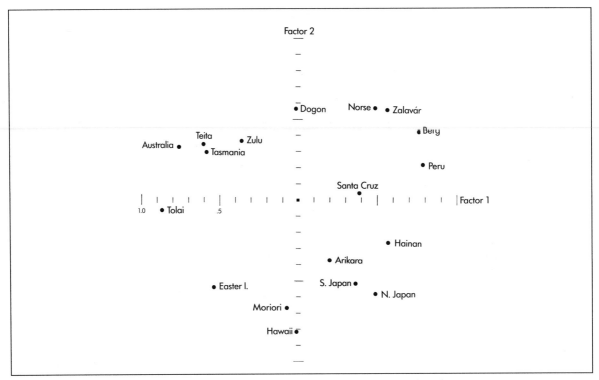

Figure 5a. Q-mode analysis of 18 male groups. Plot of factors 1 and 2.

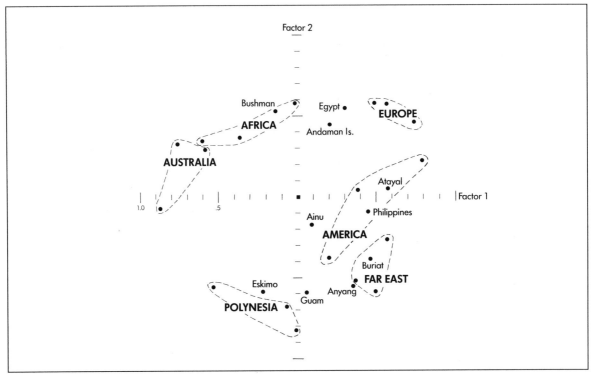

Figure 5b. Q-mode analysis of 18 male groups plotted as in figure 5a, but grouped and unlabeled. 10 labeled additional groups added by back-scoring.

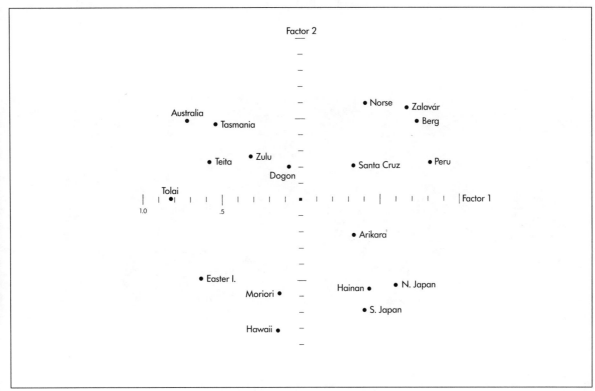

Figure 6a. Q-mode analysis of 18 female groups. Plot of factors 1 and 2.

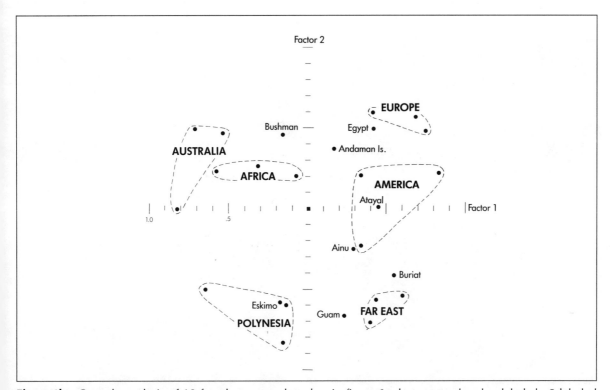

Figure 6b. Q-mode analysis of 18 female groups plotted as in figure 6a, but grouped and unlabeled. 8 labeled additional groups added by back-scoring.

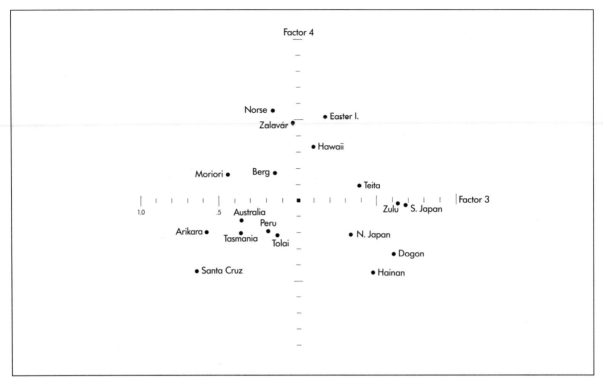

Figure 7a. Q-mode analysis of 18 male groups. Plot of factors 3 and 4.

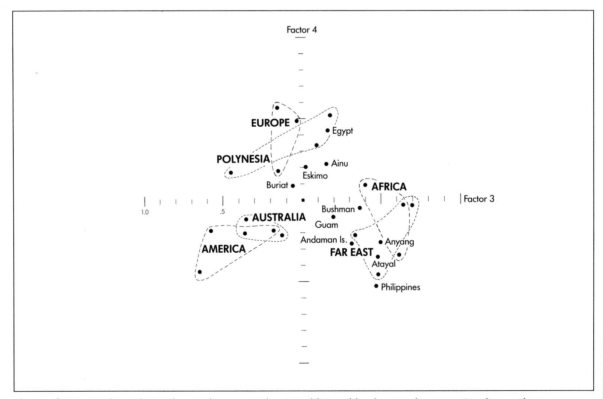

Figure 7b. Q-mode analysis of 18 male groups plus 10 additional back-scored groups. See figure 5b.

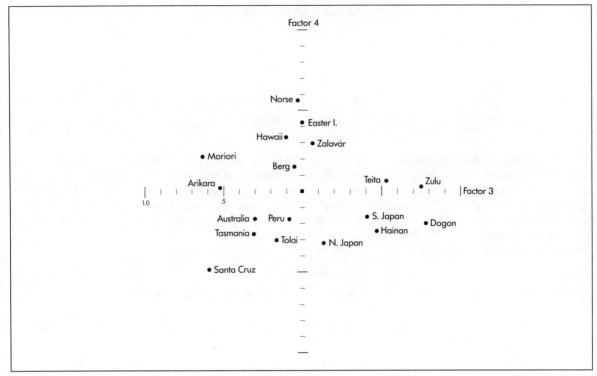

Figure 8a. Q-mode analysis of 18 female groups. Plot of factors 3 and 4.

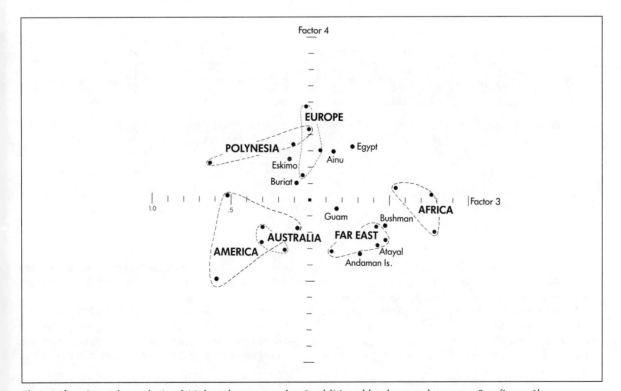

Figure 8b. Q-mode analysis of 18 female groups plus 8 additional back-scored groups. See figure 6b.

Factor 3: Abstract from measurement scores

	Male	Female		Male	Female
PAF	2.42	2.86	GLS	-2.42	-2.76
FRS	2.33	2.25	AUB	-2.09	-2.18
NLB	1.16	1.86	ZYB	-1.68	-1.49
PAC	1.27	1.45	SSS	-1.27	-1.47
STB	1.27	1.37	SIS	-1.65	-1.34
BBH	1.66	1.03	NDS	-2.02	-0.84
VRR	1.51	1.07	SSR	-0.93	-1.26

It is hard to see much of a pattern here. The positive side implies a high and long (in the parietal) vault profile with a convex forehead smooth at glabella; the negative side is the opposite, with a relative prominence of the nose and subnasal profile. It is clear that there is no great inner coherence of geographic groups, whose members are evidently divided by details. Moriori are low skulled, but other Polynesians are not; Santa Cruz Islanders are helped to a high negative score by high GLS; Arikara are low in GLS but high in the AUB. Thus, the factor is good at making such distinctions but is perhaps less so at describing groups or populations broadly.

FACTOR 4

This factor makes a still less informative arrangement, pairing Santa Cruz and Hainan against pairs of Europeans and Polynesians.

	Male	Female		Male	Female
Santa Cruz	.45	.49	Norse	-.55	-.54
Hainan	.45	.24	Easter I	-.51	-.43
			Zalavár	-.48	-.30
			Hawaii	-.33	-.34

Factor 4: Abstract from measurement scores

	Male	Female		Male	Female
MAB	2.07	2.49	BNL	-1.75	-2.19
WCB	1.76	2.00	NAR	-1.89	-2.06
ZMB	2.00	1.59	NDS	-1.76	-1.66
NLB	1.60	1.37	NOL	-2.02	-1.43
MLS	1.79	1.18	GOL	-2.00	-1.35
			DKR	-1.23	-1.36
			ZOR	-1.21	-1.16
			STB	-1.12	-1.20

The pattern of the positive end is a breadth of the lower face and palate coupled with a short skull and skull base. The opposite, a narrow palate and sphenoid region and a long base placing the upper face well forward, is characteristic of Polynesians.

SUMMARY

As a display of information explaining the relations of six areal groups, this analysis is not impressive. The last two factors mostly suggest groupings which seem to rest on secondary aspects of shape that are less helpful than previous factors in understanding relationships or other matters.

Further factors are less instructive still. **Factor 5** (figures not cited here; see appendix D) again stresses glabellar prominence, and in both sexes logically opposes Tasmanians to Dogon and Arikara (these last two were sharply separated on factor 3, which also featured GLS). At this point it is evident that factors are getting down to small distinctions such as this, i.e., differences in GLS development not fully absorbed by earlier factors.

Although interpretation may be difficult, the continuing strong agreement between the analyses for the two sexes nevertheless shows that the underlying results are coherent and firm, and are not the vagaries of residual error in the material.

Plotting the populations on the factors (figs. 5a–8b) also reveals a greater degree of order than is readily seen from the figures alone. Not only do the area groups segregate well, but the placement is highly similar in the two sexes. (There are overlaps between areas in the plots of factors 3 and 4, but it must be remembered that all factors are orthogonal, so that factors 1 and 2 separate such apparently overlapping groups from one another in the total space.)

The extra populations, when back-scored, also take informative positions. Egyptians are close to Europeans; Bushmen to other Africans; and Atayals, Filipinos, and the Anyang population to the Far Eastern groups, while Ainus are not. Eskimos are insistently close to Polynesians, but Guamanians are not.

ROTATED 18-GROUP FACTORS

An attempt may be made to sharpen relations or distinctions by rotating the above factors to new positions in the population multispace. This is done here by the VARIMAX method, which maintains the orthogonality (mutual independence) of the factors. It wrestles all the factors simultaneously into new positions by maximizing some loadings while bringing the rest as close as possible to zero.

This manhandling of the analysis can have undesirable effects and to my mind should not be used for primary interpretation. In particular, the purpose of maximizing loadings on any one factor quickly leads to singletons: i.e., factors with very high loadings for a single population and low loadings for all others, a situation which tells nothing about relationships.

Because of this nature, the rotation produces only two factors of meaning before degenerating into singletons, as above. Full tables will be omitted from the appendices, leaving only the figures extracted below. Nevertheless, the rotation does provide a second perspective.

FACTOR 2/1

In the original tables (not included in the appendices), it is obvious that the first factor in the females corresponds to the second factor in the males, and the data are so arranged below and in figures 9 and 10. In each sex, the factor explains 19% of the total covariance.

	Male (Factor 2)	Female (Factor 1)		Male (Factor 2)	Female (Factor 1)
S Japan	.96	.96	Australia	-.72	-.71
N Japan	.86	.86	Tasmania	-.57	-.69
Hainan	.70	.70	Tolai	-.46	-.40
*	*	*			
Anyang	.75	—			
Philippines	.56	—			
Atayal	.55	.44			
Guam	.40	.51			
Buriat	.41	.47			
Ainu	.19	.31			

Factor 2/1: Abstract from measurement scores

	Male (Factor 2)	Female (Factor 1)		Male (Factor 2)	Female (Factor 1)
PAF	1.75	1.42	NDS	-3.15	-2.70
WCB	1.41	1.38	SIS	-1.89	-2.10
NPH	1.33	1.91	IML	-1.81	-1.85
NLH	1.01	1.72	GLS	-1.41	-1.89
OCC	1.45	1.15	FMB	-1.29	-1.70
OCF	1.40	1.28	NAS	-1.30	-1.45
BBH	1.25	1.21	WNB	-1.50	-1.02

The positive pole, in both the male and female hyperspaces, points almost directly at the South Japanese population, with a loading or correlation of nearly 1.00 with the factor. This is followed by the other two Far East populations, all with loadings which are (when rounded to two decimal places) uncannily identical in the two sexes. By back-scoring, all the other Asiatic or near-Asiatic populations appear as the only ones with positive projections of any value on this axis, trailed well to the rear by the Ainu (figs. 9 and 10).

Accordingly, the measurement scores may be taken as a pattern set by the South Japanese. The pattern is dominated by naso-dacryal and nasal flatness seconded by glabellar smoothness and a narrow, straight, upper orbital rim, and also by a high face and high narrow nose. These are all familiar traits seen already in this set of populations.

In the vicinity of the negative pole are the three Australoid groups, the only ones with consequential loadings.

FACTOR 1/2

Factor 1/2 represents the opposite pairing: factor 1 in males, factor 2 in females. The proportions of covariance explained are 19% and 18%, respectively.

	Male (Factor 1)	Female (Factor 2)		Male (Factor 1)	Female (Factor 2)
Berg	.82	.95	Tolai	-.70	-.58
Zalavár	.90	.83	Easter I	-.36	-.57
Norse	.91	.46	Eskimo	-.31	-.48
Egypt	.66	.41	Australia	-.36	-.34
Peru	.39	.51	Moriori	-.22	-.42
			Hawaii	-.24	-.32

Factor 1/2: Abstract from measurement scores

	Male (Factor 1)	Female (Factor 2)		Male (Factor 1)	Female (Factor 2)
STB	2.42	2.83	BPL	-1.75	-1.79
XFB	2.24	2.78	PRR	-1.50	-1.43
XCB	2.30	2.26	MLS	-1.02	-1.46
NDS	2.31	1.69	ZMB	-1.57	-1.00
ASB	1.35	1.47	IML	-1.08	-0.90
SIS	1.14	1.06			
NOL	1.05	0.99			
AUB	0.96	0.99			

Given that, on other evidence, the male and female population spaces are quite similar, it is evident that here the factor axes have been rotated to somewhat different positions: closer to Norse and Zalavár in the males and toward Berg in the females; at the negative end toward Tolai in both sexes, but also more toward Polynesians in the females. (The measurement scores, without going into details, reflect a European pattern on the positive side, with particular emphasis on frontal vault expansion and nasal root prominence.)

ADDITIONAL FACTORS

As suggested above, these additional factors are essentially singletons. For **Factor 3** the male/female loadings are: Santa Cruz .93/.93, Peru .34/.34, Easter Island -.61/-.42. The high measurement scores are least cranial breadth (WCB), positive; parietal chord (PAC), negative. In these two measurements Santa Cruz is indeed extreme among the 18 populations. For **Factor 5**, loadings are: Arikara .92/.94, Zulu -.27/-.25 (inconsequential). The high measurement scores are auricular breadth (AUB), positive; frontal subtense (FRS), negative. In the relevant C-scores Arikara are pronounced or extreme. Thus these and later factors tell us nothing that cannot be read in the tables of C-scores themselves.

Nor do they help with relationships: Santa Cruz and Arikara are both American populations, and neither registers at all on factors 1 and 2 (note figs. 9, 10), but these singleton factors do not relate them to each other or to other populations.

The essence of this excursion into factor rotation is finding axes which single out Far Easterners in the first case and Europeans in the second, with Australoids in the generally opposed position. Graphing distributions on the two factors (figs. 9 and 10) emphasizes the isolation of the Australoids from others better than does their position on either factor taken alone.

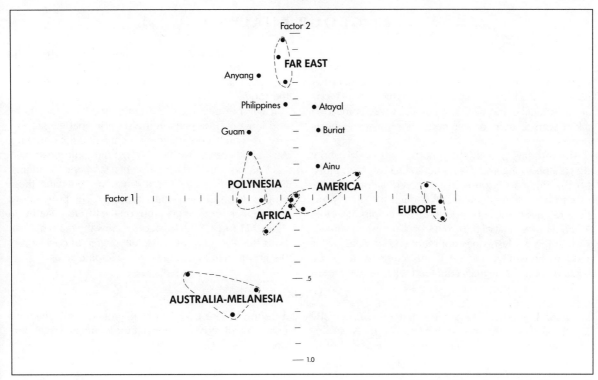

Figure 9. Q-mode analysis of 18 male groups. Plot of first 2 rotated factors, with 6 additional groups back-scored.

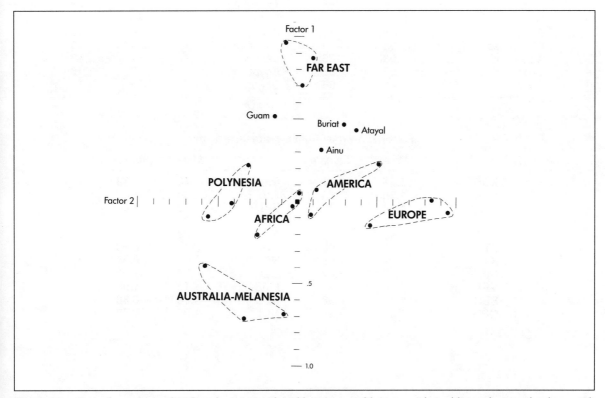

Figure 10. Q-mode analysis of 18 female groups. Plot of first 2 rotated factors, with 4 additional groups back-scored.

28-GROUP ANALYSIS

Here we use correlations (from tables 6 and 7) among all the 28 populations (26 in females), not the 18 core groups only. It might be hoped that this thicker body of information will give clearer statements as to which populations are most unlike and why; but any such results must be taken with a grain of salt because of special effects imposed by actual input.

The resulting plots of the groups (figs. 11–14) show that (1) the arrangement is similar to the 18-group plots; (2) the non-core groups, back-scored before but included here in the analysis, take much the same positions relative to the core groups; (3) the graphs of factors 1 and 2 place most of the groups on a peripheral circle, so that this analysis does not mark any as singular for modern humanity; and (4) if this circle were to be rotated about 90 degrees counterclockwise, we would have a sort of skeleton map, finding Europeans in the far west, Polynesians in the far east (in the Pacific Ocean), Far Easterners in the north, and Australoids in the south.

It will be seen at once that the first three factors by and large oppose pairs of the six principal geographic groups which contain the 18 core populations, viz., Australoids versus Far East Mongoloids, Europeans versus Polynesians, and Africans versus American Indians. Further factors find finer distinctions, breaking these groups down for secondary reasons. The populations are graphed for their positions on the first four factors in figures 11 to 14, which not only show the main oppositions but also support the actual degree of cohesion of the groups making up the six geographic areas.

FACTOR 1

Factor 1 opposes Mongoloids generally, especially Far Easterners (but not Polynesians), to Australo-Melanesians and, to a lower degree, to Africans. Below are shown these populations in gross order of the most positive and most negative factor loadings (see appendix E, table E-1).

	Male	Female		Male	Female
N Japan	.81	.72	Australia	-.80	-.84
Anyang	.80	—	Tolai	-.65	-.79
Hainan	.79	.64	Tasmania	-.62	-.68
S Japan	.71	.62	Teita	-.56	-.57
Buriat	.68	.71	Zulu	-.38	-.33
Philippines	.65	—	Bushman	-.24	-.30
Atayal	.63	.46	Easter I	-.17	-.43
Guam	.53	.52	Egypt	-.17	+.18
Peru	.42	.64	Dogon	-.09	-.11
Hawaii	.39	.16			

Factor 1: Abstract from measurement scores

	Male	Female		Male	Female
XCB	1.77	2.08	SSR	-1.43	-1.63
AUB	1.86	1.80	IML	-1.33	-1.67
WCB	1.74	1.84	BPL	-1.32	-1.62
NLH	1.41	1.56	PRR	-1.24	-1.63
WMH	1.49	1.51	AVR	-1.28	-1.38
STB	1.22	1.85	NDS	-2.24	-0.80
XFB	1.07	1.68	NAS	-1.56	-0.94
NPH	1.19	1.42	GOL	-1.25	-1.05
VRR	1.44	1.11	FMB	-1.13	-1.08
BBH	1.48	0.98	SSS	-1.18	-0.86
OBH	0.84	1.17	NOL	-1.03	-0.78

This factor makes a clear pattern. The positive, or "Mongoloid," end reflects a relatively high face which is narrow and flat across the upper part (low NDS, FMB) and also below the nose (SSR, PRR). This is joined to a vault that is moderately broad, especially at the base (AUB, WCB) and also high (BBH, VRR). The opposite or minus end signals a decided "Australoid" configuration: a short face, protruding in the mouth region (SSR, BPL), on a vault low and narrow throughout, especially at the frontal (STB, XFB).

This configuration may not be the most specifically Australoid, such as might be read directly from a profile of the C-scores, since the axis of factor 1 is partly determined by other populations, especially Africans,

who for example differ greatly from Australoids in frontal and glabellar shape. This last fact doubtless explains the absence of GLS from among the highest values above. Nonetheless, the factor to a great degree delineates the distinctive and opposing characters of Far Eastern Mongoloids on the one hand and of Australoids on the other, and seems to point to them as perhaps the most contrasting populations in modern humanity. But this may be an artifact: in this analysis, compared to the 18-group analysis, a larger number of "Mongoloid" groups is present (notably Anyang and Buriats), and this probably determines a different position for this main axis, thus diminishing the scores of European groups.

FACTOR 2

Factor 2 mainly opposes Europeans (plus Egyptians and Andaman Islanders!) to Polynesians and Eskimos.

	Male	Female		Male	Female
Zalavár	.71	.69	Eskimo	-.73	-.77
Andaman Is	.73	.62	Hawaii	-.67	-.80
Egypt	.68	.73	Moriori	-.65	-.73
Berg	.68	.63	Easter I	-.67	-.63
Norse	.61	.59	Guam	-.54	-.54
Peru	.58	.53	Tolai	-.47	-.29
Dogon	.58	.41	Arikara	-.32	-.29
Bushman	.44	.47	Buriat	-.23	-.35

Factor 2: Abstract from measurement scores

	Male	Female		Male	Female
NDS	1.65	2.27	EKR	-1.64	-1.98
WNB	1.79	1.91	FMR	-1.55	-1.72
SIS	1.67	1.92	DKR	-1.32	-1.39
STB	2.05	1.42	ZMR	-1.22	-1.21
NAS	1.27	1.46	BNL	-1.23	-1.15
PAF	1.71	1.36	ZOR	-1.11	-1.25
FRS	1.57	1.25	SSR	-1.38	-1.08
XFB	1.56	1.12	PRR	-1.16	-0.97
DKB	1.35	1.29	NAR	-1.17	-0.92
DKS	1.14	1.24	BBH	-0.90	-1.27
PAS	1.12	0.84			
XCB	1.09	0.61			

Above all, factor 2 on the positive side distinguishes a wide and prominent upper nasal region (WNB, SIS, NDS), with the orbits deep (DKR, DKS) and the face pulled back on either side, especially above (FMR, EKR) but also below and at the mouth region (ZMR, SSR, PRR). There is a moderately full and broad forehead.

This conformation is that of Europeans (but also of the small-skulled Andamanese). That of Polynesians (and also Eskimos) is one of a diminished and flattened nasal saddle and an extended (BNL) and forwardly placed facial mask generally (radii to facial points); also a flattish and relatively narrow frontal bone.

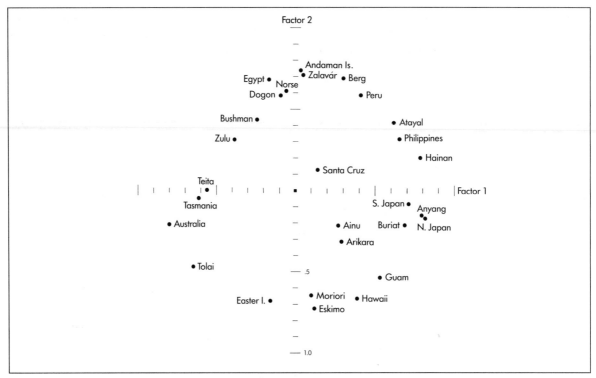

Figure 11. Q-mode analysis of 28 male groups. Plot of factors 1 and 2.

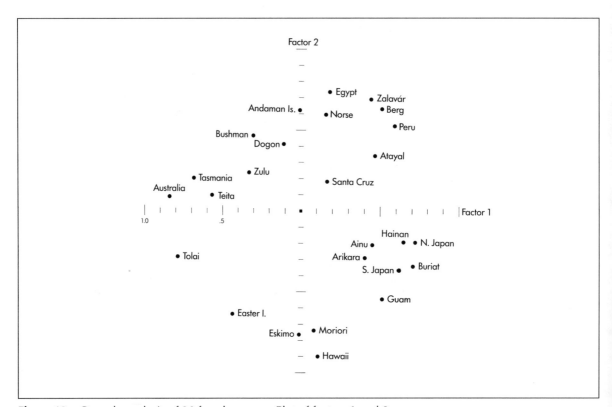

Figure 12. Q-mode analysis of 26 female groups. Plot of factors 1 and 2.

FACTOR 3

This factor opposes Africans, trailed by various Asiatic Mongoloids, to American Indians and Europeans.

	Male	Female		Male	Female
Zulu	.65	.66	Santa Cruz	-.60	-.60
Dogon	.59	.69	Arikara	-.59	-.51
Teita	.52	.53	Moriori	-.46	-.48
Bushman	.49	.43	Norse	-.46	-.31
S Japan	.47	.50	Berg	-.43	-.29
Anyang	.42	—	Peru	-.43	-.26
Philippines	.42	—	Zalavár	-.34	-.19
Hainan	.32	.55			
Atayal	.35	.44			

Factor 3: Abstract of measurement scores

	Male	Female		Male	Female
PAF	2.19	2.65	AUB	-2.24	-2.04
FRS	2.31	2.23	SIS	-2.09	-2.17
NLB	2.22	2.01	NDS	-2.28	-1.81
MLS	1.65	1.52	GLS	-1.20	-1.94
BBH	1.34	1.60	ZYB	-1.46	-1.27
DKB	1.35	1.39	XCB	-1.54	-0.96
PAC	1.35	1.37	ASB	-1.31	-1.08
VRR	0.79	1.27	SSS	-0.80	-1.27
			OCS	-0.83	-1.02
			SSR	-0.38	-1.04

This factor depicts, for Africans, a skull that is narrow behind and amidships (ASB, XCB), but particularly so at the base (AUB, ZYB). The vault, however, is convex in parietal profile, with the special feature that the point of greatest curvature is placed well back (PAF). The frontal is likewise rounded (FRS) and smooth (low GLS), and the nasal region is also broad (NLB, DKB) and low (SIS, NDS). These traits are not uniformly those of the Far East populations appearing above, who are probably arrayed here because of the upper nasal flatness.

At the opposite end of the scale, American Indians and Europeans share elevated and narrow nasal regions, and broader skulls and skull bases.

FACTOR 4

Factor 4 separates some Europeans from some American Indians, who were all grouped together under factor 3. The six major population groupings were set in roughly opposing pairs by the first three factors; here they start to be broken up, which continues in subsequent factors. This factor joins some Europeans (not Berg) with Egyptians, Ainus, and some Polynesians (not Moriori), and opposes to them a loose grouping of American Indians and Australoids. Thus coherence within geographic areas is being lost, along with some of the concordance between the sexes, as is reflected in the factor values of various measurements having lower loadings.

	Male	Female		Male	Female
Norse	.52	.59	Santa Cruz	-.55	-.45
Ainu	.37	.53	Tasmania	-.45	-.21
Egypt	.50	.34	Tolai	-.32	-.32
Zalavár	.46	.38	Philippines	-.38	—
Easter I	.44	.22	Hainan	-.25	-.29
Eskimo	.27	.30	Andaman Is	-.22	-.52
Zulu	.16	.34	Arikara	-.34	-.07
Hawaii	.30	.15	Australia	-.25	.00

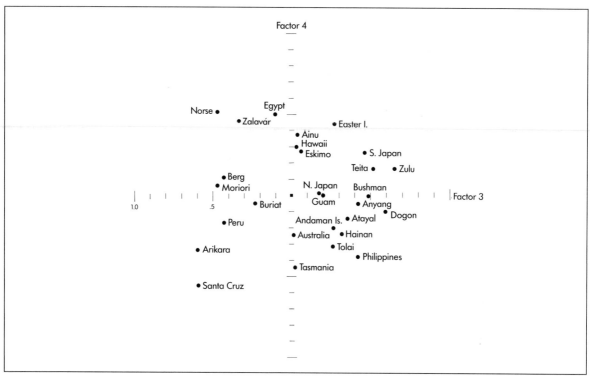

Figure 13. Q-mode analysis of 28 male groups. Plot of factors 3 and 4.

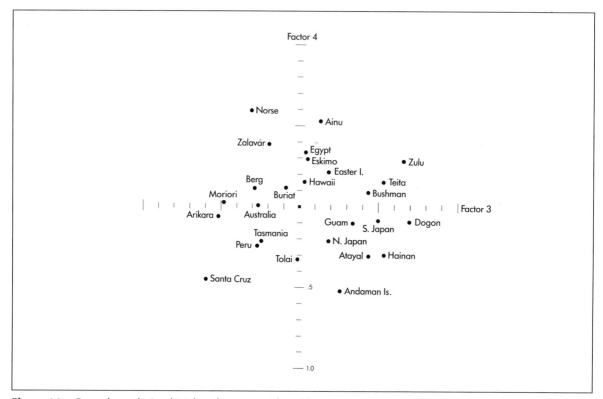

Figure 14. Q-mode analysis of 26 female groups. Plot of factors 3 and 4.

Factor 4: Abstract of measurement scores

	Male	Female		Male	Female
NOL	2.30	2.47	GLS	-1.83	-2.05
GOL	2.11	2.34	MAB	-1.54	-1.52
BNL	2.02	1.76	SSS	-1.34	-1.94
NAR	1.31	1.54	ZMB	-1.54	-1.27
STB	1.26	1.24	SOS	-1.35	-1.38
ZOR	1.20	1.23	MLS	-1.19	-1.46
DKR	1.14	1.15	IML	-1.20	-1.20
XFB	0.91	1.42	NLB	-1.89	-0.95
FRS	0.94	1.00	WCB	-1.45	-1.06
FRC	0.93	0.95	XML	-0.66	-1.11
NDS	0.82	1.17	ZYB	-1.07	-0.67

This factor accents a long cranial base (GOL, NOL, BNL, NAR; note that NOL is higher than GOL) and an orthognathous face: note the high values for BNL and NAR, with BPL and PRR not registering. Also, the prominent radii are those to the upper midface only (DKR, ZOR). The same suggestions of smaller size below, and general gracility, are seen in the measurements of the malar and the glabellar projection. This sounds Egyptian, and the retracted lower face is seen in Polynesians and Europeans, while the opposite nature goes well enough with Australoids and American In-

dians. If the apparent element of gracility does not accord with visual impressions of these latter or with Ainus, it must be remembered that this factor simply picks up secondary characters and relationships left after more important aspects have been absorbed by preceding factors.

In particular, this factor may be emphasizing the relative retraction of the lower face in Europeans and Polynesians, something that factor 2, in contrasting these two groupings, was not able to account for.

FACTOR 5

	Male	Female		Male	Female
Buriat	.49	.42	Egypt	-.36	-.44
Bushman	.43	.46	Andaman Is	-.40	-.29
Ainu	.59	.13	Moriori	-.32	-.28
Australia	.28	.28	Easter I	-.23	-.33
Berg	.32	.21	Peru	-.26	-.19

Factor 5: Abstract of measurement scores

	Male	Female		Male	Female
WCB	1.81	2.45	VRR	-2.17	-2.90
ASB	1.95	1.48	SSS	-2.52	-1.59
EKB	1.61	1.50	BBH	-1.56	-2.13
FRS	1.66	1.35	OCC	-1.44	-1.61
FMB	1.35	1.48	MDH	-1.26	-0.90
FOL	1.20	1.41	MDB	-0.93	-1.11
OBB	1.53	0.96	PAS	-1.28	-0.78
XFB	1.36	0.72	SIS	-0.65	-1.56
ZMR	0.99	1.05	NLH	-1.19	-0.85
ZYB	0.87	1.05	NDS	-0.46	-1.35
AUB	0.75	1.03			

Factor 5 bespeaks a low vault (VRR, BBH, OCC) and flattish subnasal region, together with a vault and face which are broad at their juncture (ASB, WCB, EKB, FMB, OBB). This apparently fits Buriats and Bushmen; the opposite—a high vault more constricted below—goes with Andamanese (note the separation from those other small dark-skinned pygmoids, the Bushmen) and Egyptians.

With this factor we are getting down to minor and

fugitive patterns of difference, uncovered after the effect of major axes has been absorbed. Nevertheless, there seems to be a little more substance than can be associated with the fifth factor in the 18-group analysis. The agreement between the sexes indicates that something real is being represented here, as in the minor factors of the previous analyses, though it is well past the point of having significant weight or being capable of real interpretation.

FACTOR 6

In this factor the female and male loadings have opposite signs (tables E-1 and E-2), and all female signs have therefore been reversed in the tabulations here.

	Male	Female		Male	Female
Dogon	.55	.46	Tasmania	-.49	-.41
Arikara	.35	.52	Ainu	-.33	-.24
Buriat	.26	.20	Hawaii	-.32	-.10
Teita	.12	.33	N Japan	-.20	-.26
Eskimo	.29	-.05	Atayal	-.09	-.22
			Bushman	+.01	-.22

Factor 6: Abstract from measurement scores

	Male	Female		Male	Female
ZMB	1.57	1.68	GLS	-4.04	-3.29
NPH	1.88	1.22	BBH	-1.56	-1.34
OBH	1.90	0.73	VRR	-1.85	-0.92
XML	1.46	1.14	GOL	-0.90	-1.53
NLH	1.48	0.91	PAC	-0.83	-1.51
NAS	1.23	1.05	WCB	-0.77	-1.49
IML	1.01	1.61	OCC	-0.80	-1.36
WNB	0.59	1.53	ASB	-0.78	-1.23
JUB	0.63	1.50	SSS	-1.43	-0.59
DKS	1.02	0.62			

Very few factor loadings carry any weight: a loading of 0.50 would associate 25% of the variance of that group with a given factor, but a loading of 0.20 only 4%, which is hardly of significance. The factor itself accounts for 4.5% of the male covariance matrix and 4.6% of the female.

The factor may suggest a high face (NPH, OBH, NLH), together with a marked lack of glabellar protrusion (GLS) and with some enlargement of the malar (ZMB, XML, IML, JUB) and a low vault. All of these are aspects of Dogon, Arikara, and Buriats, though not consistently (the Dogon face is low). The exact reverse is found in Tasmanians (except of course for a high vault). We are doubtless being told simply that previous factors do not account for the total difference in morphology between Tasmanian and Dogon faces.

FACTOR 7

	Male	Female		Male	Female
Eskimo	.29	.34	Ainu	-.38	-.44
Bushman	.39	.22	Teita	-.44	-.28
S Japan	.20	.20	Zulu	-.29	-.17
N Japan	.20	.15	Tasmania	+.05	-.32
Norse	.02	.27			

Factor 7: Abstract of measurement scores

	Male	Female		Male	Female
OCS	2.67	2.58	NLB	-2.26	-2.57
SOS	2.61	1.15	JUB	-1.54	-1.73
EKR	1.57	0.99	EKB	-1.42	-1.66
FOL	1.18	1.03	FMB	-1.39	-1.60
FRF	1.03	1.10	XCB	-1.23	-1.49
OCF	1.36	0.86	OBB	-1.15	-1.56
ZMR	0.79	1.30	BPL	-1.13	-0.95
			STB	-0.86	-1.17
			XFB	-1.01	-1.03

The pattern here is unfathomable and uninstructive. The positive end apparently signifies a flexed occiput and a protruding supraorbital, along with a narrow nose. Bushmen, however, have high C-scores for nasal breadth, and while Eskimos have narrow noses they lack convex occiputs or supraorbitals.

Factors 6 and 7 have been outlined here mainly to show the rapid decay in intelligibility, in spite of definite continuing agreement in the sexes, following factor 5. The proportion of covariance explained by successive factors is as follows:

	Male	*Female*
Factor 1	24%	24%
Factor 2	23%	23%
Factor 3	14%	14%
Factor 4	9%	8%
Factor 5	6%	6%
Factor 6	4%	5%
Factor 7	3%	4%
Factors 8–20	16%	16%

SUMMARY OF POPULATION SHAPE RELATIONS

The foregoing evidence supports the assumption that the primary geographical areas can be differentiated in aspects of shape. The factor plots show that the core groups, of three populations each, do indeed cohere consistently. The other populations do not, though they are distributed in generally suggestive adjunct positions.

Reading the information calls for a mental stereoscope, enabling one to look for the apparent leading characters of an area (mainly via C-scores) on the one hand, and to check their importance in distinguishing between areas (mainly via the factoring) on the other. It looks as though three areas were the most distinct: Europeans, Far Easterners, and Australo-Melanesians, particularly the last. These three are the areas picked out for mutual opposition by the earliest factors of the several Q-mode analyses. The Australoids appear to be the most isolated. The rotated 18-group factors pick them out as most distant from the other two, on different factors. In the tables of intercorrelations (see tables 6 and 7) they show the greatest distance, i.e., the most negative correlations, from the Far Easterners, except for the Tolai, who show very high negatives with Europeans. Europeans are most opposed to Polynesians, but are also strongly negative with Australoids; they and Far Easterners are mutually but less strongly negative in correlations. We now will look again at each area from all points of view.

Australo-Melanesia. The C-scores by themselves give a straightforward picture of a narrow frontal bone with heavy glabellar development, and a low face broad above and projecting below. The factor measurement scores, opposing Australo-Melanesians to both Far Easterners and Europeans, stress the narrow vault and projecting lower face. (These features are also brought out by the analyses in my 1973 report, which agree at various points with other characterizations below as well.)

Far East. The central character among Far Easterners is a narrow and flat bifrontal line, with a very low nasodacryal subtense: a depressed nasal saddle relative to the eyes, and a prominence of the latter. Face and skull are high (but the face is not broad). The face is somewhat retracted in the antero-posterior direction, particularly in the midline. The factor scores, mostly in opposition to Australoids, bring out the same features, with somewhat greater notice of cranial breadths.

Europe. The leading distinction of the Europeans, differentiating them above all from Far Easterners, is the prominence of the nasal saddle and of the nasion relative to the sides of the face, so that the eyes are deep-set. In the factors, oppositions to Australoids pick out cranial breadths in Europeans, while oppositions to Polynesians point to the retracted sides of the face. C-scores also show the European mouth region to be retracted and narrow.

Africa. Africans, the remaining eastern hemisphere population group, have some individuality but no strong position in the factor analyses: they are picked up only on factor 3, where they appear in opposition to American Indians, who are the most distant from Africa in terms of pre-Columbian travel. Africans are very narrow in the skull base, which is apparently reflected also in bizygomatic and bijugal narrowness. The frontal is convex and very low in glabella development. In the face, Africans contrast with Far Easterners in a marked breadth across the nose and between the eyes, as well as across the upper face, which is bowed forward in the midline (though without nasal prominence). Also, the face is short.

Polynesia. The contrasts between Polynesians and Europeans in factor 2 spell out main traits, but not emphatically enough: those traits are flatness and narrowness across the upper nose and upper face generally. Upper nasal diminution is extreme (more marked only in Eskimos). Also extreme is forwardness of the whole facial mask, most marked at the upper sides, and dropping off from nasion to prosthion, so that the lower part is relatively but not absolutely retracted. The palatal and sphenoidal breadths are distinctly small, as is the sagittal diameter of the foramen magnum.

Americas. American Indians are not very uniform (Peru tends to converge on Europeans in clustering) or strongly characterized. They have positions on factors 3 and 4 which accent different aspects and are best sorted out from the C-score means directly. Cranial vaults are short, and particularly broad in the base (auricular, zygomatic, and minimum cranial breadths) and lower face (palatal and zygomaxillary breadths), thus diverging from Polynesians. The nasalia are moderately prominent in American Indians (unlike other "Mongoloids"), but at the same time this region as a whole is not elevated relative to the sides of the face. Faces and vaults are high, frontals are flattish.

Calibration by Clustering

Analyses to this point have shown relationships in a general way and have confirmed some community of cranial shape within each geographical area. There are other important questions. What is the scale of differences among modern populations, viewed against the background of late hominid evolution in general? More specifically, can we use classic Neanderthals as an outgroup, both to give a yardstick and to see if any modern group is closer to that archaic population than are others? Where, on such a yardstick, lie other late prehistoric specimens of varying degrees of archaicness? How good is such a yardstick when used to place modern specimens of known derivation? Let us try to test these questions seriatim.

We have been examining Q-mode analyses of the 28 male / 26 female groups, a mode that provides a degree of stability in results but which has the effect of damping differences due to scale, and perhaps to other reasons (which I leave to others to examine). Here I shall change to R-mode analyses (canonical variates, principal components) as a more useful way of calibrating intergroup and interregion differences, since such

methods can be more specifically addressed to those differences. The differences involve measuring distances among the groups, as compared with the inspection and factorial plotting of C-scores as above. It must be realized that with these analyses the number of possible solutions is almost limitless, depending on the method of transformation chosen, the input of variables, the axes chosen, the computing of distances, and so on.

Accordingly, as practitioners of these arts know, results may be discrepant to a considerable degree, and there is the temptation, which will be yielded to herein, to choose those results which seem most satisfying. This is not evil if it is acknowledged. The object of study is the basic data, which have a hyperdimensional, normally messy, configuration that we wish to view. If this were something approaching a hypermoon, different analyses would have a roughly similar image. But such data sets as this one probably have a configuration more like the moons of Mars, with a shape that varies as we take different views of it, and we deduce what we are seeing as best we can. Some aspects are constant, others are not.

MAHALANOBIS D DISTANCES AMONG 28 MALE GROUPS + NEANDERTHALS (N = 2)

These are based on classic Mahalanobis D-square distances, using all 28 possible canonical variates to maximize discrimination, employing all 57 measurements.* The distance here is taken as the square root of those distances, a common practice, partly to arrive at a scale more like that of the Euclidean distances of the analyses following (see figs. 16 and 17). The Neanderthals are La Chapelle and La Ferrassie 1; because both crania are clearly male, and because there are two extra male series among the moderns, the analysis has been done on males only. This solution is likely to be as explicit and stable as can be achieved.

The clustering is shown in figure 15. The populations are arrayed in gratifying fashion, with the six core

groups forming up as geography would suggest. Except for American Indians, Buriats, and Eskimos, all "Mongoloids" group nicely, although Polynesians are separated from others to about the same degree as Africans (plus Andamanese) are separated from Australoids. American Indians, plus Buriats and Eskimos, join with Europeans; possibly an odd result, but see Cavalli-Sforza et al. (1988).

(Using the D-square distances instead produces a slightly different dendrogram, moving the Ainus to the European-American Indian branch and reorganizing the final branches somewhat, a reminder of the frailty of such joinings. The primary groupings of the core populations, however, remain the same.)

The main point here is the separation of the Neanderthals, who in this clustering are almost twice as far removed from all moderns as the African-Australoid branch is from other lines. A dendrogram such as this

---

*The program used is CANDISC of the SAS package. The canonical variates are standardized, with mean = 0 and within-group standard deviation = 1.0. Clustering was performed by Jones's NATURE'S GROUPS (Jones 1964).

does not suggest whether some modern populations are closer to Neanderthals than others. The actual table of distances appears in appendix F as table A-9; it shows that distances from the Neanderthal pair of modern populations are all of the same order of size, very roughly over twice that among themselves. (In the D-square differences, not shown, the magnitude is much greater.) Most distant are Eskimos; closest are Tasmanians. Among Europeans, Norse are more distant than Berg, who are about as distant as South Australians, both being more distant than Arikara or Santa Cruz Indians.

PRINCIPAL COMPONENTS ANALYSIS: 28 MODERN GROUPS + 22 PREMODERN SAMPLES

These units are scored on principal components based on raw scores of the 28 male groups. Here the measurements are converted to orthogonal scales without the element of discrimination among groups as above, and the eigenvalues associated with these are hierarchical, with much of the covariance accounted for by the first few components. (See the section on Q-mode analysis, above.)

Components 2 through 18 have been used in forming Euclidean distances for cluster analysis. The first component was discarded as a concession to the influence of size (see discussion under PENSIZE), with the idea that Neanderthal individuality need not be presumed to be a matter of size alone.

Here the two Neanderthal skulls (La Chapelle and La Ferrassie) are entered as individuals, not as a sample of two, as above. The other equally archaic specimen is Broken Hill. There are also 19 additional crania or small samples, of late Pleistocene to modern date, to test both scale and "correct" affiliation. This is not systematic, or an attempt to review a wide series of such affiliations; these are simply specimens selected from those I have measured for the test series. All, like the Neanderthals, are diagnosed as "male," and so the clusterings have been performed on males only. The specimens or samples used are listed below.

Canary Islands: a sample of 3

Kurgan: a sample of 2, from mounds of the Kurgan culture in southern Russia, dating probably to the 4th millennium B.C.

Natufian: a skull of this Mesolithic culture, early Holocene, Israel

Tepe Yahya: an aristocratic burial in this southern Iranian mound, probably 3rd millennium B.C.

Skhul 5: late Pleistocene, Mt. Carmel, Israel

Qafzeh 6: ca. 92,000 B.P., Jebel Qafzeh, Israel

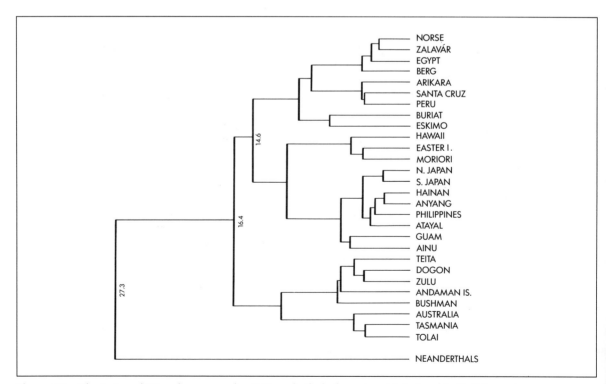

Figure 15. Clustering of 28 male groups plus 2 Neanderthals (based on Mahalanobis D distances).

Muge: a sample of 5 males from Mesolithic sites, central Portugal, ca. 7000–8000 B.P.

Teviec: a sample of 2 from the Mesolithic site in Brittany

Mladeč (Lautsch) 1: (cast; possibly female) Aurignacian of Czechoslovakia

Irhoud 1: (cast) Upper Pleistocene of Morocco

Afalou: #5 and #9, Upper Paleolithic at Afalou bou Rhummel, late Pleistocene/Holocene, Algeria

Elmenteita: sample of 2 (A and B), Bromhead's site, Kenya, ca. 7000 B.P.

Fingira: #2, Late Stone Age of Malawi, ca. 3300 B.P.

Fish Hoek: Cape Province, South Africa, 12,000–13,000 B.P.

Upper Cave 101: (cast) Zhoukoudian, China

Keilor: Victoria, Australia, >13,000 B.P.

South Maori: sample of 10, Murihiku coast, New Zealand

Tonga: sample of 4

Gilbert Islands (Kiribati): sample of 4

Broken Hill: Kabwe, Zambia, late Middle Pleistocene?

La Chapelle: Neanderthal, Corrèze, France

La Ferrassie 1: Neanderthal, Dordogne, France

To repeat, input from the material can be varied almost limitlessly, thereby also varying the results. Furthermore, as Bulbeck (1981) has astutely remarked, large samples and individual skulls are different kinds of data. Samples have central tendencies, but individual configurations—shapes—can depart considerably from the mean, and need not closely approach an actual or putative parent population in clustering. (Small samples of 2 or more tend to diminish this distinction.)

As we have seen already, results in this study have a common complexion over a number of runs. They tend to cluster members of regional groups, while placing introduced samples (and some base series like the Ainus or Eskimos) in different positions. In this dendrogram (fig. 16) groupings conform well to what might be expected. American Indians come into one group, along with the Buriats. Muge, Teviec, and Afalou join Europeans (which they do not do in all runs). There are also anomalies which do not appear in other runs:

Eskimos and Micronesian Gilbert Islanders have no business being grouped with Africans; Elmenteita should go with Africans but does so in no runs. Upper Cave 101 avoids Asiatics. Mladeč, Fingira, and Keilor might be expected to go with Europe, Africa, and Australia respectively: the first two do so in some runs, but Keilor tends to be recalcitrant.

A special group of six premodern skulls (Natufian, Qafzeh 6, Fish Hoek, Mladeč 1, Keilor, and Fingira) is set off from the moderns. (Note that Qafzeh 6 and Skhul 5 are separated here.) The two Neanderthals and Broken Hill, with Skhul 5 and Irhoud 1, are a group three times as distant as the previous group from all the living populations.

Is this last result primarily a matter of size? Not necessarily. Here are the highest mean Z-scores (PENSIZE) in the list, all from males:

La Chapelle	27.4
La Ferrassie	24.4
Broken Hill	22.3
Upper Cave 101	19.5
Irhoud 1	16.5
Keilor	13.1
Qafzeh 6	11.5
Afalou	11.1
Skhul 5	10.0
Teviec	8.7
Easter I	6.8
Tonga	6.4
Mladeč 1	6.3
Buriat	5.9
Guam	5.4

We are well down the list before the first living population (Easter Island) appears. It would seem easy to implicate simple size in these groupings, even though the first component has been suppressed. But this may not be the key explanation. For example, the largest anatomically modern skull (Upper Cave) does not join that group of six premoderns near the bottom of the dendrogram, while three members of that group have these PENSIZE values: Natufian, 2.6; Fish Hoek, -1.8; Fingira, -5.1. This is quite against size as the controlling factor.

PRINCIPAL COMPONENTS ANALYSIS: 28 GROUPS + 19 MODERN SAMPLES

As another check on the nature and scale of variation, a precisely similar clustering analysis (using the same 17 components computed just above from the raw scores of the 28 male groups) is carried out, substituting 19 samples of modern crania, all males from the test series, in place of the 22 mostly prehistoric samples of the previous run. These samples or specimens are given below.

Norse X: a possibly exceptional individual, buried in the Great Hall

Zalavár X: sample of 2 from Zalavár "village," Hungary; the main series derives from the castle and chapel (see appendix A)

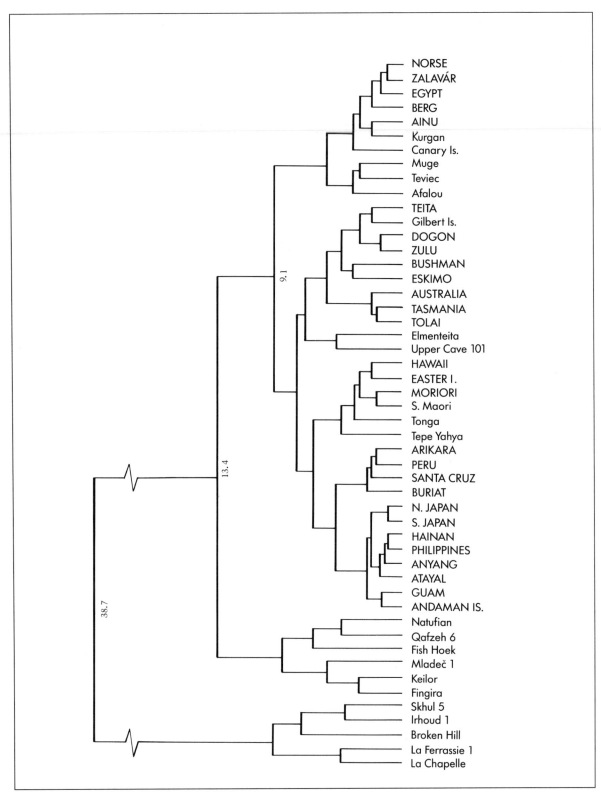

Figure 16. Clustering of 28 modern male groups plus 22 premodern samples (based on principal components analysis of raw scores).

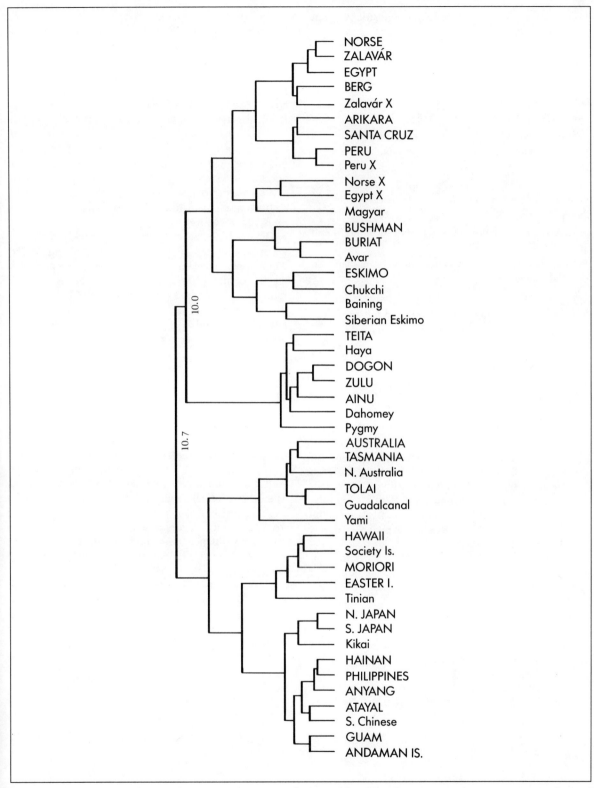

Figure 17. Clustering of 28 male groups plus 19 modern samples (based on principal components analysis of raw scores).

Magyar: sample of 3 "Conquering Hungarians" from the post-Zalavár period

Avar: sample of 4 from the pre-Zalavár Avar Empire (with Central Asian connections?)

Egypt X: sample of 2 left out of the main series

Haya, Tanzania: sample of 3

Dahomey, West Africa: sample of 3

Pygmy: sample of 3, localities in West Africa

North Australia: sample of 3, Anson Bay

Baining: Gazelle Peninsula, New Britain, west of Tolai Territory, non-Austronesian-speaking

Guadalcanal, Solomon Islands: sample of 3, different localities

Society Islands: sample of 3, different localities, Tahiti area

Peru X: sample of 10, random selection from total male pool (see appendix A)

Kikai, Ryukyu Islands: sample of 5

South Chinese: sample of 6, died in U.S.A.

Yami, Botel Tobago Island, Taiwan: sample of 3

Tinian Island, Marianas: sample of 2

Eskimo, Siberia: sample of 2

Chukchi, Siberia: sample of 3

Figure 17 gives the resulting dendrogram. The horizontal scale is the same as that for figure 16: the Euclidean distances among the 28 base groups are of course the same, as are their levels of joining, wherever the same groups have their primary connections (e.g., Norse-Zalavár, North Japan-South Japan); some differences result from the introduction of other samples.

The main point of interest is that this fairly wide coverage of moderns is totally embraced by a final union at almost the same level of joining as the modern and quasi-modern units of figure 16. In that figure, the Natufian-etc. group is somewhat more separate, and the distinction of the Skhul-to-Neanderthal branch is emphasized once more.

The rest of the dendrogram is one more lesson in the vagaries that may attend such analyses. The "hairy" Ainus appear in an otherwise exclusively African group; the lone Baining should join all the other Australoids rather than the company of Eskimos and Chukchis; and the often wayward Bushmen have no business with the possibly compatible Avars and Buriats. Nonetheless, apart from such aberrations the main branchings show the essential power of these clusterings.

SUMMARY

From the above and from other runs, the following results appear.

1. The regional groupings (core groups) retain coherence, with some, especially those of the Far East, being especially informative and consistent. American Indians and Polynesians are more apt to shift main relations and even to break down (cf. figs. 1–4). As in all the foregoing analyses, the core groups appear as trends rather than as sharply defined units.

2. Some non-core groups which lack companion populations, especially Andamanese, Eskimos, and Buriats, are apt to take varied and uninformative positions.

3. When other very small samples or single specimens are introduced, these also vary between positions that seem logical and positions that do not. Here problems of sampling and representativeness enter in, as well as those of choice of analysis.

4. When the clusterings include prehistoric specimens, these wander more freely from hypothetically expected spots. Such marginal anatomical moderns as Irhoud 1 or Skhul 5 ally themselves consistently, if not closely, with Neanderthals rather than with moderns.

5. The two French Neanderthals and Broken Hill stand well apart from everything except Skhul and Irhoud. These Neanderthals were entered as an out-group, to see what degrees of distance from all recent populations, or from particular core groups, might emerge. What stands out is the distance from moderns; no real indication appears of a closer link to one living population group (e.g., Europeans) than to others.

The answer to the primary question seems to be that modern populations taken all together are indeed limited in the geographical variation of both shape and size of the cranium, when tested numerically against Neanderthals or Broken Hill. Also, some early anatomically modern specimens may tend to fall a little out of this range. The impression, true or not, is that the modern unity is fairly recent.

8

Discussion

Some questions can be addressed by reference to the preceding work and to certain other studies that use similar materials and methods. These questions are meant to be limited, in number and scope, to this particular kind of data, and no account is taken of nonmetric or genetic evidence. It would be too blinkered an attitude, however, to ignore the latest developments in genetics, and these will be briefly discussed following this section.

Also, the cranial series herein, while assembled with some care, are few in number; many studies more restricted in area and comprising more, if smaller, series are needed and are being carried out by others.

Is modern humanity fairly limited in cranial variation?

Apparently so. The C-score analyses suggest only variations on common themes of shape. With principal components based on raw scores, two Neanderthal specimens were introduced as a means of calibrating distances. These Neanderthals are very much more distant from all modern series than are any of the moderns from one another. Even most late Pleistocene or post-Pleistocene specimens—indubitably "modern" anatomically—are somewhat separate from the modern series, with a possible implication of size in this result.

Is any modern population group significantly more removed from others?

1. Coon's (1962) candidate for this distinction was the Caucasoids. He based this opinion on his tabulation of indices of facial flatness (Woo and Morant 1934; their measures are comparable to several of the transfacial angles and measurements herein) made on many cranial series. We have seen the importance of such measures. But other measures included here, and not used in previous studies (radii from the transmeatal axis in particular), are also important. In analyses in the present study, Europeans do not appear in positions of exceptional divergence.

2. Australo-Melanesians seem possibly most divergent in the Q-mode analyses, but only slightly so and not to a degree that really distinguishes them. (And not to the degree which I suspect may exist in the minds of many students who view the living in their cultural and ar-

chaeological context.) In any case, these Australoids are not greatly removed from Africans in the Q-mode analyses and, in various clusterings not shown herein, they vary in their apparent isolation from other populations.

3. In fact, it is Polynesians that seem in some ways to be the most isolated area group. They are more distinct in the Q-mode factors than are Africans or American Indians. But I would have to ascribe some of this, at least, to the effects of size: among the "core" populations the Polynesians are distinctly high in PENSIZE averages (see table 3).

Conclusion: None of the areas specified by the core groups gives signs of being separated from the rest to a degree recognizably greater than the others. Statistically, modern cranial populations are a unit according to criteria of shape.

Causes of differences: phylogenetic pattern.

What is the evidence for or against the Weidenreich-Coon hypothesis of independent regional evolution? This is the major and long-standing question, cast in a logical format by Stringer and Andrews (1988). These authors consider the expectations in two different cases: (A) a radiation of *Homo erectus* followed by regional continuities, and (B) a radiation of recent *Homo sapiens*.

The first case (A) predicts that interpopulation (interregional) differences will be high, and will be greatest between peripheral populations; case B predicts that such differences will be low and, in the hypothesis of an African origin, that the greatest differences will be between Africans and non-Africans.

The data reviewed here favor case B, in that present regional differences are certainly not great. On the other hand, there is no sign that, cranially, Africans are set off as most distant from other populations—quite the reverse.

For the Australo-Melanesians, Weidenreich (1945) stressed the continuity of form from earlier Javanese fossils (going back from Wadjak through Solo to Sangiran, etc.), which is also generally appealing to the eye. But, over so great a time span and such important grade differences, it is hard to find special correspondences in shape. Weidenreich drew attention to one distinction between the Zhoukoudian and Javanese fossils which might find reflection in modern Far Easterners and Australians: a flatter obelionic profile in the Chinese fossils. In fact, the modern crania show the reverse.

For the Far East, Weidenreich relied mainly on epigenetic traits (e.g., inca bone, third molar agenesis) for connections over time since, as above, the grade changes are such as to make possible surviving shape differences among modern major populations perhaps too subtle to follow. We would not, for example, find specific connections from Zhoukoudian leading to the high face, narrow at top, seen in the Far East populations of the present.

The proposal (Wolpoff, Wu, and Thorne 1984) that the *Homo erectus* populations of China and Java gradually diverged, to produce "Mongoloids" and "Australoids" respectively, suggests that these two share a community which would not include people of other areas. The evidence herein, finding perhaps the greatest area difference between the Far East and Australo-Melanesia, does not at all accord with this hypothesis.

The present homogeneity is somewhat equivocal. There is clearly no evidence of any individual, diverging line of development elsewhere like that which led in Europe to development of the Neanderthals. It must be realized that *Homo erectus* and some later forms like archaic Africans (Broken Hill and others) are early in both date and grade, and that the Neanderthals are not comparable to these, being much later in time and special in development. Neanderthals now must be seen as a separate evolution from other later hominids. Compared to the Neanderthals there are far fewer premoderns, from all areas, for possible comparison in shape distinctions with the groups analyzed here.

Causes of differences: environmental effects.

There are also the problems of local environmental adaptation, as an agent in bringing about the present area differences and thus in obscuring the evidences of either long-term independent lines or a recent common source.

1. Evidence of Polynesians and American Indians shows the degree of change possible in a few or a modest number of millennia (Key and Jantz [1981] have traced slight changes in Arikara series over generations). However, the basic features discerned in each area may survive longer. But the Polynesians, in addition to the clear divergences arising within Polynesia itself, also pose the problem of a decidedly limited time for their emergence from some source of Asiatic "Mongoloids." (See Bulbeck 1981 for further consideration of this problem.)

2. Differentiation as a response to climatic factors is a familiar suggestion. It has been examined in a very interesting paper by Guglielmino-Matessi, Gluckman, and Cavalli-Sforza (1977). These authors used the 17 populations and the discriminant functions in my 1973 study, together with climatological data from the individual locales of the populations. My discriminant function 1 tended to place Australo-Melanesians and Africans together toward one end and Europeans and American Indians toward the other, while function 2 tended rather to divide Europeans and Africans from Australians, American Indians, and Polynesians. The point of this was that function 1, the primary "anthropometric" factor, correlated highly with temperature variables. As an environmental response, this tended to mask function 2 which, though related to variables of humidity, agreed with "genetic" trees that gave the grouping (joining Europeans and Africans) suggested by the authors. Accordingly, as a climatic response this would appear to relate broader skulls and higher faces (function 1) to colder habitats.

The plot Guglielmino-Matessi et al. arrived at (and in fact the similar plot in Howells 1973, fig. 7) is not unlike that of the first two factors of the 18- and 28-group Q-mode analyses herein: Africans and Australoids tend toward one pole of factor 1, and Europeans and American Indians, and also other Mongoloids, toward the other. The latitudinal distribution of these last does not agree very well with the argument of temperature control for this first factor, though it does not refute it. Van Vark et al. (1985) have done a different analysis, using all the populations of the present study. They formed sets of Mahalanobis distances between all groups, one set based on measurements and the others on different climatological variables. This was followed by correlating the distances in the measurement set with those in one or another of the climate sets. Correlations involving all climate variables were significant at a low level, especially the range of variation in humidity. The authors did not consider the distribution of populations in these respects, being primarily interested in the statistical problem of significance; however, the levels of the associations were such as to make them cautious of interpretations as to morphology.

Furthermore, Brace and Hunt (n.d.) take another view. Brace (with others) has long emphasized that due to cultural factors (i.e., softer diets) tooth size can have become substantially reduced in recent populations, with effects on supporting structures. However, he and Hunt suggest here (n.d.) that, on the other hand, craniofacial metric traits are in fact nonadaptive and thus useful in the study of relationships.

There are older investigations of the relations of nose form to humidity, etc. The striking convergence herein of the Peruvians on Europeans in measurements of the upper nose might call for a look at the high altitude of the Yauyos District. All these studies are suggestive and important. They show the problem of separating phylogeny and climate response, and particularly the uncertainty as to the stability of particular morphology as we go back in time. We seem to have become content to recognize familiar European or Australian conformation in crania of 30 to 35 millennia ago. The question is whether or not such figures as I can adduce here can be used in support. There are problems, as we have seen in the previous section.

From what period do regional skull shape differences seem to accord with those of the present?

This question returns us to Weidenreich's (1945) proposition. In terms of the data herein, the period seems actually to be fairly recent, perhaps on the order of 35,000 years. This is quite different, of course, from recognizing general anatomically modern form in substantially earlier crania.

1. *Homo erectus* specimens (see above) are too radically different from moderns to permit recognition of our regional metrical shape differences. If arguments of regional filiation are made, these have to be on other grounds.

2. Later Middle Pleistocene crania (some would be classed as *H. erectus*) are also remote, and by some tests even more so than in the present study. Stringer (1978 in particular), using measurements defined herein, has made bivariate and Penrose size/shape plots of different hominids. These vary in results, like any such tests, but as to shape in general they place Petralona, Broken Hill, Arago, and Steinheim at the greatest distances from moderns, with Irhoud and the Neanderthal average intermediate, and Skhul 5 and Qafza 6 and 9 closer to moderns and Upper Paleolithics, the last two being mutually close. But none of this draws a modern population (of the 17 in my 1973 publication) closer, in the size/shape plots, to an earlier hominid, except possibly Norse to Upper Paleolithics. The analysis is effective in relating archaics to moderns but not in tracing connections the other way, which was not its intent.

Van Vark (1985) grouped similar subjects: a sample of 14 modern individuals selected from my 1973 series; 23 Upper Paleolithics; 8 Neanderthals; Asiatic erecti; and Broken Hill, Steinheim, and Petralona. He was applying Steerneman's test for significance of the difference between two distances; he found in particular that the last three specimens, both as a group and singly, were significantly more distant from moderns than any of the other hominid groups entered (i.e., Neanderthals or *Homo erectus*). It is not clear what such special distinction of these western Middle Pleistocene archaics may mean (it is seen also in Stringer's 1978 study). But it is apparent that, in craniometric terms, these specimens are too different from moderns to allow detection of numerical distinctions among Middle Pleistocene lineages corresponding to those of today.

3. Neanderthals exhibit no evidence of special connections with any modern group—in fact, in the two studies just mentioned, as well as in the clusterings performed herein, they stand well apart from moderns altogether. Arguments have constantly been made, of course, implicating them somehow in the ancestry of Europeans. These arguments go counter to the recently developing picture of Neanderthals as a separate and isolated European lineage of hominids evolving by special adaptation (in fact, more or less what Weidenreich suggested happened in other main regions). Although expanding into Asia Minor in the last main glacial phase, they were eventually altogether replaced by about 32,000 B.P. No such trajectory of isolated development has been detected elsewhere; the Neanderthals make a foil for the rest of late Pleistocene humanity. Our problem is to interpret the general homogeneity and the minor differences among modern crania worldwide.

4. Outside Europe the only remaining material we can examine is that of the anatomical moderns (including some "archaic" forms), dating from roughly the beginning of the Upper Pleistocene, about 120,000 B.P., to its end. In fact, as I have said above, it is only the late specimens, from about 35,000 B.P., that really seem to suggest placement near particular modern populations.

The situation—and only the situation in general— can be reviewed by regions. I will not try to be encyclopedic: I do not have the material at my command and cannot undertake special studies of important partial specimens, as has been ably done by others. The main point is not identification of fossil specimens but rather the earlier presence of modern shape differences.

How far can different lineages be traced in specific terms?

Given its dimensions, this question cannot be answered systematically here. I am not attempting a searching study of relationships outside the series of this study, adding only a few extra cases or groups. However, to fill in I rely on the work of perhaps half a dozen or so students, mostly mentioned below, who have done detailed analyses of major areas, using many groups. Here I will mention an unpublished thesis by Bulbeck (1981), who has critically assembled existing data (cranial, mandibular, dental) from East Asia and the Pacific, and shown how much can be extracted from them. His method is to use detailed plots and distances among sets of the populations, comprising restricted sets of measurements relating to specific parts of the cranium rather than the whole. Much future work of the same and other kinds needs doing, in developing evidence with strong statistical support.

Europe. Upper Paleolithic crania have always been identified visually with later Europeans, though distinguished by a greater robustness. This is how the few included in the clusterings above place themselves, if not very positively. Mesolithic samples (Muge, Teviec) and even Afalou of North Africa (fig. 16), and in some runs a Natufian from Palestine, are so located, as is the early Mladeč1, which however seems no closer than are Ainus. Van Vark (1984) has used 17 of the measurements in the list of the present study, supplied to him by Stringer, to find Mahalanobis distances among a large number of series and single skulls, including 22 European Upper Paleolithic crania. (The measurements are necessarily restricted to the cranial vault, which vitiates the value of the results somewhat.) By and large these specimens are close to present Europeans (the Norse sample)—more so than to other living peoples. Only Předmostí 3 and Mladeč 5 show low distances from a few of the Neanderthals used by van Vark. Otherwise, comparisons go off the rails on getting back to the Neanderthals, signifying that connections with the past end at that point.

Search elsewhere takes us to Skhul and Qafzeh. Here results are equivocal and do not point with any emphasis toward Europe. In van Vark's distances, Skhul 5 is closer to Tasmanians than to anything else living or fossil; at the same time, it is closer to Europeans than to Neanderthals. In another tabulation by van Vark, Qafzeh 6 and 9 and Skhul 5 are generally close to one another but not to Neanderthals. But these distances are not based on a broad suite of measurements, and they leave room for future judgments, including examination of other specimens from these two sites. In any case the search for European antecedents, in terms of this study, ends in the Upper Paleolithic, not beyond 35,000 B.P.

Africa. North Africa would seem to have some continuity with Europe as far back as the Mesolithic, from the Afalou evidence, but earlier remains (Irhoud) do not suggest North Africa as an ultimate source.

As to sub-Saharan Africa, reviews by Rightmire (1975, and later) and Bräuer (1984a, 1984b) are useful. In East Africa, various late specimens (Elmenteita, Gamble's Cave, Willey's Kopje, Nakuru, and others) have in the past been suggested to represent "Caucasoid" influences in this region. Rightmire used multivariate analysis to reject any likeness of any of these specimens to Egyptians. In the present study as well no such connection is apparent, but in their C-scores the Elmenteita skulls also seem un-African: they display high faces and noses, and modest nasal and interorbital breadths. Two Willey's Kopje skulls are more equivocal. Rightmire feels that the original population of the area might provisionally be thought of as "Nilotic Negro," i.e., non-Bantu historically or linguistically.

We should be looking for signs of the African shape defined in previous sections above. A Weidenreichian stalwart would seem obliged to perceive the flat upper nose, broad upper face, and much diminished glabellar prominence as appearing in the lineage from Broken Hill, Saldanha, and Florisbad via Omo 1 and Ngaloba. These last two probably date from the beginning of the Upper Pleistocene, say 125,000 B.P. In principal components plots, Bräuer (1984b) finds a strong likeness between Omo 1 and the North African Afalou group; the high, non-projecting face of this fossil (as reconstructed) is non-African. Laetoli Hominid 18 (Ngaloba), though of probably similar age, is rather too archaic for assessment here. On the other hand, the undated but obviously archaic Eliye Springs skull from West Turkana (Bräuer and Leakey 1986), in spite of its low forehead and strong supraorbitals, has the short face and wide nasal aperture, biorbital, and interorbital breadths appropriate to Africans. But it provides us with no date.

Farther south, the Late Stone Age Fingira specimen from Malawi gives suitable C-scores, with a narrow biauricular, low face and nose, wide and low nasalia, etc. However, it clusters with Africans in some runs only. The many South African crania of past discussion (from Boskop on) might or might not be fruitfully reexamined.

The obviously early (ca. 100,000 B.P.) and much-discussed Border Cave skull has a convex frontal but well-developed supraorbitals. There is not enough of it for simple C-score comparisons. Multivariate analyses have several times over suggested a Bush-Hottentot affiliation or, less frequently, a connection with one or another Bantu people. However, the breadth of such testing has not been wide enough (being confined to recent South African samples) to judge the reliability of such affiliation, and in fact some results now suggest that Border Cave is significantly separated from all modern populations (Rightmire 1981a; Campbell 1984), and even that it is not really anatomically modern (van Vark, personal communication)—not a view I can share. This important fossil serves as an example of the difficulty in the analysis of partial specimens, and of the need for further development of the statistical treatment, advanced though this already is. At any rate, Border Cave does not now solidly demonstrate, in terms of this monograph, a local ancestry for sub-Saharan moderns, in spite of the conviction of many, myself included, that that is the true case.

The Fish Hoek skull, one of a number found in Peer's Cave on the Cape Peninsula, has an age of perhaps 12,000–13,000 years. In Rightmire's (1981) view, supported by discriminant analysis, the skull looks like a large Hottentot; in my 1973 discriminant study it appeared as least distant from Bushmen. It does not, however, approach Africans in the clusterings herein, and van Vark's distances (1984, personal communication) remove it from all modern populations and find it closest to certain Upper Paleolithic crania, especially Předmostí 4. These are unsatisfactory results which need future resolving, given the importance of knowing about African antecedents.

Still on the Fish Hoek skull, we may look more directly at matters of shape via C-scores, comparing

those of the Australian Keilor skull at the same time. This latter specimen has a comparable or greater antiquity, and its discovery in southernmost Australia puts the two at perhaps the greatest possible distance in the then-inhabited world. These C-scores should reflect differences already noted for Africans and Australo-Melanesians (male means for the populations).

	Zulu	Bushman	Fish Hoek	Keilor	Australia	Tolai
STB	6.89	5.23	16.0	-5.52	-16.47	-15.67
FRS	11.58	23.90	25.16	-17.25	-0.70	-5.34
DKS	3.21	10.23	-4.03	-8.08	-0.33	-2.16
NAS	4.58	6.45	1.41	-8.93	0.68	-1.98

Thus, in these supposedly differentiating measures, Fish Hoek shows the broader and convex frontal of Africans, Keilor the opposite; the same differences appear in the relative tendencies to prominence in the upper midface, if not as strikingly. Such comparisons of individual measurements are not very satisfactory, reminding us of the infant days of craniometry. However, we are allowed to accept that the perceived regional differences may already have existed toward the end of the Pleistocene—not exactly a sensational finding.

Australo-Melanesia. Here the Keilor skull is a principal exhibit, with the results described above. In the clusterings of the previous chapter it does not take informative positions, any more than does the Fish Hoek skull. (Bulbeck [1981], in fact, finds no evidence of its connections with Australians! or with Wadjak, which Weidenreich saw as its "twin.") There is a great range of robustness in skeletons of the late Pleistocene and post-Pleistocene of Australia, but I do not know of any craniometric evidence to sustain hypotheses of more than one population complex present in the region.

Giles (1976), in a discriminant analysis, has used 11 good-sized samples from Australia and New Guinea, including series representing the three populations of this monograph. His work shows that local individuality of form can be distinguished, especially in the case of northern Australian tribes. But the distributions on his functions seem to make it clear that the variation is simply rounding out and filling in what is established by the three Australoid groups of the present work. Various similar studies by Pietrusewsky, including more New Guinean and Melanesian samples, probably extend the range of variation, but I doubt that this would go beyond Pietrusewsky's own conclusion (1988) that Australia and Melanesia are two branches of one major stem.

In any case, such very interesting work amounts to looking for historical answers in present intraregional differences, but it is not germane here. I lack data for

the large Lake Nitchie skull and the enormous Cossack individual; they are younger than Keilor in any case. The Kow Swamp material has been only incompletely described. However, Thorne and Wolpoff (1981) have used the gnathic index (the ratio BPL:BNL, or basion-prosthion to basion-nasion) to show that the Cohuna skull, a probable Kow Swamp representative, has the high value, or projecting prosthion, of the modern Australoids included in this study. In the absence of such data from other crania, this stands with Keilor as the best signal of "Australian" shape in the late Pleistocene.

There remains the constant question of whether or not a lineage from Australians goes back to *Homo erectus* via the Solo population, something not testable here. However, there are new tentative chronometric dates (Bartstra, Soegondho, and van der Wijk 1988) for Ngandong, placing the material within the Upper Pleistocene, mostly registering less than 100,000 years. This would make that population contemporaneous with quasi-modern Qafzeh and similar Africans, thus bringing the Solo *Homo erectus* down to an overlapping time zone, and one pressing on the oldest Australians.

A final note: Christy Turner's evidence from dental variations, described immediately below, makes a sharp distinction between Australo-Melanesians and all groups possibly assignable as "Mongoloid," which argues for a longer period of distinction than can be made out from cranial shape. Turner also finds that Australoids have dental resemblances to Africans.

Far East. When we turn to East Asia, Oceania, and the Americas we are in a part of the world separate from Australo-Melanesia, Europe, and Africa. It involves a general problem of a "Mongoloid" population complex, a problem with dimensions and interconnections of its own; and it concerns more than half the series herein.

The geographical logic is plain: a continuous area along Asia's eastern lands and island festoons; linguistic-cultural and other indications of extensions north and west; obvious points of entry to the Americas in the north and to the Pacific in the south. Thus there is subcontinental community on the mainland, with pinch-points in the Bering Strait and Indonesia. We know from geology that in the Pleistocene these points, and the offshore island chains, were larger masses (especially Beringia and Sundaland) connected with the mainland; and so the arena of human movement and contact would have been wider, not narrower. And we know something about archaeology throughout, including some signs of isolation from the western Old World during the Paleolithic, with suggestions, in the southern part of the region at least, of more dependence on wood-shaping for tools. Culturally and biologically, we can say that the borders of the whole area were Australia/New Guinea to the south, and somewhere in Siberia and India to the north and west.

Cranial data are not copious, but as an obligatory orientation we have Christy Turner's extensive work (many papers), on tooth variations, expanded from Hanihara's recognition (1969) of the "Mongoloid dental complex." This work identifies a number of special dental traits, of which a well-known and important example is shovel-shaped incisors. Turner has discerned two levels of complexity. The less rich of these he calls Sundadont, which is expressed in a southern distribution of populations including the Sunda chain and Southeast Asia up to the Philippines, but also including Micronesia, Polynesia, and, very significantly, Jomon Japan and the Ainu. Thus it is southern and Oceanic, and gives the impression of being early and, at the present time, peripheral.

The more intense expression Turner calls Sinodont, with a distribution that is northern and extends into the Americas. It characterizes modern Japanese and Chinese as well as boreal peoples of eastern Siberia, where there is a hard boundary, just to the west, with "European" populations who lack the complex. All American tribes possess it.

Sinodonty has a certain antiquity, Turner has pointed out, which is determined by its presence in all American populations and possibly in the Upper Cave skulls from Zhoukoudian. This all suggests a minimum of 20,000 years, and possibly a good deal more. But Turner believes the Sundadont pattern is also old, and probably the matrix from which Sinodonty developed. In other words, Sundadonty was not produced as an intermediate stage, by gene flow from Sinodont peoples into Southeast Asian populations with an amorphous dental pattern. Rather, Turner sees an autochthonous development of Sundadonty, from which Sinodonty in turn emerged.

How does this accord with the cranial evidence developed here? Very well. (Of course, my series are relatively few and lack the representation of Southeast Asia, while Turner has a great many, if mostly smaller, dental samples.) My Polynesian series have their own

cranial traits that suggest a separate history of development but not one that conflicts with a southern origin. Guam, on the other hand, tends to go with Asians more than with Polynesians. And the Asians all have a certain community: the Japanese and Anyang are a relatively compact group such as might have expanded from a northerly center, but at the same time tend to be joined more broadly, via the Hainan Chinese, to the peripheral (early?) Taiwanese Atayals and Filipinos. The Ainus appear as the most tangential.

In a discriminant analysis using 16 of these series (Howells 1984), I found good separation (on four functions) among pairs of Europeans, Australoids, Polynesians, and American Indians. Distinct from these but tightly clustered were North and South Japanese, Hainan, and Anyang with, nearby, Atayals and the Filipinos. Ainu, however, were located at some distance, and were associated with no other populations. The whole is a particularly clear result which, like those here and elsewhere, brings together northern Far Easterners while associating with them nearshore peoples such as the Taiwanese Atayals and Filipinos. (The latter are Sundadonts; however, Turner thinks that the Atayals have been affected by gene flow from Sinodont Chinese immigrants to Taiwan.)

In another study (Howells 1986) I used these same Asians and a number of other small Asiatic samples or individuals in a cluster analysis using C-scores and 20 principal components. This provided as one major branch a broad skein like that above, with the Japanese, Chinese, and other East Asiatic specimens, and including other Taiwanese, Ryukyuans, Ainus, Yayois, and Jomons. In a separate very small branch were four individual Jomon skulls, which I would guess are Sundadonts; and in a third branch were a modest number of far northern Siberians which, I have to suppose, from Turner's groupings, to be certified Sinodonts.

Brace et al. (1987, 1989) have used a battery of 18 measurements, of which two thirds relate to the nasal skeleton. In clusterings, Korean, Japanese, and several Chinese series form a main group. Once again Ainu and Jomon samples are separate from these, and go instead with generalized Polynesian and Micronesian (largely from Guam) samples. This leads Brace to formulate a Jomon-Pacific cluster of populations. One interesting point: most removed from the main Asian group but still allied with it are samples of Thai, Vietnamese, and Filipinos; this agrees with Turner's tooth evidence that these are all Sundadont dental "Mongoloids." Another interesting point: within the main group the Japanese Yayoi sample is joined to a sample of Mongols—interesting because of cultural and other hints that this western region has ultimate links with the origins of the recent Japanese.

Hanihara (1985) has done a Q-mode correlations analysis of Asian and a few Pacific series, using nine cranial measurements. His results are clearcut: in one dendrogram of 30 series his three main branches are (1) modern Japanese (including two Korean samples); (2) Yayoi/North Asia/Siberian Neolithic; and (3) Ainu/Jomon.

Turner (1985) estimates from all the evidence that Sinodonty appeared in North Asia between 40,000 and 20,000 years ago out of Sundadont predecessors, so that Sundadonty would be older still. The dental characteristics of Europeans had appeared by 22,000 B.P., and an Upper Paleolithic culture of European affinity was present at the site of Mal'ta, near Lake Baikal, with a date of 18,000 B.P. Teeth recovered from that site are of European type, so we have a boundary marker well eastward in Asia, and also a minimum date for distinction between these major dental populations.

These last dates are earlier than modern cranial shape characteristics can be recognized in the Far East, where they may be seen in Chinese Neolithic crania going back to 7000 B.P. Such samples are small and poor, but they demonstrate the relatively long face and nose present in the later populations (Howells 1984), and photographs make the same traits clear, together with the characteristic marked flatness across the whole upper face (ibid.)

Older crania do not readily conform. In the clusterings, Upper Cave 101 completely fails to conform to any expectations of the kind, but with its age of possibly 18,000 years it calls for close consideration.

The Upper Cave skull is very large (PENSIZE = 19.5). My measurements were made on a surviving cast, and in a few comparable major diameters these are about 2 mm greater than Weidenreich's (1938–39) measurements made on the original. This is unlikely to affect either shape (C-scores) or any overall effects of size. Measurements, especially on the face, correspond well with those taken by J. Kamminga (Kamminga and Wright 1988; see below) on another first-generation cast.

Weidenreich, from his inspection of the original 101 skull, found suggestions of Upper Paleolithic European, Ainu, and "primitive Mongolian"; he diagnosed the other two Upper Cave crania as Melanesoid and Eskimoid. He distinguished all three from recent Chinese or Mongols. Other writers, especially G. Neumann (1959), have found 101 to resemble American Indians. From their appearance it is not clear that skulls 102 and 103 need be excluded from Far Eastern populations, although they are rather short faced and short nosed individually. As to 101, its C-scores would make it not European or Far Eastern or Ainu or American Indian, but Polynesian. It has the greater prominence at nasion compared to prosthion coupled with high radii from the meatus to facial points, also narrow nasalia (WNB) and low dacryon subtense (DKS). Some of these characteristics, however, together with flatness across the sub-

nasal region, are not inappropriate to Asiatics generally, or to Eskimos in particular. Upper Cave 101 has no C-score likenesses to the American Indians herein. The skull remains difficult to diagnose; it does not forecast the present, as do the Upper Paleolithics of Europe. On the other hand, there seems no greater reason to dismiss it from a broad Mongoloid brotherhood than there is to do the same with Ainus. And it must not be forgotten that Turner finds (at least provisionally, from casts—the originals are lost) that the Upper Cave teeth are Sinodont, which would secure a North Asian affiliation for the population.

In an intensive and persuasive study which I received after arriving at the above conclusions, Kamminga and Wright (1988) express stronger reserve all around as to viewing these skulls as Mongoloids-to-be. In a principal components analysis using the samples in this work, and the same measurements, they arrive at a plot of populations corresponding well with the plot seen here in figures 11 and 12 (of 28 and 26 groups): all the Mongoloid peoples, including American Indians and Polynesians, can be put in an envelope distinct from Europeans and Africans, while Upper Cave 101 lies in the opposite quadrant, between the last two sets. (Bulbeck [1981], in plots of available measurements, places all three Upper Cave skulls similarly.) However, the always recalcitrant Ainu behave similarly.

There is a question as to the date of the Upper Cave skulls. Kamminga and Wright cite recent evidence that the 18,000 year date is probably from a part of the site which is earlier than that containing the human bones. However, a new radiocarbon date is about 20,000 years (cited by Stringer, in preparation). Furthermore, Kamminga and Wright feel that Turner's diagnosis of the teeth as Sinodont, made on a cast, is not entirely secure. All this hardly ameliorates the problem of very dubious Mongoloids in the Upper Cave coming down in time rather close to their Chinese successors of the Neolithic. This does not resemble the European lineage. Certainly, the Upper Cave population continues to ask more questions than it answers.*

The undated but presumably Pleistocene Liuchiang skull (clearly anatomically modern) has been diagnosed as suggesting Australoid affinities (Coon 1962) and as incipient Mongoloid (Woo 1959). The latter affiliation

---

*Various special analyses, including CRANID recently developed by Wright (Department of Anthropology, University of Sydney) have been done since publication was begun. These place Upper Cave 101 varyingly least distant from Moriori, Arikara, and Tasmanians—hardly a definitive location—but fully confirm Kamminga and Wright in separating the specimen from northern Asiatic Mongoloids. For what it may be worth, the same kinds of test associate Fish Hoek quite strongly with Bushmen, and Fingira (Later Stone Age of Malawi) somewhat less clearly with the same, rather than with other Africans. Keilor appears least distant from the Australo-Melanesians and Arikara. Work continues.

is more likely from skull measurements: BNL is greater than BPL, and SSS is low (flat across subnasal area). Facial height is equivocal, as are upper facial measures of flatness. Forehead and basal cranial breadths are high, certainly for a female. It might be equally appropriate as Atayal, Filipino, or Ainu; without fuller analysis little can be said.

There is little other material that can be used. The Dali skull of early Upper Pleistocene date, with its heavy supraorbitals and broad, short face, does not predict late Far Easterners. Arguments for regional evolution may go forward from the early fossils on the basis of sagittal keeling, inca bones, and third molar agenesis, but attempts to go back, looking for antecedents of local shape deviations from the generality of present skull form, tell us little.

Polynesia. Here the problem of regional antecedents does not arise, since we are aware of the recency of occupation of these parts of the Pacific. Polynesian origins and migrations are not the subject of this treatise. (It might be mentioned here that Turner [1987], in addressing these matters via dental traits, has found Micronesians and Polynesians to be close in distance measures, and about equally distant from Southeast Asia-Indonesia. On this same dental evidence he would rule out Philippine or Taiwanese origins.) More pertinent are the problems of Polynesian large size, shape discreteness, and the diversity which has arisen among Polynesian populations since their arrival. Again, these are not things we can deal with here.

A good deal of craniometric analysis has been carried out recently, however, and should be reviewed. We have new studies by Pietrusewsky (1987, 1988) and by Brace with others (Brace et al. 1989; Brace and Hunt n.d.), using more restricted measurement lists but many samples.

To begin with, all those authors' groupings set Australians and Melanesians clearly apart from other Pacific and Asian groups; Pietrusewsky, on the basis of this and much earlier work, is satisfied that they form a distinct branch and ancestry, though with Australia and Melanesia as subdivisions.

In Pietrusewsky's 1987 paper, 38 samples divide into five branches: north and south Asian plus Indonesian; Micronesian (7 groups); Polynesian (8 samples); Melanesian; and Australian. However, Saipan and Truk lie in the Polynesian branch, and Ponape, dismayingly, in the Melanesian.

A larger clustering of 54 groups in Pietrusewsky's 1988 paper produces a similar Asian-Indonesian plus Polynesian main division (also large Melanesian and Australian branches); however, five Micronesian samples are splattered around from the Asian to the Melanesian groupings. Most of this evidence manifests an ordered Asian-to-Polynesian continuity. The disor-

dered Micronesian affiliations, especially with Melanesia, also appeared in my analysis (Howells 1970) of a large number of living groups, something that seems to reflect a history of settlement and contact more complicated than that of Polynesia.

Brace and others get more disciplined results. Brace et al. (1989) find as before that Ainu and Jomon go with broad Polynesian and Micronesian groupings, instead of falling into a cluster of North and South Asiatics. This finding is the basis for Brace's "Jomon-Pacific" cluster. In a Pacific clustering, three Australian-Melanesian samples oppose seven Polynesian-Micronesian groups including Guam and Yap (but this case may he strongarming the Micronesians, given the limited choice of populations).

In a later study using 24 measurements, Brace and Hunt (n.d.) in one analysis find these three clusters: 10 Australo-Melanesian to Fiji (including Andaman Islands); 8 Ainu-Jomon, Polynesia, Micronesia (including Guam and Ponape); and 11 Japan (+ Yayoi), China, Siberia, Southeast Asia. In a broader set of 38 samples, they find the same divisions plus two branches made up respectively of six American Indian and seven European samples (these two branches join before uniting with all the rest). This neat result may in part reflect judicious pruning (e.g., leaving out Andaman Islanders) and balancing numbers from major areas. But the net result is a regional distinction like that among five of my own areas herein, plus a more constant position for Guamanians and Ainus.

To summarize East Asia and the Pacific, we find one general complex of populations in East and Southeast Asia and the offshore islands (covering both Turner's Sinodonts and Sundadonts), with signs in some data of a greater degree of differentiation in Siberia to the north and west. In the Pacific, Polynesians are somewhat set apart, and the Micronesians are somewhat heterogeneous. I believe all this appropriately registers the picture of East Asia and the Pacific in which the populations studied here are embedded and which they are expressing. My series conform to this picture, with the Ainus, Guamanians, and Buriats refusing to take constant positions among the others, although in the simplest clusterings they are found with East Asiatics generally.

America. With the Americas, coverage is thin. That is to say, for the answers sought here, three samples for the whole hemisphere are a relatively poor muster. Consider, too, the context: compared with Polynesia-Micronesia, the area to be represented is enormous, with extremes of climate and ecology. Also, the evident time interval allowable for dispersion, adaptation, and microevolution is on the order of 15,000 years. At the same time, however, this gives us a minimum for the migration of peoples who were purely modern anatomically, and a date to contemplate in looking for surviving common cranial shape features of such people.

The material is also thin when we consider the unparalleled collections from North America, which are well documented as to source. These have been subjected to increasingly sophisticated analyses of population relations (e.g., Ossenberg 1977 and earlier; Heathcote 1986 and in progress). Key and Jantz (1981; Key 1986) have not only shown differences among inhabitants of the Plains in terms of cranial shape factors but have tracked these through time, with important historical implications.

These and many other cranial studies have been leading toward suggestions of population histories in a way not equaled in other areas. At a higher level they promise to provide detail in the gathering arguments for three main groupings or original migrations, now sustained by linguistics, dental traits, and genetic data (especially Greenberg, Turner, and Zegura 1986). But these fairly impressive results have not led to equally persuasive suggestions of cranial affinity with particular peoples of North Asia. It is true that the archaeologists have important clues, and Turner is willing to hypothesize very general routes for the postulated migrations (e.g., Turner 1985). The essential evidence just now would be the flatly Sinodont character of all American Indian dentitions.

The foregoing has little to do with the main question here, which is the degree to which present regional shape characters extend into the past. The Americas give some clues here. The hypothesized three migrating groups are probably, from last to first, the Eskimo-Aleut, the Na-Dene of northwest North America, and the Paleoindians. Our three core samples—Arikara, Santa Cruz, and Peru—would be derived from the last-named, and so would project their common features to about 15,000 B.P. Given their recent geographical distribution, we may suppose that their last common source was earlier rather than later in this period.

These three samples indeed have some common features, partly "Mongoloid" and partly not. Let us refer to the plots of the populations in the Q-mode analyses. In the 28-group and the 18-group sets, the Americans place themselves among the East Asiatics generally on factors 1 and 2, but on factor 3 they are grouped together and removed from the Asiatics *except* for the Siberian Buriats. In the rotated 18-group factors, the first factor strongly registers East Asiatics, but the American Indian groups have virtually zero loadings. Morphologically, all this translates especially as elevated and narrow nasal regions (which the Americans share with Europeans) and distinctly broad skull bases (AUB).

There are subsidiary questions. The American Indian group is not a very tight one in the above plots; in the other clusterings it may break up, with Peru in particular cozying up to Europeans. Even when clustering together, the American groups are more apt to join Europeans than Asiatics. But one should be wary of this. Note again that the Americans are resoundingly Sinodont; Turner does not want to hear further talk of "Causasoid" contributions or origins for American Indians.

Eskimos, or at least those of my sample, do not align themselves with American Indians but with Polynesians. I do not read history from this; rather, I suspect that the forward placement of the facial skeleton is an independent development and has an undue effect on apparent relations.

The Buriats are another matter. With many extreme C-scores they nonetheless approach the Americans, in particular the Arikara. There are archaeological signs that the Plains Indians were an agglomeration of late arrivals in the Great Plains, drawn from different linguistic families, suggesting that any common cranial and skeletal form is a late development. At any rate, no one is likely to propose a recent special migration of Siberians to the middle of North America. But this peculiar pairing has surfaced before. Brennan and I did a cluster analysis (Brennan and Howells n.d.) using nine measurements, of Hrdlička's many published North American samples. This analysis also brought together a number of Plains tribes with Siberians and Mongolians (but also an Iroquois sample).

Opportunity exists for much fuller solutions of these questions. But—setting Eskimos aside—we have indications that the Americans are cranially less varied than might be expected from past opinion, and that this may be important in working out the course of developments in North Asia.

9
Evidence from Molecular Biology

In a much-discussed study Cann, Stoneking, and Wilson (1987) analyzed 147 individuals of five geographic regions by mapping variants in mitochondrial DNA found using restriction enzymes. In a "genealogical tree" a cluster of individuals of sub-Saharan descent appeared as most isolated from the rest of the Old World. Although there was no exclusiveness of lineages, there was a degree of clustering among individuals from different regions. The apparently oldest cluster with no African members was calculated to have originated 80,000 to 190,000 years ago, thus marking a separation from Africa during that time. This study has been a main support of the "out of Africa" hypothesis, and of the idea of an African "Eve," a possible bottleneck event near the origin of moderns establishing a single mitochondrial DNA lineage from which all others, African or not, have mutated.

Broadly reviewing these and other data, Spuhler (1988) disagrees. The essence of his argument is that many mitochondrial DNA types are unique and apparently old in their several areas, so that the estimated age of the founding populations would take them back to the time zone of *Homo erectus*, beyond the limits of any known moderns. This therefore supports the Weidenreichian hypothesis of regional transitions and separate evolution of major Old World populations, and not the replacement hypothesis. But in both these recent analyses the control of populations needs to be improved. As acknowledged, the "Africans" of Cann, Stoneking, and Wilson are almost exclusively American blacks, and their "Europeans," which include North Africans, etc., become Spuhler's "Caucasians," so that geography and the Neanderthal question are not addressed.

With a population structuring more like that presented herein, and with more familiar genetic material, Cavalli-Sforza et al. (1988) have developed a tree with highly interesting results. This is the most comprehensive such study to date. It uses up to 120 alleles from a large number of polymorphisms and 38 populations, of which one, "European," was composed of five compactly clustered samples (Basque, Dane, English, Greek, and Italian).

The primary split is between Africans (sub-Saharan) and non-Africans. The second, among non-Africans, is between North Eurasians (subdivided into Caucasoids and Northeast Asia-America) and Southeast Asians (subdivided into Southeast Asia-Pacific and New Guinea-Australia.) (This supersedes earlier trees developed by this group of workers, e.g., Guglielmino-Matessi, Gluckman, and Cavalli-Sforza 1977, in which Caucasoids and Africans were paired against Asians and Australians.)

Allocations by geography are satisfactory throughout. Assignment to major linguistic phyla is extremely coherent, which suggests recency of modern human expansion and favors the replacement model, not that of regional evolution supported by Spuhler, above. In general, the concordance of Cavalli-Sforza's findings with those here from cranial evidence is good, although there are differences in emphases such as the closer connection found by those authors of Australoids with South Asians. We might note once more the differences in material: the blood samples used by Cavalli-Sforza et al. are often composite as to localities, while my cranial samples are meant to be strictly localized; and of course one study analyzes frequencies of discrete alleles and the other continuous metric variables. Considering this, the correspondences between the two studies are all the more impressive.

10
Conclusions

There are signs of evolutionary divergence in cranial shape among recent populations of different geographic areas, but this divergence is of a highly limited degree compared with the distance separating any of the modern populations from Neanderthals.

Size is generally comparable throughout, with Polynesians, Guamanians, and Buriats being cranially the largest. Small-bodied Andamanese and Bushmen are cranially small. The impression is one of a universal loss of robustness leading to the present general size; whether this stems from a common genetic source or from a common environmental response is not demonstrated.

Variation in shape seems to be largely located in the upper face, and particularly the upper nose and the borders of the orbits. This was virtually ignored in the earlier preoccupation with the shape of the braincase.

The scale of shape differences may be uncertain, but it seems to be uniform: no main area sticks out like a sore thumb. Nor are there persuasive constant branchings among the main areas, other than the shifting connections seen in the various dendrograms. Only in the case of the "Mongoloid" areas (i.e., including Polynesians and Americans) may there be some support for overall connections, though if the populations were all to be blind-labeled (called Populations A, B, C, etc.) such connections might be difficult to see.

As to the age of differentiation, on the face of things the above evidence would suggest it to be recent. It is notable that, if anything, intraregional heterogeneity is greatest in Polynesia and the Americas, the two regions we can certify as the latest to be occupied. This goes counter to any expectation that such recency would be expressed in cranial homogeneity.

Altogether, the whole foregoing analysis must be recognized as a rather blunt instrument, and one giving largely negative signals. Such negatives are as follows:

No support for lineages deriving separately from the stage of *Homo erectus*

No support for a special eastern common ancestry for East Asiatics and Australians

No support for a sub-Saharan first source for anatomical moderns, i.e., *Homo sapiens sapiens*

These conclusions are not disproofs of anything, and they may be taken with all the salt one wishes. More complex analyses of the data might give finer clues. Studies of transformations of one population "shape" into others produced statistically or by computer-imaging might be applied to such problems as the apparent connection of Polynesians to Eskimos rather than to Far Easterners. I have wanted only to complete the rather simple and straightforward study ending here.

Bibliography

Bartstra, G.-J., S. Soegondho, and A. van der Wijk. 1988. Ngandong man: Age and artifacts. *Human Evolution* 17:325–337.

Brace, C. L. , M. L. Brace, Y. Dodo, W. R. Leonard, Li Y., Shao X.-q., Sood S., and Zhang Z. 1987. Micronesians, Asians, Thais and relations: A craniofacial and odontometric perspective. Paper presented at the Micronesian Archaeological Conference, Guam, September 9–13, 1987. To appear in *Micronesica*.

Brace, C. L. , M. L. Brace, W. R. Leonard. 1989. Reflections on the face of Japan: A multivariate and odontometric perspective. *American Journal of Physical Anthropology* 78:93–113.

Brace, C. L., and K. D. Hunt. n.d. A non-racial craniofacial perspective on human variation: A(ustralian) to Z(uni). In preparation.

Bräuer, G. 1984a. A craniological approach to the origin of anatomical *Homo sapiens* in Africa and implications for the appearance of modern Europeans. In *The Origins of Modern Humans*, F. H. Smith and F. Spencer, eds., 327–410. New York: Alan R. Liss.

———. 1984b. The "Afro-European *sapiens*-hypothesis," and hominid evolution in East Asia during the late Middle and Upper Pleistocene. In *The Early Evolution of Man with Special Emphasis on Southeast Asia and Africa*, P. Andrews and J. L. Franzen, eds., 145–165. Senckenberg: Courier Forschungsinstitut 69.

———. 1988. Osteometrie. In *Anthropologie: Handbuch der Vergleichenden Biologie des Menschen*, R. Knussmann et al., eds., vol. 1, p. 2, pp. 160–232. Stuttgart: Gustav Fischer.

Bräuer, G., and R. E. Leakey. 1986. The ES-11693 cranium from Eliye Springs, West Turkana, Kenya. *Journal of Human Evolution* 15:289–312.

Brennan, M., and W. W. Howells. n.d. A craniometric and linguistic grouping of selected North American and Asian peoples. Manuscript.

Bulbeck, F. D. 1981. *Continuities in Southeast Asian Evolution Since the Late Pleistocene. Some New Material Described and Some Old Questions Reviewed.* 2 vols. Ph.D. thesis, Australian National University, Canberra.

Campbell, N. A. 1984. Some aspects of allocation and discrimination. In *Multivariate Statistical Methods in Physical Anthropology*, G. N. van Vark and W. W. Howells, eds., 177–192. Doordrecht: D. Reidel.

Cann, R. L., M. Stoneking, and A. C. Wilson. 1987. Mitochondrial DNA and human evolution. *Nature* 325:31–36.

Cavalli-Sforza, L. L., A. Piazza, P. Menozzi, and J. Mountain. 1988. Reconstruction of human evolution: Bringing together genetic, archaeological, and linguistic data. *Proceedings of the National Academy of Sciences* 85:6002–6.

Coon, C. S. 1962. *The Origin of Races.* 724 pp. New York: Knopf.

Coon, C. S., with E. Hunt, Jr. 1965. *The Living Races of Man.* 320 pp., 128 pls. New York: Knopf.

Corruccini, R. S. 1973. Size and shape in similarity coefficients based on metric characters. *American Journal of Physical Anthropology* 38:743–754.

———. 1987. Shape in morphometrics: comparative analyses. *American Journal of Physical Anthropology* 73: 289–303.

Giles, E. S. 1976. Cranial variation in Australia and neighboring areas. In *The Origin of the Australians*, R. L. Kirk and A. G. Thorne, eds., 161–172. Human Biology Series 6. Canberra: Australian Institute of Aboriginal Studies.

Greenberg, J. H., C. G. Turner II, and S. L. Zegura. 1986. The settlement of the Americas; A comparison of the linguistic, dental, and genetic evidence. *Current Anthropology* 27:477–497.

Guglielmino-Matessi, C. R., P. Gluckman, and L. L. Cavalli-Sforza. 1977. Climate and the evolution of skull metrics in man. *American Journal of Physical Anthropology* 50:549–564.

Hanihara, K. 1969. Mongoloid dental complex in the permanent dentition. *Proceedings of the VIIIth International Congress of Anthropological and Ethnological Sciences* vol. 1:298–300.

———. 1985. Origins and affinities of the Japanese as viewed from cranial measurements. In *Out of Asia. Peopling the Americas and the Pacific*, R. Kirk and E. Szathmary, eds., 105–112. Canberra: The Journal of Pacific History.

Heathcote, G. M. 1986. *Exploratory Human Craniometry of Recent Eskaleutian Regional Groups from the Western Arctic and Subarctic of North America. A New Approach to Population Historical Reconstruction.* BAR International Series 301. 348 pp. Oxford: B.A.R.

Howells, W. W. 1957. The cranial vault: Factors of size and shape. *American Journal of Physical Anthropology* 15:19–48.

———. 1970. Anthropometric grouping analysis of Pacific peoples. *Archaeology & Physical Anthropology in Oceania* 5:192–217.

———. 1973. *Cranial Variation in Man. A Study by Multivariate Analysis of Patterns of Difference Among Recent Human Populations.* Papers of the Peabody Museum, Harvard University, vol. 67. 259 pp.

———. 1984. Prehistoric human remains from China. In *Rassengeschichte der Menschheit*, I. Schwidetzky, ed., Lieferung 10, Asien III, 29–38.

———. 1986. Physical anthropology of the prehistoric Japanese. Chap. 4 of *Windows on the Japanese Past: Studies in Archaeology and Prehistory*, R. J. Pearson, G. L. Barnes, and K. L. Hutterer, eds. Ann Arbor: Center for Japanese Studies, University of Michigan.

Jones, K. J. 1964. *The Multivariate Statistical Analyzer.* 179 pp. Cambridge: Harvard Cooperative Society.

Kamminga, J., and R. V. S. Wright. 1988. The Upper Cave at Zhoukoudian and the origins of the Mongoloids. *Journal of Human Evolution* 17:739–767.

Key, P. J. 1986. *Craniometric Relationships among Plains Indians.* Report of Investigations 34. 189 pp. Knoxville: Department of Anthropology, University of Tennessee.

Key, P. J., and R. L. Jantz. 1981. A multivariate analysis of temporal change in Arikara craniometrics: A methodological approach. *American Journal of Physical Anthropology* 55:247–259.

Knussman, R. 1967. Penrose-Abstand und Diskriminanzanalyse. *Homo* 18:134–140.

Neumann, G. 1959. Race, language and culture in aboriginal North America. Paper presented at the 28th annual meeting of the American Association of Physical Anthropologists. Title, no abstract, in *American Journal of Physical Anthropology* 18:362.

Ossenberg, N. 1977. Congruence of distance matrices based on cranial discrete traits, cranial measurements, and linguistic-geographic criteria in five Alaskan populations. *American Journal of Physical Anthropology* 47:93–98.

Penrose, L. S. 1954. Distance, size and shape. *Annals of Eugenics* 18:337–343.

Pietrusewsky, M. 1987. Craniometric variation in Micronesia and the Pacific: A multivariate study. Paper presented at the Micronesian Archaeological Conference, Guam, September 9–13. To appear in *Micronesica*.

———. 1988. Cranial variation in Australia, Melanesia and the Pacific. Paper presented at the annual meeting of the American Association of Physical Anthropologists, Kansas City, Mo., March 22–26.

Rao, C. R. 1971. Taxonomy in Anthropology. In *Mathematics in Archaeology and Historical Sciences*, 19–29. Edinburgh: Edinburgh University Press.

Rightmire, G. P. 1975. Problems in the study of later Pleistocene man in Africa. *American Anthropologist* 77:28–52.

———. 1981a. More on the study of the Border Cave remains. *Current Anthropology* 22:199–200.

———. 1981b. Later Pleistocene hominids of Eastern and Southern Africa. *Anthropologie* 19:15–26.

Sokal, R. R., and P. H. A. Sneath. 1963. *Principles of Numerical Taxonomy*. 359 pp. San Francisco: Freeman.

Spuhler, J. N. 1988. Evolution of mitrochondrial DNA in monkeys, apes, and humans. *Yearbook of Physical Anthropology* 31:15–48.

Stringer, C. B. 1978. Some problems in Middle and Upper Pleistocene hominid relationships. In *Recent Advances in Primatology*, D. Chivers and K. Joysey, eds., vol. 3, Evolution,395–418. London: Academic Press.

Stringer, C. B., and P. Andrews. 1988. Genetic and fossil evidence for the origin of modern humans. *Science* 239:1263–68.

Thorne, A. G., and M. H. Wolpoff. 1981. Regional continuity in Australasian Pleistocene hominid evolution. *American Journal of Physical Anthropology* 55:337–349.

Turner, C. G. II. 1985. The dental search for Native American origins. In *Out of Asia. Peopling the Americas and the Pacific*, R. Kirk and F. Szathmary, eds., 31–78. Canberra: The Journal of Pacific History.

———. 1987. Origin and affinity of the people of Guam: A dental anthropological assessment. Paper presented at the Micronesian Archaeological Conference, Guam, September 9–13. To appear in *Micronesica*.

van Vark, G. N. 1984. On the determination of hominid affinities. In *Multivariate Statistical Methods in Physical Anthropology*, G. N. van Vark and W. W. Howells, eds., 323–349. Doordrecht: D. Reidel.

———. 1985. Multivariate analysis in physical anthropology. In *Multivariate Analysis* VI, P. R. Krishnaiah, ed., 599–611. Elsevier Science Publishers.

van Vark, G. N., P. G. M. van der Sman, A. den Arend, and S. K. Hazewindus. 1985. The statistical significance of an association between skull morphology and climatic conditions. *Homo* 36:232–241.

Weidenreich, F. 1938–39. On the earliest representatives of modern mankind recovered on the soil of East Asia. *Peking Natural History Bulletin* 13:161–180.

———. 1945. *Apes, Giants and Man*. 122 pp. Chicago: University of Chicago Press.

Wilmink, F. W., and H. T. Uytterschaut. 1984. Cluster analysis, history, theory and applications. In *Multivariate Statistical Methods in Physical Anthropology*, G. N. van Vark and W. W. Howells, eds., 135–175. Doordrecht: D. Reidel.

Wolpoff, M. H., Wu X.-z., and A. G. Thorne. 1984. Modern *Homo sapiens* origins: A general theory of hominid evolution involving the fossil evidence from East Asia. In *The Origins of Modern Humans*, F. H. Smith and F. Spencer, eds., 411–483. New York: Alan R. Liss.

Woo J.-k. (Wu Rukang). 1959. Human fossils found in Liukiang, Kwangsi, China. *Vertebrata Palasiatica* 3:109–118.

Woo, T. L., and G. M. Morant. 1934. A biometric study of the "flatness" of the facial skeleton in man. *Biometrika* 26:196–250.

Appendices

Appendix A
Description of Populations

1

NORTHERN EUROPE: MEDIEVAL NORSE, OSLO
55 males 55 females
Anatomical Institute, University of Oslo

The Anatomical Institute possesses a large collection of skulls and skeletons from the vicinity of Oslo, excavated at different times (mostly by Schreiner and his associates and later by Torgersen and his associates) and representing different periods, the excavations usually resulting from the disturbing of ancient graveyards by construction work. The sample used here comes from medieval parish graveyards, representing the early period of general isolation of the area, and thus a population which was less cosmopolitan than that of later times (as represented by the main Maria Kirche and Gamlabyen collections which probably vary as to social level and include foreigners). The sample is about 85% from the graveyard of St. Nicolaus, with some from St. Halvard, fewer from St. Olav, and two of each sex from the early period of the Maria Kirche. Other more recent European populations might have been used, especially those known as to individual sex, but this one was favored because its parochial nature and simple conditions of life should make it more comparable with others of the study. The good teeth, and the total lack of malocclusions pointed out to me by Dr. Olav Bergland, epitomize the situation.

SELECTION: Most of the crania in the sample were included in a large group of both sexes already set out from the collection for dental study, and thus accompanied by mandibles and in generally excellent condition. I took those from early graveyards, filling out with some 20 more of each sex from the collection, all from St. Nicolaus parish. No selection beyond good condition was applied, except the cases of metopism were held to about 10% of the total arbitrarily in order not to err in the direction of too great inclusion of this feature, common in Norway.

SEXING: All the skulls had already been sexed by Schreiner and his associates (1939, p. 7), by inspection, the estimate being supported by presence of a skeleton in a "limited number" of cases. Schreiner and two experienced associates made independent estimates for each case. Where all three agreed, the case was taken as settled; otherwise the specimen was restudied by all three and then discussed. According to Dr. Bergland, Schreiner made a notebook recording these determinations, which showed that the cases for special discussion as doubtful amounted to about 28%; unfortunately the notebook has not lately been seen.

The skulls of my sample were already separated by sex following Schreiner's determination, or else, in the supplementary cases, were taken from boxes labeled with this determination in obvious fashion. Therefore, I clearly did not approach the skulls free of previous suggestion. In working, I noted those cases in which it seemed at all possible to reconsider the sex as given—not because of distinct disagreement with Schreiner but to make sure I could agree after careful consideration. This reserved group amounted to 11 "males" and 5 "females" (an odd balance, since in general the apparent females seem to be relatively robust and masculine). For the 16, skeletons were available for 8 "males" and 1 "female," which except for one "male" appeared to me to support Schreiner's decision. My final estimates agreed with his in every case but 2 out of 110. These two were in any event so difficult to decide upon—and one appeared morphologically unusual for the population as a whole—that I settled the matter by transferring them from the series to the test group and replacing them with two more ordinary citizens. Thus the sexing of the sample as constituted agrees 100% with that of Schreiner and his co-workers.

Bibliography

Schreiner, K. E. 1939. *Crania Norvegica*. I. Instituttet for Sammenlignende Kulturforskning, Serie B: Skrifter 36. 201 pp., 53 pls. Oslo: Aschehoug.
Torgersen, J., B. Getz, and E. Berle. 1964. Die mittelalterliche Bevölkerung von Oslo. *Zeitschr. Morphologie u. Anthropologie* 56:53–59.

2

CENTRAL EUROPE: ZALAVÁR, HUNGARY

53 males   45 females

Natural History Museum, Anthropological Section, Budapest

The cemeteries at Zalavár, situated 16 km from the western shore of Lake Balaton in western Hungary, date from the 9th to the 11th centuries A.D. and represent a rather complex population. Following the destruction of the Avar Empire in wars with the Franks at the beginning of the 9th century, this region became a Frankish protectorate controlled by the Bishop of Salzburg, with Zalavár as an important stronghold. Ethnic shifts in this post-Avar period created a general population which was heterogeneous, with distinct local differences. The inhabitants of Zalavár comprised three main elements: surviving Avars, surviving Romanized and newly arrived Germanic and Slavic elements (probably the most important), and small numbers of the earliest Magyars.

The skeletal material was excavated by Dr. Janos Nemeskéri in the course of general archaeological work at Zalavár carried out in the years 1948–52 by Professor G. Fehér and later by A. Sós for the Hungarian National Museum. Four cemeteries have been excavated, as follows: Zalavár village—the local common people (this might have been the best for study, but numbers were too limited); Zalavár castle—very cosmopolitan, with surviving Avars, Romanized Germans, Slavs, Frankish officials of court, church, and army, and toward the end Hungarians; Zalavár chapel—more homogeneous, largely restricted to ancient inhabitants and the western elements; a fourth cemetery akin in nature to the last two mentioned. Except for one skull from this last, the sample comes entirely from the castle and chapel cemeteries; none is from the village. It includes all the skulls from these cemeteries in condition suitable for my measurements.

SEXING: This population is one of those subjected to a systematic paleodemographic analysis by the methods developed by Nemeskéri. Part of this involves individual sex determinations by the methodical scoring of 12 different traits of the skull, and 9 additional traits of the post-cranial skeleton when possible. In preparation for full publication on the Zalavár population, this sexing has already been carried out for a first determination by Dr. Nemeskéri, and the skulls were set out (through the kindness of Dr. T. Tóth, then director of the Anthropological Section, and his assistants, especially Dr. Kinga Kralovánkiné Ery) already grouped according to this preliminary sex assessment, though it was not guaranteed that this had been followed absolutely. While acknowledging this division, I made my own estimate of sex as I went along. I noted all cases in which, considering my inexperience with the population, I thought any question at all could be raised, totaling 23 specimens for further consideration. Most of my doubts as to sex were quickly resolved on a further examination of these. I then checked the whole sample of 100 with Nemeskéri's manuscript list, and found 3 cases of disagreement.

For completeness, Dr. Nemeskéri then reviewed with me almost all of the 23 cases in which I had had a degree of uncertainty, getting out the skeletons where possible for final analysis (in a few cases after I had left Budapest, because of the shortness of time). This resulted in final complete agreement in all these cases. However, I discovered one case in which neither I nor Dr. Nemeskéri (in his original list) had been able to arrive at a decision, and which for some reason I did not review with him. I have eliminated this skull from the series. Another was dropped in a later assessment.

Bibliography

Acsádi, Gy., and J. Nemeskéri. 1970. *History of Human Life Span and Mortality.* Budapest: Akadémiai Kiado.

Acsádi, G., L. Harsányi, and J. Nemeskéri. 1962. The population of Zalavár in the Middle Ages. *Acta Archaeol. Acad. Scientiarum Hungaricae* 14:113–141.

Howells, W.W. 1974. The Population of Zalavár: A Problem in Cranial Variation. *Anthropologiai Közlemenyek* 18:91–96.

3

CENTRAL EUROPE: BERG, CARINTHIA, AUSTRIA

56 males   53 females

American Museum of Natural History, New York

Berg is a small mountain village near Greifenburg on the Drau River in western Carinthia. The skulls are part of the collection of Felix von Luschan, acquired by the American Museum in 1924 through a gift of Felix Warburg. This extraordinary series numbers 496 individuals obtained by von Luschan from a charnel house where, as elsewhere in Austria, bones have been placed following exhumation enforced by the limited size of church cemeteries. At the time of acquisition (1911), according to von Luschan, the village itself had about 30 houses and had harbored in recent centuries hardly more than 100 souls; he supposed therefore that he had collected virtually all the crania representing some five generations of this isolated village's population, excluding only some badly preserved skulls of children. The series as a whole has been fully described by H. L. Shapiro (1929), of the Department of Anthropology, to whom I am of course much indebted for its present use.

SELECTION: From the total of nearly 500 skulls Mrs. Priscilla Ward of the Department of Anthropology selected and put out for me 146 in the most complete condition. Of these, I rejected 35 for deficiencies and probable immaturity, coming to the end with 111 suitable (not necessarily complete) specimens, of which I measured 110 in the time allotted.

This is a "brachycranial" population; however, skulls vary from quite long and narrow to short, with a pronounced lambdoid flattening. The depressed cerebellar region, the frequent secondary growth of the occiput making a step along the lambdoid suture, the bulging parietals, and prominent foreheads, often very broad, suggest that cradling practices have been influential in shaping heads to varying degrees. The fact that asymmetry of the flattening is not common indicates however that cradling is probably not the only influence—i.e., a purely artificial effect on an actually long-headed population—but rather that round-headedness and flattening mingle effects in a way that is difficult to assess visually. Skulls which appeared to be naturally brachycranial, with no signs of secondary

effects, were few. I rated the specimens in this respect. In 46 cases flattening was possibly present, i.e., could not be excluded but was not clearly present (36 cases), or was entirely absent (10 cases). In the remaining 64 skulls flattening was either evident (52) or pronounced (11), being so extreme in one case that it was finally omitted from the series. The 35 skulls originally rejected also included a few with such extreme shortening that they were rejected for that reason. Thus the sample was selected to the extent that a few extremely short and flattened skulls—those I felt had undergone a marked unintentional deformation—were arbitrarily excluded, though no further attempt to control the effect (which was done in the case of the Hawaiian skulls, q.v.) was made.

Metopism is fairly frequent in the population but was disregarded as a regular variation; the proportion in the sample (14/109) should approximate that in the Norse sample.

SEXING: This impressed me as a particularly difficult population, and no mandibles or skeletal parts are available to aid in diagnosis. Sex was assessed by inspection during work, followed by two complete further reviews; all three judgments agreed for 44 "males" and 47 "females." Further study and shuffling of the other skulls assigned another 13 as 7 male and 6 female. The remaining 6 combined male and female traits so as to resist my powers of discrimination completely; I decided provisionally that they were, in fact, all male. A statistical comparison with Shapiro's 1929 results is not possible, since he met the same situation by excluding a number of doubtful specimens from his study. However, in all cases where we disagree, my "females" were his "males."

Bibliography

Shapiro, H. L. 1929. Contributions to the craniology of Central Europe. I. *Crania from Greifenberg in Carinthia.* Anthropological Papers of the American Museum of Natural History 31/1.

4

EAST AFRICA: TEITA, KENYA

33 males   50 females

Duckworth Laboratory of Physical Anthropology, Cambridge

These skulls were collected by I. S. B. Leakey in 1929. According to Leakey (see Kitson 1931) the Teita are a small group of Bantu-speakers living in the hilly country south of the Kenya-Uganda railway in the neighborhood of Voi, i.e., the southeast corner of Kenya; they are allied to the Wa-Chagga of the slopes of Kilimanjaro and to the Wa-Pare. The Teita formerly exhumed the skulls of the dead (usually without the mandibles) after about two years, and placed them in rock shelters or caves, which thereby became ancestral shrines. Leakey was allowed to visit such shrines and collect skulls of those dead who were no longer remembered by the living, or whose relatives had all become Christian; however, none is believed to have been deposited more than three or four generations prior to Leakey's collecting them.

All shrines were in the territory of a single clan, and since the Teita are patrilineal and patrilocal, the males in the series should all have been members of this clan, except for a few possible slaves from other tribes represented by skulls with avulsion of the incisors, which the Teita do not practice. (Leakey also felt that skulls with excessive nasal flatness might also be non-Teita, the flatness stemming from the mother's expressing mucous from the newborn's nose by pressing down with her thumb, again a custom not practiced by the Teita.) The Teita being exogamous, most of the females, contrary to the males, should be derived from other clans and might therefore be less homogeneous. Kitson, however, found the females to be, if anything, less variable than the males in measurements, and both sexes to be low in variability in any case. (The standard deviations reported herein likewise fail to indicate higher variability in females.) From their appearance she judged the series to be "racially as pure as any with which the biometrician usually deals." I was likewise struck by the marked homogeneity of appearance of the skulls. From the above and other findings in the studies of Kitson and Crichton, I consider that this sample conforms to the ideal of a local or tribal population about as well as any in this study.

SELECTION: This was hardly a problem. Of 123 adults in the series about 75 skulls were in moderately good condition, but teeth were remarkably bad throughout and a number of crania were damaged around the orbital margins by the gnawings of rodents, making various of the facial measurements difficult to take. By the laborious process of estimating measurements from one half of the face when the other was badly damaged, and similar devices, the total was eventually run up to 84 (one of which was eventually transferred to the test series because of bad condition). Although the number of males is limited, the specific nature of the population and its apparent morphological homogeneity make it acceptable for purposes of this study notwithstanding.

SEXING: No evidence except the skulls themselves was available for sex. Contrary to Miss Kitson's impression, I found the assignment of sex particularly difficult in the series. I judged the series twice: first while doing the skulls individually and then all at once, and got 7 cases of disagreement which I resolved by final examination without particular confidence in the results. Pearson and Morant sexed the series for Miss Kitson's study; in the 84 cases used by me there were 14 disagreements with my final judgments (4 of my males called female, 10 of my females called male), a high proportion of disagreement compared with the other series in this study where previous expert workers had recorded estimates of sex.

Bibliography

Crichton, J. M. 1966. A multiple discriminant analysis of Egyptian and African Negro crania. Papers of the Peabody Museum, Harvard University, vol. 57, no. 1: 45–67.

Kitson, E. 1931. A study of the Negro skull with special reference to the crania from Kenya Colony. *Biometrika* 23:271–314.

5

WEST AFRICA: DOGON, MALI
47 males   52 females
Musée de l'Homme, Paris

These skulls derive from burial caves in the territory of the Dogon tribe on the slopes of the Bandiagara plateau, east of the Niger in the vicinity of 14°30′N 30°30′W, in the Mali Republic. All were collected in 1934 on an expedition of Professor Marcel Griaule, from whom they came to the Musée de l'Homme in 1935.

They have been reported upon, for certain measurements, by Dr. J. Leschi (1958, 1959). According to her, the series comprises two lots, from different localities near Sanga, of which the later lot, from Bara, dates to about 200 years ago, and the earlier, from Toloy, corresponds to the time of the occupation of the escarpment by the Dogon. Although the females of the two groups appear to differ somewhat (the later being wider in maximum breadth), the small numbers and the general correspondence of the more numerous males of the two groups render a real distinction uncertain. At any rate, all are treated as one population here. However, Huizinga et al. (1967) also made collections from these caves, and they raise the question as to whether the crania, at least of their collection, represent the Dogon or their legendary predecessors in the region, the Tellem, who used such caves as burial places up to the 14th and 15th centuries. According to the authors, the present-day Dogon are quite willing to have "Tellem" caves investigated, but strongly discourage visits to their own burial caves, still in use. The skulls assumed to be Tellem appear to differ in form from those of Dogon when living Dogon are used for comparison, at the same time the "Dogon" skulls (in Paris) and the "Tellem" skulls (in Utrecht, at the Institute of Human Biology) do not appear to differ markedly. In the absence of a better basis for decision, the series used here will be accepted as Dogon, in view of the presumed dating of the material, although Dr. Vallois (1968) accepts the possibility that the Paris collection contains both populations, i.e., that the earlier lot is of Tellem origin. Since the desideratum for the study as a whole is a good local West African series, its actual application within the region is not of primary importance here.

SELECTION: None was involved; all adult skulls in usable condition were included.

SEXING: The whole series was judged twice, first individually during measuring, then all at once in a review of the storage shelves. This produced 7 difficult cases, which I set out in order from the most "male" to the most "female," reshuffling and repeating until the order stabilized. I then divided them at what seemed like the appropriate point.

Leschi's division of the same skulls was of the order of 70 males and 44 females (different numbers in different measurements and a larger total number considered). This implies a considerable divergence in assignment between us, and a greater tendency to assign skulls as female on my part. However, an even balance of sexes is more likely. In a study of innominate bones (disassociated from the skulls) in the "Tellem" caves, Glanville (1967) found that these were very largely of male sex in one cave, where the cultural material was also strongly male in nature, but were approximately equal as to sex in three other caves.

Bibliography

Glanville, E. V. 1967. Sexual dimorphism in the pelvic bones of the Tellem, a medieval Negro population from the Mali Republic. Koninkl. Nederl. Akad. van Wetenschappen, *Proceedings*, series C, 70:368–377.

Huizinga, J. 1968. New physical anthropological evidence bearing on the relationships between Dogon, Kurumba and the extinct West African Tellem populations. Koninkl. Nederl. Akad. van Wetenschappen, *Proceedings*, series C, 71:16–30.

Huizinga, J., N. F. Birnie-Tellier, and E. V. Glanville. 1967. Description and Carbon-14 dating of Tellem cave skulls from the Mali Republic: a comparison with other negroid groups. Koninkl. Nederl. Akad. van Wetenschappen, *Proceedings*, series C, 70:338–367.

Leschi, J. 1958. Premières données craniométriques concernant des Noirs Dogon de la boucle du Niger (Soudan Français). Variations des indices craniens. *Bull. et Mém. Soc. d'Anthrop. de Paris*, ser. 8, 9:160–168.

———. 1959. Quelques mesures concernant la tête osseuse de Noirs Dogon de la boucle du Niger (falaise de Bandiagara). *Bull. et Mém. Soc. d'Anthrop. de Paris*, ser. 10, 10:186–195.

Vallois, H. V. 1968. Dogon et Tellem, un problème anthropologique. *L'Anthropologie* 72:411–413.

6

SOUTH AFRICA: ZULU

55 males   46 females

R. A. Dart Collection, University of the Witwatersrand

This osteological collection, now named in Dart's honor, stems largely from the dissecting room of the Department of Anatomy, though it also includes archaeological specimens. It was instituted in the 1920s and has continued systematically to the present; due to the anthropological orientation of the department from its beginnings under Professor Dart, it is clear that the identification of subjects has been professional and as correct as information would allow. As to the tribal identity of Africans included, Dr. Hertha de Villiers, in her general study of the Bantu (1968), has this to say:

> As detribalisation is occurring to a marked degree in the Wits area, from which the cadavers were obtained, it may be assumed that many of the present day *children* of Africans in this area are 'intertribal hybrids,' whereas the adults, such as those of the present study, represent as yet unhybridised individuals, belonging in most cases to the first generation of urbanized Africans, whose parents on both sides were of the same tribe. It is, therefore, considered justified to break down the data of the present Wits series according to tribal origins.

I must particularly thank Dr. de Villiers for her guidance and suggestions in the selection of my own series.

The condition of the skulls was in general excellent, since they were affected less from accidental damage, frequent in other series, than by tooth loss and occasional other age effects. A special condition affects the majority (62 skulls): removal of the calotte during dissection. In some specimens this resulted in a small degree of warping of the calotte; however, in all cases

used I was able to join it to the rest of the skull with plastic tape in such a way that the measurements must be essentially the same as in the original condition.

SELECTION: Though other neighboring Bantu tribes, e.g., Sotho, are closely related to the Zulu—and no special physical differences from them could be found by de Villiers in her study—it was possible to restrict the sample to Zulus alone, and thus to one tribe and area (19th-century history of course suggests that the Zulus are a rather cosmopolitan tribe). This meant, however, scratching for every available female Zulu specimen in the collection.

SEXING: This is one of three series in the study which is entirely composed of individuals of known sex (and approximate age). Some of the skulls would certainly have been assigned to the wrong sex if sexing had been done by inspection; in a few cases this impression was strong enough so that I checked the mortuary book, to be able to say that no error had occurred in transfer, after preparation, to the Dart Collection. The largest skull in the whole series was that of an authentic female; it was included in the female series of my 1973 publication but has been dropped from the present study as aberrant.

Bibliography

de Villiers, H. 1968. *The skull of the South African Negro—a morphological study.* Johannesburg: Witwatersrand University Press.

7

AUSTRALIA: LAKE ALEXANDRINA TRIBES, SOUTH AUSTRALIA

52 males   49 females

South Australian Museum, Adelaide

This sample represents the Jarildekald and Warki-Korowalde tribes of the lowermost Murray, the latter tribe being an offshoot of the former not over four generations ago. The territory involved is, for the Jaril-dekald, the east bank of the Murray River below (but not including) Murray Bridge, the east shore of Lake Alexandrina, and all of Lake Albert except the south shore; for the Warki-Korowalde the remaining shore of Lake Alexandrina and a short distance west. The female group was filled out by including 6 skulls from the territory of the linguistically related (and intermarrying) Tanganekald of the Coorong (shores of the lagoon to the south, behind Younghusband Peninsula).

This is thus a well-defined local population, and the linguistic and archaeological evidence indicates long-time stability (2000 years?) in the area given. Place names are entirely in the local languages. Relationships with other peoples are up the Murray River and eastward, and down the shore southward; just to the west was a hard cultural boundary (at the mountains east of Adelaide) with circumcising tribes who had no contact with the people described.

SELECTION: The above information was given me by Norman Tindale of the South Australian Museum, on whose firsthand knowledge of the area from archaeology and from surviving aboriginals the delimitation of the sample entirely depends. It was picked out locality by locality from the large collection in the museum by following his detailed advice, and also with constant help from Graeme Pretty of the museum in using the catalogue. I must express again my appreciation to both for making possible the assembling of this series. It is one of the nearly ideal samples in the present investigation: a real local and time-limited population.

The majority of skulls derive from a cemetery at Swanport, found in 1911 and ascribed by some to a smallpox epidemic in the area, just before the settlement of Adelaide in 1836 (see Stirling 1911). Mr. Tindale, however, doubts this, and believes it represents a more normal accumulation of burials of the Mulbarapi horde of the Jarildekald. Other vicinities yielding more

occasional finds were Talem Bend, Poltalloch, Lakes Albert and Alexandrina generally, Milang, Port Elliot, and the Coorong.

SEXING: Australian skulls give the impression of being difficult to sex visually by the canons of experience with other populations. Female-appearing specimens may have wide and flaring malars, and "males" sometimes seem to have reduced and rounded supraorbitals. This sample was sexed by inspection as I measured (using the mandible where possible, although this bone also seems less informative than in other series). Then all were reviewed together at once, for a second independent list of assignments; and 9 cases of disagreement between first and second judgments resulted. These particular cases were then reviewed again at length for final decision. Skeletons were available for only 11 individuals in the whole sample. The sex as determined from the skeletons supported that determined from the skull in 10 cases in which I had not disagreed with myself; one of the doubtful cases, which I had finally called female on the third review, I changed back to male after seeing the skeleton. (There was a further, apparently very vexing, case, that of #A 61. This had a definitely male-appearing skull and a skeleton with a definitely female-appearing pelvis. Since skulls and skeletons are not stored together, I wrote Mr. Pretty later asking him to bring them together in this case: he was able to report that atlas and skull did not fit anatomically, and that the different coloration of skeleton and skull showed that they clearly belonged to different individuals.)

Bibliography

For a review, with references, of work on Australian crania, see T. Brown, *Skull of the Australian Aboriginal; A Multivariate Analysis of Craniofacial Associations* (Department of Dental Science, University of Adelaide, South Australia, 1967).

Stirling, E. C. 1911. Preliminary report on the discovery of native remains at Swanport, River Murray; with an inquiry into the alleged occurrence of a pandemic among the Australian aboriginals. *Transactions of the Royal Society of South Australia* 35:4–46, pls. 2–9.

8

TASMANIA: GENERAL

45 males　42 females

The specimens are located in the following institutions:

Tasmanian Museum, Hobart	20
Queen Victoria Museum, Launceston	13
South Australian Museum, Adelaide	5
Department of Anatomy, Melbourne	6
National Museum, Melbourne	1
Musée de l'Homme, Paris	7
British Museum (Natural History)	9
Oxford University	5
Cambridge University	1
University of Edinburgh	9
Royal Scottish Museum, Edinburgh	1
American Museum, New York	7
Field Museum, Chicago	2
Naturhistorisches Museum, Vienna	1

The problem of assembling a Tasmanian series is acute, although different from the case of the Bushmen (see below). A regional rather than a local population must be accepted. There is the similar danger that skulls of other ethnic varieties may be labeled Tasmanian because of the rarity and romantic interest in the case of the latter.

Tasmania is an island, and thus constitutes an area both smaller and better delimited than the territory from which Bush skulls might emanate. Also, the aboriginals came to a rather quick end, and so the chance of finding the remains of hybrids is greatly reduced (certain late burials at Oyster Bay, of Flinders Island survivors, are believed mixed; none of these is included here). European skulls can readily be detected, even though labeled Tasmanian. The real hazard lies in the fact that Melanesians, Maoris, and above all, Australian aboriginals, did come to the island in the 19th century; and those that came from Australia furnish the greatest chance of erroneous acceptance, as Tasmanian, from three sources: (1) Australian emigrants who died in Tasmania (such a known case is represented by a skull in the Musée de l'Homme); (2) a 19th century physician coming from Australia to take up practice in Tasmania and bringing an Australian skull or two along with his medicine cabinet, to be presented eventually by his heirs to some institution as the skull of an "aboriginal"; and (3) skulls acquired by museums from collectors who had those of both Australians and Tasmanians in their possession. In existing collections outside of Tasmania itself, other errors are possible, because of the general interest in Tasmanian natives: thus "Tasmanians" acquired from dealers or received in old phrenological collections are distinctly suspect. Material in European museums (except for the Musée de l'Homme) is especially poor in documentation. There is of course a large literature on all this, fortunately admirably reviewed by Macintosh (Macintosh and Barker 1965), by Abbie (1964), and by Plomley (1962).

SELECTION: I have been particularly helped by Mr. Frank Ellis, director of the Queen Victoria Museum in Launceston; by Dr. N. J. B. Plomley, former director of the same museum; and by the late Professor N. W. G. Macintosh of the University of Sydney.

I cannot go deeply into details of authenticity here. In Tasmanian museums I avoided all crania which seemed suspect by reason of appearance or documentation, but accepted undocumented "Tasmanians" which were clearly not of European or some other extraneous derivation. It is conceivable that one or two actual Australians may have been included but I doubt it. Elsewhere I accepted on about the same basis: clear labeling as Tasmanian and no reasons for suspicion.

The problem may be put in perspective in this way. Macintosh is optimistic; he says (Macintosh and Barker 1965, p. 43): "We are on quite safe ground if we accept 90% (or even a little higher percent) of the Tasmanian cranial collections as being genuinely Tasmanian." My feeling is that he is probably correct, and that by judicious omissions the present series, on such a standard, would be closer to 100%. On the other hand, Dr. Plomley has very kindly given me an estimate of the status by actual documentation of most of the skulls in the present series (omitting some for which he has no information leading to a decision). This makes less serene reading than Macintosh's opinion. He has classed the skulls (the sexing is mine) as follows:

	Males	Females
A. Known individuals	2	2
B. Good data as to locality of origin making it likely, but not certain, that they are Tasmanians	7	8
C. Other specimens obtained by "reliable" collectors and likely to be Tasmanian (von Luschan's 5 in the American Museum came from G. A. Robinson as "Tasmanian," but fall in this group rather than in B since, in view of Robinson's long sojourn in Australia, it is not certain that he had only Tasmanian skulls in his possession).	5	5
D. Specimens for which information is poor, or does not go beyond a labeling as "Tasmanian," or which derive from a collection that contained a miscellany of crania (e.g., that of Crowther).	24	21
Unclassified	6	6

This indicates that only 14 males and 15 females of this series can be rated as having positive historical reasons for being used as actual Tasmanians. (I would be inclined to add one unclassified male in the South Australian Museum on geographical grounds, as well as one D male [Edinburgh XXXII] and one ungraded female [Field Museum 27295] on the basis of charring of the skull, as a sign of the aboriginal practice of burning the dead body without always achieving complete cremation.)

Thus, independent documentation does not cover many specimens. I have, however, accepted a large body of skulls simply labeled "Tasmanian," in Tasmania and elsewhere, with little pricking of conscience, since there is a Tasmanian look to the majority which is rather clear, and different from Australians. (This is *not* the same thing as assembling a "Tasmanian" series on a typological basis, since it is used simply as a principle of nonexclusion of skulls already labeled Tasmanian.) Some specimens, especially males, do in fact look Australian, but having decided that construction of a Tasmanian series calls for accepting the specimens graded D by Dr. Plomley, I have done so across the board, excluding only skulls which seem illegitimate to me on other grounds, or which have simply turned up,

within the last generation or so, in a doctor's cabinet in Tasmania, without any legitimate claim to being of Tasmanian origin rather than Australian.

To use everything possible, some badly damaged skulls were included, as long as these were not distorted in the remaining parts, and so allowed acceptable approximations to probable original form. Also included are some possible late adolescent skulls (on the basis of spheno-occipital synchondrosis and third molar eruption—the latter may not be a reliable sign of immaturity) which seemed adult in general morphology and development.

SEXING: This was catch-as-catch-can, under the circumstances, not systematic. Four skulls came from definitely or allegedly identified individuals ("Cobia" was not included in the series; "William Lanney" in Edinburgh is probably female, and in my view, based on comparing photographs, almost certainly not Lanney); two more were accompanied by pelvic parts.

There is a traditionally recognized "Tasmanian" skull form, doubtless valid in general, which has pronounced parietal bosses and a pentagonoid horizontal vault outline, and a short broad face with low orbits. In several collections I got the strong impression that this was exhibited by the "female" skulls, and that "males" often appeared to be longer-headed, lacked the pentagonoid form (probably a size effect) and looked like particularly rugged and gerontomorphic Australians. On getting home from the main trip for collection of data, I received the Macintosh and Barker paper which points out (p. 13) that Hrdlička, on several occasions in reviewing small groups of Tasmanian skulls, described all or nearly all the males as "Australian" or "near Australian" in type, without commenting on the females. As Macintosh notes, this has doubtless been a factor both in authentification of crania by some authors and in ideas as to the degree of distinction between Australians and Tasmanians.

Bibliography

Abbie, A. A. 1964. A survey of the Tasmanian aboriginal collection in the Tasmanian Museum. *Papers and Proceedings of the Royal Society of Tasmania* 98:53–62.

Hrdlička, A. 1928. Catalogue of human crania in the United States National Museum Collections. Australians, Tasmanians, South African Bushmen, Hottentots and Negro. *Proceedings of the U.S. National Museum,* 72/24:1–140.

Macintosh, N. W. G., and B. C. W. Barker. 1965. *The Osteology of Aboriginal Man in Tasmania.* Oceania Monographs 12. 72 pp.

Plomley, N. J. B. 1962. A list of Tasmanian aboriginal material in collections in Europe. *Records, Queen Victoria Museum,* n.s. 15. 18 pp.

9

MELANESIA: TOLAI, NEW BRITAIN

56 males   54 females

American Museum of Natural History, New York

These skulls, to the total number of 194, form part of the collection of Felix von Luschan acquired for the American Museum in 1924 by gift of Felix Warburg. Except for a small group purchased in Sydney in 1914, they were procured for von Luschan by Richard Parkinson, the naturalist who was "Queen Emma's" brother-in-law and estate manager. Exactly how they were obtained is not recorded (Parkinson is exasperatingly silent about this in his book), but they were apparently gathered as opportunity afforded, and evidently forwarded to von Luschan in two lots, bearing accession dates (also marked on the individual skulls) of 1900 and 1908. For long, this collection remained in the Königliche Museum für Völkerkunde in Berlin, where the earlier lot was studied by Müller (1905). Still other skulls of the same population, collected by Parkinson, are in the Field Museum in Chicago (von Bonin 1936).

The skulls are all lettered "Ralûm," which is the name of a general area, not of a specific village, tribe, or district; the name was adopted by Queen Emma for her plantation (she called her own house and grounds Gunantambu; Robson 1965). In a letter dated October 24, 1898, Parkinson wrote von Luschan: "Dieselbe (Schädel) sind ausnahmslos von Eingeborenen aus den Dörfer zwischen Ralum und dem Varzin," i.e., the southwest shore of Blanche Bay and Varzin or Vunakokor mountain. This is Tolai territory; Parkinson (1907) does not use the name but refers to the whole ethnic group as simply the natives of the northeast Gazelle Peninsula. It is clear from his book that he distinguishes them from other tribal groups: Baining, Nakanai, Taulil, Butam, Sulka, with which there might be any confusion. In 1962, a one-legged Tolai named Leg-he-broke remembered seeing the skulls collected in a storehouse; he asserted Parkinson and Queen Emma got them locally, and that they were all Tolai, victims of interclan killings. The Tolai were head-takers and cannibals at the arrival of the Germans, but Parkinson says nothing about this, ascribing cannibalism only to places farther away. The skulls themselves are clean but usually have rootlets or vine parts in the apertures, whatever this may signify. Actually, ordinary burial of the dead and later exhumation and skull storage are probably responsible for much of this collection. Parkinson elsewhere (1887, p. 101) indicates that burial was the general mode of disposal, and Kleintitschen (1906) says: "Gewöhnlich graben sie einen Toten aus und stellen den Schädel in die Mitte der Tamburollen."

So it is apparent that the collection derives from a limited number of Tolai villages in a small part of their territory. It is unlikely that the series contains non-Tolais, and most unlikely that it contains Europeans, though some were eaten at about the right time. By all tradition, the Tolai came a few centuries ago from southern New Ireland (lying to the eastward) across the Duke of York islands to the Gazelle Peninsula (according to Mr. Terry Daw of the administration, the languages in the two areas are mutually intelligible). Traditionally, it has been assumed that they settled in the Gazelle Peninsula by conquest, after scouting parties from the Duke of Yorks witnessed very large taros being boiled in hot springs. Parkinson's belief was rather that they took up empty territory after a volcanic explosion had driven the Baining westward into the mountains (the lethality of such explosions, and the quick regrowth, have been demonstrated all too recently). There is certainly no sign of the Tolai having mixed with previous inhabitants such as the Baining; the living Tolai and their neighbors in southern New Ireland are somewhat "Australoid," heavy-faced people, compared with tribes southward in New Britain and, with less difference, northward in New Ireland.

SELECTION: This was made according to condition, more or less undamaged skulls being accepted in order of number, though in some cases estimates of readings had to be made, as in other series. Metopic skulls were avoided arbitrarily—they were few, but in one or two cases gave the impression of a modified forehead form. As to sex, no selection was made until I came to the last 11 skulls, when skulls readily assignable by sex were taken to balance final numbers. One skull (#V.L.1571) was rejected for abnormally large size, leaving 110.

SEXING: This was done by inspection, during measuring. The principal previous worker used for checking was myself; I studied the same skulls in 1932 and sexed them jointly with H. L. Shapiro. Of the 111 cases measured here, comparison showed 8 disagreements on first judgment, and 4 on final assessment (the 1966 determination of course being followed herein). Von Luschan, in the catalogue, recorded his opinion as to sex in 28 of these 111 cases (probably he avoided most of the doubtful cases), and in these there are no disagreements with my own determinations. Müller studied 52 of the same skulls (the 1900 shipment, and in 20 of the 52 gives a different estimate of sex, in every case recording male where I record female: his division is 40 males and 12 females (against my 20 males and 32 females). Because of their generally rugged and "Australoid" features the skulls on the average look "male" by European standards. Nevertheless, after having reviewed 12 other widely differing series of skulls before doing this one, I arrived at a division by sex (of the total of 111) in which 4 skulls were called *female* which I had called male in 1932 (all of course in the highly dubious category); in other words my standards of estimate were slightly further from Müller's, not nearer, after all this experience. (In 1966, I rated one skull as female without question, which in 1932 was the single skull both Shapiro and I had excluded from the series as impossible to decide upon.) Since 1973 I have shifted one "female" to the males.

Bibliography

Howells, W. W. 1934. The peopling of Melanesia, as indicated by cranial evidence from the Bismarck Archipelago. Ph.D. thesis, Harvard University.

Kleintitschen, P. A. 1906. *Die Küstenbewohner der Gazellehalbinsel.* 360 pp. Düsseldorf.

Parkinson, R. 1887. *Im Bismarck Archipel. Erlaubnisse und Beobachtungen auf der Insel Neu-Pommern (Neu-Britannien).* 154 pp. Leipzig.

_____. 1907. *Dreissig Jahre in der Südsee.* 876 pp. Stuttgart: Strecker & Schröder.

Müller, W. 1905. Beiträge zur Kraniologie der Neu-Britainnier. Mitteilungen aus dem Museum für Völkerkunde in Hamburg. 5. *Beiheft zum Jahrbuch der Hamburgischen Wissenschaftlichen Anstalten* 23:71–187.

Robson, R. W. 1965. *Queen Emma. The Samoan American Girl Who Founded an Empire in 19th Century New Guinea.* 239 pp. Sydney: Pacific Publications.

von Bonin, G. 1936. On the craniology of Oceania. Crania from New Britain. *Biometrika,* 28:123–148.

10

POLYNESIA: MOKAPU, OAHU, HAWAII

51 males   49 females

Bernice P. Bishop Museum, Honolulu

The skeletons were recovered (in a few cases by accident) from burial plots in sand along the north shore of Mokapu Peninsula. Extensive excavations were carried out from March, 1938, through early 1940 by the Bishop Museum, under the direction of Kenneth Emory (briefly) and Gordon T. Bowles (then of the University of Hawaii); later occasional finds were made and brought to the museum, and in 1957 Robert N. Bowen carried out further excavations. The number of burials discovered totaled over 500. (For further remarks see Pietrusewsky 1971.)

The graves gave no indication of European contact, and lay in three different subareas, from west to east as follows: Heeia or Hawaiian, Castle, and Navy (designated on excavation cards as H, C, and N respectively). These areas may represent corresponding extended family (*'ohana*) divisions in adjacent habitation sites but, except for the geographical separation, nothing is known from archaeological evidence which would distinguish the three groups as different populations. The most likely period of burial is the latter half of the precontact Hawaiian occupation period, or some time between 1400 and 1790 A.D.

The skeletal material was studied in detail by the late Charles E. Snow of the University of Kentucky, who died before publication of his report (except for an oral presentation, 1966). His 1974 volume, published after my 1973 study, is comprehensive as to the details given here from other sources. It is also detailed as to characters of the skeletal material. His measurement means, done on a larger number of specimens, do not coincide very closely with mine herein. He did not supply individual measurements.

I had only brief correspondence with him on the subject before his unexpected and deeply regretted death, but his notes on sexing are recorded in the museum catalogue. For my own work with the series I am most grateful to Mr. Bowen for a great deal of help, and for the above information on the collection, which I have from him personally and also from his published note on the burials (in Sterling and Summers 1961).

SELECTION: Of all the series studied, this is the only one clearly affected by artificial deformation, or "head-shaping," a custom recognized for Polynesia but dealt with in the literature far less than a physical anthropologist might wish (but see Pearson 1921). In the Mokapu series, its presence and effect were variable, posing the difficult problem of trying to eliminate it by selection as far as possible, without overdoing the process and in this way creating a sample which would be dolichocephalic to a false degree (a stroll in the street will show that the modern population of Hawaiian descent is not a dolichocephalic one).

Head-shaping manifests itself here in an obvious vertical flattening of the back of the skull, often accompanied by a small asymmetry of the flattened area. Skulls which do not show this clearly may nevertheless have an occiput with only a moderate curve, i.e., a rather flat nuchal plane, together with a high vertex, a marked curve of the profile at lambda, and prominent parietal bosses. As far as I know, this pentagonoid skull is a natural Polynesian form, not necessarily reflecting actual deformation, and grading into crania which are more frankly oval and dolichocephalic.

In going through the storage of material, I rejected out of hand any skulls with obvious flattening which could have been caused only artificially. The remaining crania were put out for study, during which I continued to set aside doubtful cases. Finally, I reviewed the entire lot set out (doubtful cases included) and classified them once again, as A, frankly ovoid, with no likelihood of their having been shaped; B, pentagonoid, as described, with a flattish nuchal area, but showing a definite rounding of the occiput in both lateral and vertical views and having no convincing signs of artificial shaping or flattening; C, those approximating the original rejections, i.e., having flattening or asymmetry, and with insufficient rounding of the occiput to be convincing as to *lack of* deformation completely.

As a result, 6 skulls already measured were rejected, the residuum representing every usable skull from Mokapu in the collection. At this stage it was not possible to make any better judgment as to the presence of shaping effects, beyond the knowledge that such effects may in fact survive every effort to eliminate them in this way from a series. For example, the high standard deviations for cranial length, breadth, and index in Hooton's "undeformed" Pecos series, selected as a small proportion of the whole Pecos collection, show that this sample was not sufficiently pruned so as actually to remove the effects of deformation.

No careful count was kept of skulls, otherwise in good condition, which were left in storage because of evident shaping, but I estimate that one-third of the whole collection would be classifiable as C, above, and hence clearly influenced by deformation.

SEXING: Skulls were removed from their boxes in a few large lots. As this was done, I made and recorded for each skull a snap judgment of sex, with appropriate expressions of doubt where called for. I then inspected the accompanying skeleton, which was largely present in most cases, and recorded a separate estimate of sex, also noting the degree of my conviction about this estimate. (As elsewhere I lacked time to do full determinations using discriminants or other systematic methods.) Finally, on measuring the skull, I reconsidered and made a third estimate.

I then checked all assignments with those made previously by Snow, as shown in the catalogue. Of 105 possible comparisons I found 3 cases of disagreement. I sexed these 3 carefully once more from skull and skeleton without reference to previous decisions, and arrived at a different opinion for one, leaving only 2 cases (obviously, they were difficult ones) of disagreement between myself and Snow, certainly a very low figure for two workers. It is my impression that

Hawaiian skeletons are easy to sex, but it also remains my conviction that a skeleton is not necessarily male just because two, or ten, anthropologists say it is.

Bibliography

Pearson, K. 1921. Was the skull of the Moriori artificially deformed? *Biometrika* 13:338–346.

Pietrusewsky, M. 1971. *Human skeletal collections in the Bishop Museum*. 35 pp. Department of Anthropology, B. P. Bishop Museum, Honolulu, Report 71-B.

Snow, C. E. 1966. Hawaiians past and present. A comparative study of prehistoric Hawaiians and those "pure" Hawaiians living in 1920 and 1965 (Abstract). Pacific Science Congress, Tokyo, September 1966.

Snow, C. E. 1974. *Early Hawaiians. An Initial Study of Skeletal Remains from Mokapu, Oahu*. 179 pp. Lexington: University Press of Kentucky.

Sterling, E. P., and C. C. Summers. 1961. *The sites of Oahu*, vol. 1, p. 5:184–188. Honolulu: Bishop Museum.

11

POLYNESIA: EASTER ISLAND

49 males   37 females

The crania used for this series are located in the following institutions:

	Males	Females
Musée de l'Homme, Paris	30	20
British Museum (Natural History)	13	11
Naturhistorisches Museum, Vienna	5	5
Peabody Museum, Harvard University		1
Canterbury Museum, Christchurch	1	

This population, on its spectacularly isolated island, surely represents a limited breeding population, as was sought for the present study, both spatially and apparently temporally as well, though it does cover some centuries. The bulk of the Paris collection (made by Pinart in the 1870s) comes either from La Perouse Bay in the northeast or Vaihu in the south; but this cannot connote geographic variation, in spite of traditions of battles between Long-ears and Short-ears. R. I. Murrill reported (1968) on a limited number of crania recovered under good archaeological and chronometric control in 1955–56 by the Norwegian Expedition under Thor Heyerdahl. No burials could be assigned to the Early Period (400–1100 A.D.). Murrill could find no indications of difference between those of the Middle (1100–1680) and Late (1680–1868) Periods.

SEXING: This was done by inspection. It struck me as particularly difficult, in contrast to the Mokapu Hawaiians. It is clear that large mastoid processes and well-developed supraorbitals need not exclude female sex, as was apparent in the case of a mounted skeleton, fully female otherwise. The same female robustness is evident in the Moriori series herein. Sex was assigned during work except that in Paris, where more than half of these crania reside, the most difficult cases of all were kept out and studied at length at the end. As always, a number of departures from true sex must enter, but these are assumed to do little violence to variation between and within the sex groups, the main effect probably being to exaggerate somewhat sex differences when human judgment rather than nature is in control of division. Few assessments of sex by previous workers could be usefully consulted. Matchable specimens in the British Museum used by von Bonin came out with no disagreement among 12 of my males, and 1 disagreement among 3 of my females. There was no overlap with Murrill's specimens.

I am indebted, as often before, to colleagues and friends for access to collections. I warmly remember, at the Musée de l'Homme, the late Robert Gessain, then director, and Mme. Y. Azoulay; at the British Museum, C. B. Stringer and R. Kuszynski; and at the Naturhistorisches Museum, Vienna, J. Szilvássy and H. Kritscher.

Bibliography

Murrill, R. I. 1968. *Cranial and Postcranial Skeletal Remains from Easter Island.* 105 pp. Minneapolis: University of Minnesota Press.

von Bonin, G. 1931. A contribution to the craniology of the Easter Islanders. *Biometrika* 23:249–270.

12

POLYNESIA: MORIORI, CHATHAM ISLANDS

57 males   51 females

The Chatham Islands lie athwart 44°S latitude and thus are well below the tropics. About 500 miles east of the south island of New Zealand, they are also isolated in other directions. It is not now clear archaeologically whether they were settled directly from Central Polynesia or by an early movement from New Zealand; it was probably the former. In any case it can be assumed that the Moriori have an ultimate relationship with the New Zealand Maori and that they were essentially isolated from other Polynesians until they were overrun in 1835 by Maori freebooters who had learned of the existence of the Chathams from English navigators. Although the bulk of these Maori returned to their homeland, the shock led to rapid decline of the indigenous islanders, and the last survivor died in the 1930s.

The Moriori were selected for inclusion in this work, in preference to Maori, because of availability of material and the restricted and definable nature of the population. Nothing comparable exists in New Zealand, and Maori sensibilities there do not favor recovery of skeletal material. I have not attempted to track down possible details of dates and circumstances of recovery of the Moriori skulls, but the chances of inclusion of Maoris dying in the Chathams is small. Most specimens came piecemeal into the collections given below, apparently during the last 20 years of the last century, by gift or purchase from individuals. A few derive from known old burial grounds but many were randomly picked up, particularly as exposures by beach erosion of seated interments. This mode of burial existed in New Zealand as well, but the likelihood of such burials in the Chathams being actually those of Maoris is extremely small.

SEXING: Like Easter Islanders but unlike the Mokapu Hawaiians, these crania (very seldom with accompanying postcrania) seemed difficult to diagnose by inspection. I feel this is partly due to the "male" appearance of many females, especially because of the strong necks which may be seen in many living Polynesian women. At the same time occipital crests, though well developed, seem to be less so than in Hawaiians or Easter Islanders. At any rate, where I disagreed with the assessments of previous workers this was due, as in many other series, to my assigning as "female" skulls which others called "male." Of the specimens in the British Museum (most of which had originally been in the Royal College of Surgeons), Eveline Y. Thomson in 1915 (among specimens used by both of us) rated 1 skull female out of my 26 males, and 3 as male out of my 17 females, a good match.

Impressions of morphology: The Moriori have a general Polynesian appearance, with narrow frontals and rather prominent nasal-glabellar regions. I am unable to say how or whether they have any special resemblance to Maoris. Their special character is flatness of the frontal (without signs of artificial deformation), which is extreme for the species in some individuals (Howells 1979). Third molar agenesis and exostoses of the auditory canal are common, though I did not keep count of these.

The specimens were found in the following institutions:

	Males	Females
British Museum (Natural History)	31	22
University of Otago Medical School	17	17
Canterbury Museum, Christchurch	8	10
Auckland Museum	1	2

I am grateful, once again, to the British Museum and to all in the Sub-Department of Anthropology for hospitality, working space, access to the collections, and general kind assistance; to Dr. Philip Houghton of the University of Otago's Medical School and to Mr. John Dennison, for every kind of cordiality and assistance in Dunedin; to the late Roger Duff, director of the Canterbury Museum in Christchurch, and to the Auckland Museum, for similar hospitality in those places.

Bibliography

Howells, W. W. 1979. "Was the skull of the Moriori artificially deformed?" *Archaeology & Physical Anthropology in Oceania* 13/2:114–119.

Scott, J. H. 1893. Contribution to the osteology of the aborigines of New Zealand and of the Chatham Islands. *Transactions of the New Zealand Institute* 26: 1–64, plus tables.

Thomson, E. Y. 1915. A study of the crania of the Moriori, or aborigines of the Chatham Islands, now in the Museum of the Royal College of Surgeons. *Biometrika* 11:82–135.

13

NORTH AMERICA: EARLY ARIKARA

42 males   27 females

U.S. National Museum, Washington
Museum of Natural History, University of Kansas, Lawrence

This series comes from a single village site (the Sully site, 39 SL 4) near the center of South Dakota, believed to have been occupied by protohistoric Arikara from about 1600 to 1750 A.D. Now covered by the waters of the Oahe Reservoir, the village was situated on the east bank of the Missouri River just below the site of old Fort Sully, and was the largest of the earth lodge villages along the river. It was excavated, under the direction of Dr. Robert Stephenson, by the Missouri Basin Project of the Smithsonian Institution's River Basins Surveys, and Professor William M. Bass of the University of Kansas, removing a total of 566 human burials during the summer seasons of 1957, 1958, 1961, and 1962. Dr. Bass published (1964) a study of osteological variation in prehistoric Plains Indians which incorporated the Sully site material of the first two seasons.

The skulls used here are partly at the U.S. National Museum (28 males, 16 females) and partly at the University of Kansas (14 males, 11 females). I am indebted to Dr. T. D. Stewart, director, and Dr. J. L. Angel, curator of Physical Anthropology, at the U.S. National Museum, and above all to Dr. Bass, who with great hospitality suggested to me the suitability of the series for the present study and invited me to use it.

SELECTION: Although the number of burials found was large, the youth or fragmentary condition of many in-dividuals reduced the number of specimens available for use here. The skulls included in the series are all those at either museum which were in good enough condition.

SEXING: The disparity in proportions of the sexes is somewhat unusual among the series in the study. Sex was assigned by me, as in other cases, as I worked, to arrive at a first estimate. At the University of Kansas (Dr. Bass was unfortunately in the field) I reviewed all cases several times. In Washington, his previous sex determinations, as recorded on the skull itself, agreed in all cases with mine. Here, 6 determinations could be checked on the accompanying skeleton. One skull, no. 39SL4.6055, was judged definitely male by both of us (and also, at my request on the spot, by several colleagues at the National Museum), but was accompanied by a skeleton which seemed equally definitely to be female, and the problem was met by omitting this skull from the series and trans-ferring it to the test group. This does not seem likely to be a case of wrong association of skull and skeleton in cataloguing, as was evidently so in an Australian specimen.

Bibliography

Bass, W. M., III. 1964. The variation in physical types of prehis-toric Plains Indians. *Plains Anthropologist* 9/24 (Memoir 1).

14

NORTH AMERICA: SANTA CRUZ ISLAND, CALIFORNIA

51 males   51 females

Peabody Museum, Harvard University
National Museum of Natural History, Smithsonian Institution

Santa Cruz is the largest of the islands in the Santa Barbara Channel. At the time of first contact it was inhabited by Chumash, associated with the Canaliño archaeological culture. The natives were all removed to missions on the mainland in the first half of the 19th century; Santa Cruz has been essentially uninhabited since then, having been used for some years as a cattle ranch by a resident private owner. At his death it became the property of the Nature Conservancy (New York Times, May 16, 1978). The terrain is rugged; archaeological work has been carried out from time to time, though less than in the other islands.

In May and June of 1875 Paul Schumacher, under the auspices of the Smithsonian Institution, conducted a whirlwind expedition to collect skeletal and cultural material from the islands, including seven coastal sites on Santa Cruz. From six of these he recorded a rough total of 565 "skeletons" from burials; actually his collecting seems to have been confined to skulls. In a letter of May 14, 1876, to F. W. Putnam, director of the Peabody Museum, he reported that his collection included 16 boxes from Santa Cruz containing 250 "varnished" skulls, explaining that because of the pace of his work he could not give more details as to locality, let alone individual burials.

This letter seems to be the total surviving documentation of the collection. It is evident that about 100 of the skulls came to the Peabody Museum and something under 150 to the Smithsonian. These last were transferred from the Mammal Department to the Army Medical Museum, and then back to the Smithsonian's Physical Anthropology Division in two or three batches from 1898 to 1904. Records connected with the skulls, if any there were, have disappeared. But it is apparent that the lots in the two museums can be treated as an undifferentiated pool.

According to information given me by Professors Clement Meighan and Michael Glassow, any sizeable cemeteries on the island are assignable to the late Canaliño time period of a few recent centuries. Earlier deeper strata are known, but Schumacher's modes of collection, and impressions from the artifacts he collected, make it unlikely that early remains are present in the series. The skulls are in good condition, and suggest recovery from sandy soil; Schumacher's belief was that burials were made in middens, in neither loose sand nor natural soil, in which latter interment would have been harder to dig with aboriginal tools.

The series is thus judged to be relatively homogeneous genetically: not tightly restricted temporally or locally, but nonetheless one restricted to a single island, culture, and tradition.

SEXING: This appeared difficult to me, with the conventional criteria of sex tending to lack congruence in direction. Refractory cases were reviewed several times. Nonetheless, agreement with previous opinions was good. E. A. Hooton had assigned sex in the Peabody collection. Here as in other series I tended toward females: all of my 39 "males" were male to Hooton, while of my 28 "females," 7 were males to Hooton. At the Smithsonian Hrdlička had marked his sex estimate on 30 of the 36 skulls used by me; there were no disagreements with my assessments.

I am most grateful to the late J. Lawrence Angel, then head of the Physical Anthropology Division at the Smithsonian, for hospitality and help there, and for old friendship. I was also given valuable advice by Michael Glassow, Clement Meighan, and Gordon Willey.

Bibliography

Schumacher, P. 1877. Researches in the kjokkenmoddings and graves of a former population of the Santa Barbara Islands and the adjacent mainland. *Bulletin of the United States Geological and Geographic Survey of the Territories,* vol. 3, no. 1:37–55, 18 pls.

15

SOUTH AMERICA: YAUYOS, PERU

55 males   55 females

Peabody Museum, Harvard University

The collection as a whole, comprising the skulls or parts thereof of 536 individuals, was drawn from the very large body of skeletal material exhumed by Dr. J. C. Tello of the National Museum of Anthropology and Archaeology in Lima. This particular collection was selected by Dr. Tello, apparently largely to illustrate trephination, in 1890, and was purchased and presented to the Warren Anatomical Museum of the Harvard Medical School by Dr. Charles G. Weld on February 28, 1911. In July 1956 the collection was transferred to the Peabody Museum.

Each skull bears one of 16 place names, which however cannot be located geographically from records or published information. My archaeological colleague, Thomas Patterson, believes that the designations are actually extremely local names for fields or locally known archaeological sites, and that they probably derive mainly from the mountainous central part of the old province of Yauyos, which lies about 50 to 100 km southeast of Lima on the western slopes of the Andes near the headwaters of the Lorin, Mala, and Cañete Rivers. His estimate is partly based on information given me by Dr. Pedro Weiss, then director of the National Museum in Lima, who wrote that Dr. Tello told him that the skulls of his collection came from the provinces of Huarochiri and Yauyos, and that the place names connected with the skulls are linguistically appropriate to that region.

SELECTION: All of the usable skulls in the collection were measured, meaning those in which breakage, dry tissue, or trephine wounds did not preclude measurement, and in which there was no evidence of artificial or natural shaping or distortion of the vault (uncommon in this population in any case). This gave a total of just 150 from the whole collection. Of these, 4 were sent to the test series forthwith because of my inability to make up my mind as to the sex of these individuals at all. The remainder were ordered by catalogue number (which in turn followed the "place" names in alphabetical order), and approximately every fourth skull was taken out to form a test series of 18 "males" and 18 "females." This procedure was followed in the attempt to produce a test series corresponding as well as possible in distribution to the base series of 55 of each sex, so that any comparisons of the two should not be biased by geographical differences in their makeup.

SEXING: This was done by inspection, in the absence of any information from grave goods, postcranial bones, etc. Each skull was judged as to sex during measuring, followed by complete surveys of the whole series laid out (two reviews for most of the series). This produced agreement among (generally) three judgments in 130 cases. Of the remaining 20, 4 were sent to the general test series (see above) as resisting classification, and the rest were resolved after two further examinations of each. The fact that 146 skulls eventually divided exactly evenly as to estimated sex is a matter of chance.

16

NORTH JAPAN: HOKKAIDO

55 males   32 females

Hokkaido University, Sapporo, Japan

This is the dissecting room collection of the Anatomy Department of the University Medical School, used through the unfailing generosity and hospitality of Professor S. Kodama and his son and later successor, Professor George Kodama. The Japanese immigration to Hokkaido began just a century before the time of my study (1968), and so the collection does not represent a strictly regional population in the sense of long establishment and local isolation.

Sex is known from the cadaver records, as is age and cause of death. Selection presented no difficulty in the case of the males, since a sufficient number could be obtained while avoiding subadult individuals, and those showing accidental occipital flattening, as well as those with serious ante mortem tooth loss. Those with sawn calottes could also be avoided. This was not so for the much smaller number of females in the collec-

tion: for these, sawed-off calottes were replaced with masking tape where the broken edges (not the sawn edges) showed precise fit and normal total outline. The total was eked out using all in which tooth loss had not left an unmeasurable palate and in which both zygomata had not been cut out.

The series, especially the females, corresponds closely to that measured by myself in 1961 and reported on in 1966, more so than in the case of the Ainu series herein, used in the same study.

Bibliography

Howells, W. W. 1966. The Jomon population of Japan. A study by discriminant analysis of Japanese and Ainu crania. In *Craniometry and Multivariate Analysis*. Papers of the Peabody Museum, Harvard University, vol. 57, no.1:45–67.

17

SOUTH JAPAN: NORTH KYUSHU

50 Males   41 Females

Department of Anatomy, Kyushu University, Fukuoka

These crania are from the dissecting room collections of the Department of Anatomy. The first was started in 1904 under Professor T. Shindo and continued, decades later, under Professor M. Mori. The second collection was made by Professor R. Ono of the Pathological Institute from 1910 to 1928. Sex is recorded for each specimen and, in the case of the Ono collection, age as well. Place of origin is generally that of birth, and also the birthplace for two generations back.

The population of North Kyushu is considered by authorities to differ from that of southern Kyushu, and to be more like that of the nearer parts of Honshu. Choice of specimens, for both sexes, was therefore limited to these prefectures: Fukuoka, Saga, Kumamoto, Nagasaki, and Eito, plus a few from Yamaguchi on Honshu. The Anatomy Department collection was sufficient to produce 50 males; the Ono collection was

resorted to in order to reach the maximum number of females possible.

SELECTION AND CONDITION: In dissection, the calotte had been cut off in most cases, and replaced using wax as a filler at the joint making allowance for the gap caused by sawing. In some cases, joints at breakage where removal had been made without complete sawing confirmed that restoration of the original form was about the best possible. Crania were avoided which exhibited deformation or serious breakage. Cases of metopism were also avoided as well, generally, as were those with an os japonicum.

The warm hospitality of Professor Masafumi Nagai, in and out of the laboratory, was something we shall never forget. We were also greatly aided by Miss Hajime Sano in every aspect of our work. I am of course also grateful to the Department and the University for their generosity in permitting our work.

18

CHINESE: HAIKOU CITY, HAINAN

45 males   38 females

Academia Sinica, Nankang, Taiwan
National Taiwan University, Taipei, Taiwan

The series represents settlers in Hainan, largely from the Canton region originally. First Chinese arrivals were about 200 B.C., but the main immigration was much more recent. The population should be a good representation of South China generally. Skulls and skeletons were excavated from burials by the able and energetic T. Kanaseki during his tenure at National Taiwan University. Part of the collection is stored at Academia Sinica in Nankang; apparently all these were selected as being male, since all were so marked, evidently by Professor Kanaseki. Of the 24 measured, I classed 3 as female. In the main part of the collection in the Medical School of National Taiwan University, I had few disagreements in sex as previously assigned, although all told I found assignment of sex to be difficult. Total numbers were limited by condition of the crania, namely general damage, asymmetry, and evi-

dent accidental occipital flattening from cradling practices, which was common, as Professor Yü agreed. Possible residual effects of this may be present in the series, as with the Mokapu Hawaiians accepted.

I am indebted to the late Professor Li Chi and to Professor Yang Hsi-mei (now at Beijing) of Academia Sinica for the use of this and other series there, and to Professor Yü Chiu-chuan of the Anatomy Department at National Taiwan University.

Bibliography

Huang H.-m. 1948. Anthropologische Untersuchungen über die Schädel von Hainan. *Bulletin, Anatomical Department, National Taiwan University*, fasc. 8:123–211. In Japanese. This treats of 198 males and 111 females in the series (no individual measurements are supplied).

19

TAIWAN ABORIGINALS: ATAYAL

29 males   18 females

Academia Sinica, Nankang, Taiwan
National Taiwan University, Taipei, Taiwan

These crania are all from the Atayal, second largest of the nine surviving aboriginal tribes and one of the least acculturated. All specimens come from one area on the southern edge of their territory, and stem all or mostly from the so-called Wu-Sha or Wushei incident of 1932. After tribesmen had taken some Japanese heads (the last head-taking on record), the Japanese authorities sent other Atayals on a punitive action, in which one village was annihilated. Crania of the victims were in due course collected by T. Kanaseki, and these are distributed between Academia Sinica and National Taiwan University.

Damage, avulsion of lateral incisors, and immaturity reduced the number of usable crania. Sexing of these relatively gracile skulls was difficult. For those at Academia Sinica I assigned sex provisionally as I went along and then lined all skulls up as best I could on a scale from maleness to femaleness. This resulted in my changing some of Kanaseki's males to females, and getting 21 males and 16 females. Only 10 at National Taiwan University could be used, all except 2 rated as male.

It may be mentioned that the aboriginal tribes of Taiwan are extremely differentiated linguistically, more than any other region of Austronesian-speakers. They are also markedly differentiated physically, as Chai has demonstrated. This bespeaks long mutual isolation among them and so suggests a genetic integrity for such a sample as that here.

Bibliography

Chai C. K. 1967. *Taiwan Aborigines. A Genetic Study of Tribal Variations.* 238 pp. Cambridge, Mass.: Harvard University Press.

Chang C. 1949. Anthropologische Untersuchungen über die Schädel von Atayal in Formosa. *Bulletins of the Anatomy Department of the National Taiwan University,* fasc. 6:59–154. This includes means based on all crania available for each measurement, but gives no lists of individual measurements.

20

PHILIPPINE ISLANDS: GENERAL

50 males

Medical School, University of the Philippines, Manila

These crania, stored in the Anatomy Department, are a collection made by Professor Juan C. Nanagas before World War II. The subjects were convicts who died in prison in Manila and who were not claimed for burial by relatives. Accordingly, it contains relatively fewer individuals from Manila and more from remoter parts; in fact, many have combined Tagalog and Hispanicized names, or names indicating varied origin; some have no Hispanicized names and are labeled "Moro." Thus the series must be accepted as a very general one for the islands. It was the best available at that time (1969).

A broad study of more specific Philippine groups, using the measurements herein, has been carried out by Uytterschaut (1983). Between two large samples (Ibaloi of north central Luzon and Tagalogs of central Luzon and Mindoro) she found relatively small D^2 distances; they were slightly greater than between the North and South Japanese samples of this study, which she used in the distance matrices. Figures for direct comparison with the Philippine sample herein are not available, but it does not appear that Philippine populations, excluding Negritos, show anything like the diversity of Taiwan aboriginal tribes.

I chose crania in good condition for measurement, avoiding asymmetry, intentional deformation (not a widespread ethnographic feature in the Philippines, although most crania in the National Museum exhibited it), and any which had a combination of features, or lack of indigenous features, suggesting a possible European component.

I thank Professor of Anatomy Vicente S. Vergoza, Jr., and the dean of the Medical School, Dr. Forentino Herrara, Jr., for the opportunity to use the collection.

Bibliography

Uytterschaut, H. T. 1983. *Affinities of Philippine Populations. An Application of Multivariate Techniques to Human Skull Data.* 128 pp. Groningen: Regenboog.

21

GUAM: LATTE PERIOD
30 males   27 females
Bishop Museum, Honolulu

The series was collected during the 1920s by Lieutenant H. G. Hornbostel. Skeletons and crania were excavated around various latte sites (supports for raised houses consisting of stone columns bearing mushroom-like plano-convex capstones). The sites formerly existed, where tourist hotels now stand, along Tumon Beach on Tumon Bay on Guam's western shore (erroneously identified by Hornbostel as Ypao Beach to the south, also on Tumon Bay; see Graves and Moore 1985). These sites are currently thought to date from about 1100 A.D., and the population is surely entirely pre-Spanish. In any case the morphology of the skulls was in general rather individual: decidedly massive, they would stand comparison with a group of European Upper Paleolithic crania. Shoveling of the incisors was rather limited, while third molar agenesis was frequent.

This valuable material has also been used by Michael Pietrusewsky, Christy Turner, C. L. Brace, and myself in various publications, including presentations at the Micronesian Archaeology Conference of 1987, to appear in *Micronesica*.

All usable specimens were measured, including some with more damaged palates than I would ordinarily accept. I avoided cases of asymmetry and of clear occipital deformation, fortunately uncommon. Sex assignment was done by inspection and, as with the Mokapu Hawaiian series, did not seem to be difficult: in all those cases where postcrania were present, these seemed to support the assessment from the skull. Of the 58 skulls I used (one was put in the test series), I had only 3 disagreements with M. Pietrusewsky, who gave me his assessments of some years ago. I had no disagreements with R. W. Leigh, who published on the dentition (1929).

The administration and staff of the Bishop Museum cannot be thanked enough (the then director was Roland Force) for permission to work and general help and hospitality. Michael Pietrusewsky has helped me considerably with information about the origins of the sample.

Bibliography

Graves, M. W., and D. R. Moore. 1985. *Tumon Bay overview: Cultural and historical resources.* Micronesian Area Research Center and the Department of Anthropology, University of Guam, Mangilao. Manuscript.

Leigh, R. W. 1929. Dental morphology and pathology of Prehistoric Guam. *Memoirs of the Bernice P. Bishop Museum*, vol. 11, no. 3:1–18.

Pietrusewsky, M. 1971. *Human Skeletal Collections in the Bishop Museum.* Department of Anthropology Report 71–8. Honolulu: B. P. Bishop Museum.

Thompson, L. 1932. *Archaeology of the Mariana Islands.* Bernice P. Bishop Museum Bulletin 100. Honolulu.

22

EGYPT: GIZEH, 26th-30th DYNASTIES

58 males　53 females

Duckworth Laboratory of Physical Anthropology, Cambridge University

This is the well known "Egyptian E" series of the Biometric Laboratory under Karl Pearson, now transferred to Cambridge University. It was excavated by Flinders Petrie from a single cemetery, located south of the Gizeh pyramids, of the 26th to 30th Dynasties (about 600–200 B.C.), and comprises nearly 1800 skulls in varying states of preservation.

Pearson wished to undertake a study of variability and correlation in a very large series of crania, and Petrie furnished him with this remarkable collection. It appears to have arrived in London not later than 1907. Pearson did not publish his proposed report (with A. Davin) until 1924, but the material was used by workers in the Laboratory in publications from 1911 on (e.g., Crewdson Benington 1911).

SELECTION: The skulls are stored in individual boxes, not at present in order of catalogue number. At the end, when I had enough "males," I selected 5 more apparent "females" in order, otherwise I selected at random, from the most convenient part of the stacks, any skulls in sufficiently good condition.

SEXING: I assigned sex by inspection to each skull as I measured, noting doubtful cases but not following with a general review. I then consulted original working notebooks on the series, kept by (?) Evelyn Y. Thomson, which were in Dr. Trevor's possession. One of these, dated May 1907, has the following entry:

> The sexes of the skulls were determined separately by two people & then checked by Dr. Derry; if opinions differed, the points were discussed, & the opinion of the majority was taken. If no decision could be come to, Professor Pearson decided.

The chief points taken into consideration were as follows—the general appearance, size & contour; the size of mastoids, the presence of superciliary ridges; parietal bulging; the general weight & massiveness of the bone. Whether smooth or rugged base. Size of Teeth, & palate.

A typical male had weight, & general massive appearance; large mastoids, & superciliary ridges; a rugged base, & probably large teeth & palate.

A typical female was light in weight, small mastoids, parietal bulging; smooth forehead. No superciliary ridges. Smooth base.

N.B. Dr. Derry laid great stress on the nose for deciding the sex. If on passing the finger up the nose & forehead, there was a considerable 'break', this was a male characteristic. If no break, or very little—a female characteristic.

Other notebooks record the sex as assigned to each skull. I checked my sample of 111 against the "committee" decisions of 58 years before and found 8 cases of disagreement. I got these skulls out once more as a group and restudied them at length without reference to any previous notes. These final assignments turned out to reduce disagreement to 4 cases in which, as in other samples, I abided by my own decision. Later on, however, one of these cases, particularly difficult to assess, was withdrawn, and a "male" from the test series exchanged for it.

Bibliography

Crewdson Benington, R. 1911. Cranial type-contours. *Biometrika* 8:123–201.

Pearson, K., and A. G. Davin. 1924. On the biometric constants of the human skull. *Biometrika* 16:328–363.

23

SOUTH AFRICA: BUSHMAN (SAN)
41 males   49 females

This series is in a different category from most of the others. It does not pretend to be a localized population, and defining it is rather unsatisfactory. It is meant to represent not the whole of pre-Bantu South Africa, but that part which has been generally recognized as occupied by "Bushman," or more properly San. (I continue deliberately to call the series "Bushman" because of the slightly greater imprecision.) Even this approach does a kind of violence to the ideal of a localized sample as sought herein, but with relatively nomadic hunter-gatherers it is hard to do better.

Morris (1984), basing his work on four osteological samples from locales in the northern Cape and the Orange Free State (i.e., on the northeast periphery of "Bushman" territory), has shown (1) local distinctions among ethnic groups (e.g., Griqua) probably going back into the late Iron Age, but (2) a general distinction of all from Bantu peoples and likeness among Khoi-San remains, and (3) the problem, even early, of probable admixture of European or Bantu derivation. Thus, easy visualization of a widely homogeneous "Bushman" population turns out to be a chimaera.

Forming the present series has meant selecting individuals who were recognized ethnically as Bushman when living, whether wild or acculturated ("farm" Bushman), or specimens found where the likelihood is very small of their having been Hottentot, Korana, "Strandlooper," or Bantu. The actual cranial distinctions of San and Khoi (Bush and Hottentot) are little known (but see Rightmire 1970; Wilson 1986), and they will remain so while rigorous efforts are made in regard to authentification of specimens.

An exacting review of the material, also by Morris (1986), catalogues all the "known-in-life" San or Khoi individuals in the collections in South Africa and Europe, a total of 56 specimens, including 31 of all ages encountered by me. This study makes plain the dubious nature of much of the documentation of supposed Bush and Hottentot crania. Morris points out that over three quarters of my sample herein depends on archaeological evidence, and must be viewed skeptically. I agree, but have ventured to accept these specimens, in order to have a statistically useful "Bush" series, on the following grounds. Actually, my process was not so much one of selection as one of exclusion, due to doubt as to appropriateness of area or lack of any supporting evidence. Advised by the late Lawrence Wells, in a few cases I used burials in what he considered good Bush country where the later Bantu were

also present, if morphologically it was clear to me that the skull could not be Bantu. This was my only use of morphology as a criterion of acceptance.

I also accepted two particular lots in spite of some reservations as to documentation: the Pöch Collection and the Colesburg cemetery (see below). Museum collections, of course, contain many skulls labeled "Bushman" but lacking evidence of authenticity. Most such skulls in fact look convincingly Bushman and have apparently been accepted on a typological basis by such seasoned observers as Broom. I have rejected them, however, assembling the series rather by the external evidence such as it is; a typological approach would be ruinous to the purposes of this investigation. I was largely guided by Lawrence Wells, whose knowledge of Bushman distribution, and of the then-existing materials, alone made such a procedure possible. The skulls were drawn from the following collections described below.

Anthropological Institute, Vienna: From the Rudolf Pöch collection, 35 skulls, mostly from various parts of the Kalahari, and apparently mostly excavated by Pöch himself. These are most of the skulls labeled "Bushman," out of the total of 113 which includes Hottentots, hybrids, and unknowns. Pöch's original travel records are lost, but H.-M. Pacher, who did the definitive study of the material (1961), most carefully reviewed the surviving evidence of acquisition and identification, while also pointing out to me the imprecision of Pöch's records. Of the 35 specimens, 8 belong to identified individuals (some murdered or executed); others come from graves pointed out by living Bushmen; a few were found "auf freiem Feld" in the Kalahari. I found no good reason for not accepting Miss Pacher's allocations in toto.

South African Museum, Cape Town: 30 skulls. Of these, 16 come from a cemetery at Colesburg, Cape Province (see Slome 1929) and are supposed to be the remains of Bushman victims of a smallpox epidemic in 1866. The graves all had heaps of stones on them, and a group of Bushmen is known to have been living on the spot. The graveyard apparently contained some non-Bush as well, but the skulls and skeletons included here can on the evidence be accepted as Bush, I believe, without going too far in the direction of exclusion to look for "typical" Bush only. The other 14 skulls from various localities either are those of known individuals (4), or were passed as Bush on evidence of finding or locality by Dr. Wells. Most of this collection had been sent on loan to Professor Pittard in Geneva for a number of years, and was returned to Cape Town at the beginning of World War II.

Department of Anatomy, University of Cape Town: 10 skulls. All of these certified, on the grounds given above, by Dr. Wells, 4 being of known individuals.

Department of Anatomy, University of the Witwatersrand, Johannesburg: In the R. A. Dart Collection, 4 specimens, of which 2 were known individuals.

American Museum of Natural History, New York: 3 skulls (2 from von Luschan, 1 from Broom, out of at least 14 catalogued as Bush), all accepted jointly by Dr. Wells and myself on strong evidence of Bush origin.

Musée de l'Homme, Paris: 3 skulls. One from the Colesburg cemetery, and one from Beaufort West, both presents from the South African Museum; one, that of Sarah Bartman, the "Hottentot Venus" (neither Hottentot nor Venus), who died in Paris in 1816 at the age of 38.

University of Edinburgh: 4 skulls (out of a possible 8 adults) from acceptable areas, one being a known individual who died in "captivity."

Department of Human Anatomy, Oxford: One skull from Schietfontein in the heart of Bush territory.

Thus of the above there is a total of 20 adults reportedly or actually known to have been Bushmen in life; it is worth noting that some of these do not look "typically" Bush. I cannot pretend that the ideal has been achieved of an unimpeachable Bush series, but only that mistakes of inclusion should be relatively few. Specimens come from all over "Bush" territory but, obviously, not in due proportion, so that the Bushman population as a whole cannot be considered as represented in all its variation.

SEXING: In addition to the 20 known individuals, 43 of the skulls were accompanied by at least part of the post-cranial skeleton or other evidence of sex such as the presence of a fetus. Except in 2 cases, such evidence either confirmed sex as I judged it from the skull or else indicated sex fairly positively when indications from the skull were ambiguous. This led to determinations in the 35 specimens of the Pöch collection which disagreed with those of Miss Pacher (who applied the ischium-pubis index to available innominate bones) in 2 cases only. Thus, of 90 skulls, there was some independent indication of sex in 63. The remainder, of course, I sexed by inspection alone.

Bibliography

Morris, A. G. 1984. An osteological analysis of the protohistoric populations of the northern Cape and western Orange Free State, South Africa. 398 pp. Ph.D. thesis, University of the Witwatersrand, Johannesburg.

Morris, A. G. 1986. Khoi and San craniology: A re-evaluation of the osteological reference samples. In *Variation, Culture and Evolution in African Populations*, R. Singer and J. K. Lundy, eds., ch. 1. Johannesburg: Witwatersrand University Press.

Pacher, H.-M. 1961. Anthropologische Untersuchungen an den Skeletten der Rudolf Pöch'schen Buschmannsammlung. 1. Heft: Herkunft des Sammlungsgutes, Massbefunde und Lichtbilder der Schädel. *Rudolf Pöchs Nachlass*, Serie A: *Physische Anthropologie*, 12. Band.

Rightmire, G. P. 1970. Bushman, Hottentot and South African Negro crania studied by distance and discrimination. *American Journal of Physical Anthropology* 33:169–195.

Slome, D. 1929. The osteology of a Bushman tribe. *Annals of the South African Museum* 24:33–60.

Wells, L. H. 1957. Some Bushman skulls from the old Cape frontier. *Africana Notes and News* 12/8:289–290.

Wilson, M. L. 1986. Khoisanosis: The question of separate identities for Khoi and San. In *Variation, Culture and Evolution in African Populations*, R. Singer and J. K. Lundy, eds., ch. 2. Johannesburg: Witwatersrand University Press.

24

ANDAMAN ISLANDS: GENERAL

35 males   35 females

This population presents again the problem of the Bushmen and the Tasmanians, though in less acute form. The islands form a small area with a population probably genetically less varied than the other two, and actually more like the local populations sought for the study generally. Certainly it is more isolated morphologically from its immediate neighbors in Asia or Indonesia; thus there is virtually no problem here of confusing different ethnic groups in a region, as with Bushmen, Hottentots, and Bantu in South Africa. Natives of the islands were hostile to outsiders, as castaways found to their sorrow, and remained so after settlement until very recent times. The British established a penal colony in 1789 but abandoned it in 1796, reinstating it only in l857. Under these conditions of late and localized occupation and continued avoidance by natives, there is a high probability that specimens stated to be those of aboriginals are such in fact, unless there is strong suggestion of error (as there was in one or two cases). Skeletal remains of off-islanders are the less likely to be confused because of the dwarfishness of the natives, particularly if the post-cranial skeleton is represented.

Furthermore, there is frequently "documentation" of authenticity of several kinds: in addition to a dwarfish skeleton or identification of a known individual in the records, there is the native practice of carrying around the skulls of dead relatives and of decorating these by painting them with red ocher and/or by incising some kind of a pattern, especially cross-hatching, on the bone of the vault. At least 15 of the males and 6 of the females gave one or more of such demonstrations of authenticity. On general grounds, however, all specimens definitely labeled Andamanese in collections were accepted unless there was some reason to be suspicious, i.e., the specimen seemed incongruent with the fairly individual morphological character of Andamanese skulls.

At the beginning, I did not expect to assemble a population of Andamanese and made records of those I came across simply to have examples of various populations not used in the basic comparisons (and, frankly, because it is difficult to resist measuring specimens of this people, so recherché in anthropology). I had little information as to where Andamanese skulls might be, and certainly knew of no large collection. As it turned out, the skeletal collections at Cambridge University were relocated after my first visit. This resulted in the uncovering of 16 further Andamanese skulls which had been deeply buried in stacked material in the Anatomy Department. The discovery allowed a gratifying increase in the total series, and accounts for the difference in numbers shown here and in my 1973 report.

The following are locations of specimens used.

	Males	Females	Total
British Museum (Natural History)	9	17	26
University of Edinburgh	3	4	7
Royal Scottish Museum, Edinburgh	1	1	2
Cambridge University	11	8	19
Oxford University	2		2
Musée de l'Homme	2	1	3
Copenhagen, Anthropological Institute	1	1	2
American Museum, New York	3	2	5
Peabody Museum, Harvard University	1	1	2
Field Museum, Chicago	2		2
Total	35	35	70

25

AINU, JAPAN: SOUTH AND SOUTHEAST HOKKAIDO

48 males   38 females

**Faculty of Medicine, University of Hokkaido
University Museum, Tokyo University**

Sampling Ainu crania, as with South African Bushmen, Andamanese, or Tasmanians, presents the problem of a recently vanishing people. Except for the oldest generation, the living Ainu have no interest in preserving an ethnic identity, preferring to be assimilated to more prestigious Japanese life in spite of the scientific, and now tourist, interest in Ainu culture. After a drastic 19th century decline caused by introduced diseases, the number of ethnic "Ainu" has for some time remained stable at about 16,000. Genetically, however, they have been increasingly affected by Japanese admixture. This has resulted from ordinary contact in the past, but also from the adoption into Ainu families of Japanese infants unwanted by their parents. This is a particularly effective source of admixture, since such an adopted child brings twice as many non-Ainu genes into the population as does the child of an inter-ethnic union. At any rate, by 1970 authorities were of the opinion that Ainus with no Japanese ancestry numbered in all no more than 20 or 30 elderly people, meaning that at present or in the immediate future there will be none at all. Skeletal remains from Ainu settlements must therefore be assumed to be less and less representative of aboriginal Ainu as their dates approach the present. (For details, see Watanabe 1964.)

Ainu skulls outside of Japan are few, except for a number from Sakhalin now in the Soviet Union. In Japan the collections total about 800, largely made by Professor S. Kodama and his students over 40 years, and deposited in the Faculty of Medicine at the University of Hokkaido in Sapporo.

These are mostly but not exclusively from Hokkaido, as are those collected in 1888–89 by Koganei, which are at Tokyo University. Remains derive almost entirely from abandoned graves and cemeteries, the dates and affiliations of which are known, so that some discrimination can be exercised as to the degree of "purity" as Ainus attaching to them. Certain villages represented by cemeteries were recognized by Professor Kodama as having been admixed with Japanese, due to their recent date or to special conditions of contact in the 19th century.

In addition to increasing Japanese contact in the south of Hokkaido, the northern Ainu were certainly affected genetically by contact with other boreal peoples: Gilyak, Orochi (Orok), Kamchadals. There is also the well-known evidence of actual settlement of such people in northeast Hokkaido itself, in the Okhotsk culture of the Moyoro Shell Heap at Abashiri, dating to about 1000 A.D. General opinion and evidence now favor the view that Hokkaido has been the seat of the Ainu, as a segment of the late Jomon population, for a long period of time (Mitsuhashi, in conversation; Chard 1972; Howells 1966, 1986). Chard believes that northeast Hokkaido was the Ainu center, with later expansion to the south and still later migration up the Kurile chain and down across the Tsugaru Strait to northeasternmost Honshu, where actual skeletal remains have been reported by Suzuki (1951). Chard and Suzuki are skeptical of any but the most transient presence of Ainus here, although Mitsuhashi (1966) perceived some evidence from fingerprints of an Ainu component in the Japanese population of Tohoku district.

SELECTION: Professor Ito (1967) surveyed all the Ainu cranial material in Sapporo and Tokyo for regional differences, and concluded that south and southwest Hokkaido formed one homogeneous unit cranially; also, Professor Kodama believed that south-central Hokkaido remained the area least affected by Japanese contact. Because of this, and in line with the ideas of Mitsuhashi and Chard, I decided—Professor Kodama agreeing—that this southern territory would provide the best available population to represent the Ainu, after exclusion of material from villages known to be affected by Japanese admixture (such as Shizunai in Hidaka province, and Mori and Yakumo villages in Oshima, which were much visited by Japanese from Hakodate in the early days of contact).

The effort therefore is not simply to get "pure" Ainu. It must be supposed that Ainus, like other tribal peoples, varied locally, so the attempt here has been to assemble a more specific population as well as one for which Japanese admixture could be assumed to be minimal. This entails a more rigorous selection than that in my 1966 study, which was a pilot study addressed to discrimination between Ainus and Japanese generally; in this, such outriders as Sakhalin Ainu were included as well as the probably adulterated Yakumo cemetery. The result is a smaller series, of which the composition is shown in the following tabulation.

	Otoshibe (Oshima)	Oshamambe (Oshima)	Urahoro (Tokachi)	Hidaka province	Tokachi province	Total
Males						
Total	7	8	7	17	9	48
Sex known	6	7	3	12	6	34
Females						
Total	5	7	13	11	2	38
Sex known	5	6	2	8	0	21
Total	12	15	20	28	11	86
Sex known	11	13	5	20	6	55

Otoshibe, Oshamambe, and Urahoro are known Ainu villages. The burials at Otoshibe date from about 1870 back to about 1830, and perhaps into the 18th century (Sakakibara 1940), those at Oshamambe to about 1870 (Kodama and Kodama 1967), and those at Urahoro to roughly 1870 to 1910 (ibid.). The first two thus antedate the period of actual Japanese administration and colonization of Hokkaido, which began in 1868. Urahoro is thus the most recent, but in Tokachi Province Japanese contact and immigration were also relatively late. Skulls in Sapporo from Hidaka province do not come from a single cemetery but were received from various collectors, having been excavated singly or in groups in different villages in good Ainu territory. Many belong to identified, named individuals, the majority being Japonified Ainu names. Although some are rather recent, recovered as late as 1933 but within a generation of burial, they are presumably remembered individuals who were labeled as Ainu on this basis. Other Tokachi and Hidaka specimens in Tokyo, collected by Koganei, were accepted on the same grounds, i.e., definitely Ainu villages or personal identification. It is most unlikely that Japanese parentage has been fully excluded from the series, but I think that the latter achieves its aims as well as can now be done. SEXING: The above tabulation shows sex as "known" for 55 of the 86 crania involved. This knowledge is based about equally on names of individuals and on grave goods in a burial or, in a few cases, on style of grave marker. In some of the remaining cases (Tokyo), judgment of sex could be supported from the post-cranial skeleton, but the post-cranial parts of the Hokkaido skeletons could not be brought out for inspection because of storage difficulties. (Since that time this admirable collection has been rehoused in a new building.)

The tabulation shows that the sex distribution is not well balanced for locale, a possible biasing factor in the matter of sex differences in the series.

For his generosity in allowing me to study his invaluable collection once more I am greatly indebted to the late Professor S. Kodama. For the checking of records I am still further indebted to him and to Professor George Kodama, and to the late Professor Ito, who went over his own records of Koganei's materials with me to select appropriate localities for specimens to use. I am also indebted to Professor J. Nakai and Dr. T. Kamiya of Tokyo University for help with the collections there.

Bibliography

Chard, C. S. 1972. Prehistoric Japan: A survey of cultural development down to the Late Jomon Stage (approximately 2000 B.C.) In *Early Chinese Art and Its Possible Influence in the Pacific Basin*, Noel Barnard, ed., vol. 2:373–393. New York: Intercultural Arts Press.

Howells, W. W. 1966. *The Jomon Population of Japan: A Study by Discriminant Analysis of Japanese and Ainu Crania.* Papers of the Peabody Museum, Harvard University, vol. 57, no. 1:1–43.

Howells, W. W. 1986. Physical anthropology of the Prehistoric Japanese. In *Windows on the Japanese Past*, R. Pearson, ed., ch. 4. Ann Arbor: Michigan Center for Japanese Studies.

Ito, S. 1967. Local differences in Ainu skulls—Metrical observations. *Bulletin of the Institute for the Study of North Eurasian Cultures* 2:191–238.

Kodama, S. 1970. *Ainu. Historical and Anthropological Studies.* 294 pp. Hokkaido University Medical Library Studies 3.

Kodama, S., and G. Kodama. 1967. Studies on artificial injuries in Shizunai Ainu skulls. *Bulletin of the Institute for the Study of North Eurasian Cultures* 2:239–258.

Mitsuhashi, K. 1966. The distribution of Japanese finger prints. *Proceedings, 11th Pacific Science Congress.* 5 pp.

Sakakibara, T. 1940. Kraniologie der Otoshibe-Aino. In *Crania Ainoica*, S. Kodama, ed. 168 pp., 5 pls. Sapporo.

Suzuki, H. 1951. Ainu skeletons excavated at the north end of Honshu, Japan. *Zinruigaku Zassi* 62:1–10. In Japanese, English summary.

Watanabe, H. 1964. The Ainu: A study of ecology and the system of social solidarity between man and nature in relation to group structure. *Journal of the Faculty of Science*, University of Tokyo, Section 5, *Anthropology* 2/6. 164 pp.

26

SIBERIA: BURIATS

55 males   54 females

Institute of Ethnography, Academy of Science, Leningrad

Buriats are pastoralists occupying the region on either side of the southern end of Lake Baikal, but having affiliations with Mongolia. The institute's collection of Buriat skulls number at least 258 (see bibliography for partial enumeration and other collections).

SELECTION: All those in sufficiently good condition were used, to a total of 112 (3 being finally omitted; see below).

SEXING: In 4 cases the skeleton was present; all other skulls were sexed twice by inspection, first as worked on, then in the major groups in which they were brought out of storage for my use (largely through the constant kindness of Mrs. Evgenia Semenovna Ryasanzheva and Mrs. Julia Dmitrievna Benevolenskaya). Of 12 disagreements between my first and second estimates, all were resolved to my satisfaction except 3, which proved so baffling that I have omitted them, having a good series without them.

Bibliography

Firstein, B. V. 1964. Kraniologicheskii kollectizii Muzeya Antropologii i Etnografii. *Sbornik Muzeya Antropologii i Etnografii* 22:169–190.

Ginzburg, V. V. 1949. Kraniologicheskoe sobranii Muzeya Antropologii i Etnografii. *Sbornik Muzeya Antropologii i Etnografii* 12:402–416.

27

GREENLAND: INUGSUK ESKIMO

53 males   55 females

Anthropological Laboratory, University of Copenhagen

The skulls are all from a continuous area of west and southeast Greenland as far as Scoresby Sound, and were all associated with the Inugsuk culture, following the early Norse settlement but antedating Danish colonization about 1750; the specimens are from graves giving no evidence of contemporaneity with Danish settlement. They were collected on various expeditions, mostly under Therkel Mathiassen, from 1898 to 1935. This series constitutes a sub-sample of Jørgensen's (1953) Group I, Inugsuk area.

SELECTION: All usable skulls were included, as restricted to the period and area described, and as indicated to me by Dr. Jørgensen. Eventually, one was transferred to the test series because of general peculiarity and questionableness as to sex.

SEXING: This was done first by inspection of the skulls as I measured, and again in groups of 8 to 12 before putting the skulls back in the cabinets. Dr. Jørgensen then checked over with me his own original assignments. Finally, skeletons, which were available for a large number of the individuals, were examined. Between myself and Dr. Jørgensen 13 cases of disagreement eventually remained.

Bibliography

Jørgensen, J. B. 1953. *The Eskimo skeleton. Contributions to the physical anthropology of the aboriginal Greenlanders.* Meddelelser om Grønland, vol. 146, no. 2, 154 pp., 16 pls.

28

SHANG DYNASTY CHINESE: ANYANG

42 males

Academia Sinica, Nankang, Taiwan

These Bronze Age crania derive from the sacrificial burial pits in and around the imperial tombs of the Shang Dynasty at Anyang, Honan Province. The collection was first studied by T. L. Woo, who however never published his work (Li Chi in Institute of History 1986). Originally numbering in the thousands, much of the material was destroyed in World War II, but an important number of crania were removed to the southwest and eventually to Nankang in Taiwan upon the establishment there of Academia Sinica. These have been reported on in detail by Professor Yang Hsi-mei (1966, 1986), formerly of the Department of Physical Anthropology, Academia Sinica in Taiwan, now of the Institute of History, Beijing.

The number of specimens complete enough for my own purposes was limited by damage. The skulls were set out for me in batches of 30 to 40 by Mrs. Lin of the department, and I measured those in sufficiently good condition, assigning sex as I went along. In no case did I find myself in disagreement with Professor Yang's previous assessment. The sex problem was self-resolving: although there were 51 females (by our joint assessment), this was a small minority of the total series, and it did not afford any complete enough for use. However, a few very good male skulls were excluded: these

had been selected by Professor Yang as "types" of possible racial components forming the population (see Yang 1966), and these particular specimens were therefore withheld from the basic series for special investigation later (see Howells 1983).

I must warmly acknowledge the continuing goodness of Professor Yang and the late Professor Li in allowing me to work with this most important material, and helping with the work then and later. I am also in debt to Mrs. Lin for her time and patience in taking out and putting back the large numbers of crania involved.

Bibliography

Howells, W. W. 1983. Origins of the Chinese people: Interpretation of the recent evidence. In *The Origins of Chinese Civilization*, D. N. Keightley, ed., ch. 11, pp. 297–319. Berkeley: University of California Press.

Institute of History and Institute of Archaeology [Yang H.-m. et al, eds.]. 1986. *Contributions to the Study on Human Skulls from the Shang Sites at Anyang.* 377 pp., 88 pls. Beijing: Cultural Relics Publishing House. In Chinese with English abstract and some translations.

Yang H.-m. 1966. A preliminary report of human crania excavated from Hou-chia-chuang and the Shang Dynasty sites at An Yang, Honan, North China. *Annual Bulletin of the China Council for East Asia Studies* 5:1–13.

Appendix B
Measurements: Group Means

TABLE B-1
Means of Measurements

	Number of Crania		Glab-Occip Length GOL		Nasio-Occip Length NOL		Bas-Nasion Length BNL	
	Male	Female	Male	Female	Male	Female	Male	Female
Norse	55	55	188.47	179.98	186.18	178.69	101.80	97.31
Zalavár	53	45	185.13	176.44	182.26	174.51	101.28	96.51
Berg	56	53	180.32	170.53	177.29	168.55	98.59	92.92
Teita	33	50	184.00	174.72	182.48	173.54	102.21	96.42
Dogon	47	52	177.70	169.83	175.74	169.02	98.49	94.87
Zulu	55	46	185.13	178.96	183.36	177.91	102.00	97.28
Australia	52	49	190.31	181.10	185.42	177.29	101.98	96.16
Tasmania	45	42	185.36	177.81	180.07	173.40	99.73	94.79
Tolai	56	54	183.52	174.59	179.04	171.91	101.50	95.59
Hawaii	51	49	186.31	175.39	183.29	173.78	107.00	101.45
Easter I	49	37	192.14	180.76	187.78	177.14	111.29	104.46
Moriori	57	51	188.40	178.14	185.95	176.55	105.65	101.29
Arikara	42	27	179.48	171.11	177.69	170.22	102.83	97.52
Santa Cruz	51	51	179.82	172.18	177.04	170.76	97.31	92.78
Peru	55	55	177.96	169.00	176.18	168.13	96.00	90.58
N Japan	55	32	183.09	171.09	180.11	169.53	101.49	95.63
S Japan	50	41	181.30	172.49	179.18	171.24	101.94	95.63
Hainan	45	38	176.38	170.63	174.36	169.39	99.47	94.74
Atayal	29	18	177.03	168.11	174.38	166.11	97.93	93.89
Philippines	50	–	176.92	–	174.82	–	98.48	–
Guam	30	27	185.60	175.26	182.63	173.70	104.97	100.04
Egypt	58	53	185.62	175.58	183.57	175.04	101.50	95.89
Bushman	41	49	178.37	171.71	176.10	170.35	94.76	91.67
Andaman Is	35	35	168.86	160.11	167.54	159.43	93.86	89.43
Ainu	48	38	189.98	178.74	187.04	177.00	106.60	99.92
Buriat	55	54	181.64	171.83	179.04	170.69	101.85	96.70
Eskimo	53	55	188.30	180.95	184.47	178.56	106.49	100.25
Anyang	42	–	181.00	–	178.86	–	101.29	–

TABLE B-1. Continued.
Means of Measurements

	Bas-Bregma Height BBH		Max Cranial Breadth XCB		Max Frontal Breadth XFB		Bistephanic Breadth STB	
	Male	Female	Male	Female	Male	Female	Male	Female
Norse	131.73	125.96	141.87	136.29	119.13	114.31	115.55	111.71
Zalavár	134.85	128.76	141.40	136.89	119.30	115.67	117.04	113.56
Berg	130.25	124.47	147.61	140.36	124.63	118.74	122.73	117.66
Teita	129.06	125.12	129.82	126.46	111.33	108.06	105.67	103.38
Dogon	132.13	128.10	137.47	132.10	114.34	109.08	110.66	106.62
Zulu	133.67	128.74	134.11	131.72	115.84	113.70	113.89	112.28
Australia	129.62	123.53	131.94	127.51	110.10	106.22	101.35	100.22
Tasmania	132.07	126.36	138.40	132.76	113.02	106.81	106.24	102.69
Tolai	134.88	127.20	130.48	127.94	109.73	106.72	101.41	100.61
Hawaii	144.04	136.57	143.73	138.67	117.22	111.98	115.10	109.59
Easter I	144.82	137.08	135.02	128.51	112.41	106.38	109.37	103.68
Moriori	136.00	131.63	142.77	137.67	113.26	109.98	106.46	104.86
Arikara	133.36	126.81	141.55	136.48	116.43	112.81	108.43	107.93
Santa Cruz	129.02	123.94	139.90	135.02	113.82	108.73	108.76	104.27
Peru	130.53	124.91	137.95	134.93	115.24	112.07	110.07	109.24
N Japan	136.84	129.53	141.62	133.47	116.64	110.59	111.76	108.44
S Japan	138.34	130.85	138.30	133.71	115.12	110.56	112.20	107.71
Hainan	136.71	132.13	138.44	134.97	114.73	111.84	110.89	109.95
Atayal	133.52	129.33	135.76	131.89	113.28	109.06	109.52	106.28
Philippines	134.80	–	139.80	–	115.16	–	112.42	–
Guam	143.73	136.89	140.80	136.37	115.30	112.04	112.40	110.59
Egypt	133.74	127.42	139.22	135.57	115.47	111.38	112.90	109.79
Bushman	122.54	119.51	133.59	128.57	110.07	106.67	107.56	104.02
Andaman Is	129.40	123.51	135.66	131.09	110.54	106.11	107.97	103.51
Ainu	138.56	132.47	142.96	137.11	119.65	114.89	115.08	111.92
Buriat	132.55	127.17	154.91	148.35	126.47	121.83	119.65	118.57
Eskimo	139.06	132.85	134.04	130.98	112.23	108.76	101.94	100.84
Anyang	140.26	–	138.79	–	114.81	–	110.21	–

TABLE B-1. Continued.
Means of Measurements

	Bizygomatic Breadth ZYB		Biauricular Breadth AUB		Min Cranial Breadth WCB		Biasterionic Breadth ASB	
	Male	Female	Male	Female	Male	Female	Male	Female
Norse	134.44	124.44	124.67	117.65	71.42	68.09	111.09	106.71
Zalavár	133.00	125.44	123.74	118.62	73.72	71.82	110.98	107.78
Berg	135.55	126.38	127.52	120.32	74.84	71.06	113.61	108.19
Teita	131.06	124.24	117.42	112.42	67.70	64.48	104.52	100.88
Dogon	129.57	121.04	115.32	109.42	68.30	65.75	103.30	100.54
Zulu	129.95	122.78	116.24	112.83	71.98	69.02	105.31	103.30
Australia	136.77	125.78	120.13	113.24	71.31	68.53	109.75	104.49
Tasmania	135.82	125.45	123.56	116.50	71.93	68.00	109.27	105.00
Tolai	135.98	126.24	120.04	114.98	70.86	67.80	105.95	103.20
Hawaii	138.82	126.88	128.10	119.02	72.76	68.47	108.96	102.65
Easter I	136.63	125.54	123.90	115.89	68.90	64.38	108.51	101.54
Moriori	139.84	130.84	128.95	122.61	70.75	67.43	109.88	104.88
Arikara	140.88	130.67	131.33	123.89	74.40	71.26	109.02	105.41
Santa Cruz	136.94	126.65	126.22	119.33	75.41	70.80	111.71	106.45
Peru	134.93	125.60	123.51	117.56	71.60	67.65	108.16	105.25
N Japan	135.73	124.56	124.47	116.63	75.95	71.94	109.53	104.09
S Japan	133.56	124.80	122.86	117.29	73.38	69.76	108.10	103.68
Hainan	133.96	125.55	123.62	117.45	73.87	71.34	105.96	101.63
Atayal	133.07	124.22	122.97	116.61	74.17	70.83	108.41	105.39
Philippines	133.16	–	122.96	–	74.66	–	107.32	–
Guam	142.53	132.04	130.33	122.63	73.93	71.74	110.07	105.33
Egypt	128.83	120.06	118.62	112.55	68.64	66.09	107.55	104.42
Bushman	123.56	116.53	113.17	107.63	70.00	66.27	106.78	102.04
Andaman Is	123.83	117.60	113.34	108.51	69.17	65.77	100.26	95.74
Ainu	138.94	128.24	125.75	118.45	75.69	71.79	112.46	106.71
Buriat	144.35	134.35	136.33	129.17	79.98	76.50	117.00	112.13
Eskimo	139.74	130.20	126.40	120.49	74.17	70.93	109.66	105.53
Anyang	135.95	–	125.69	–	74.19	–	108.24	–

TABLE B-1. Continued.
Means of Measurements

	Bas-Prosth Length BPL		Nas-Prosth Height NPH		Nasal Height NLH		Orbit Height OBH	
	Male	*Female*	*Male*	*Female*	*Male*	*Female*	*Male*	*Female*
Norse	96.96	94.02	68.93	64.25	51.96	49.16	33.75	33.22
Zalavár	97.06	92.13	68.45	63.18	51.43	48.49	32.68	32.09
Berg	93.75	89.91	67.89	63.49	51.71	48.23	33.75	32.75
Teita	102.45	96.28	66.21	60.94	50.21	46.42	33.21	32.26
Dogon	99.98	96.08	64.72	61.58	47.72	46.17	33.74	32.79
Zulu	102.38	98.72	67.33	63.41	50.00	47.30	33.76	32.87
Australia	105.50	100.45	64.77	61.14	49.69	46.51	33.46	33.10
Tasmania	103.24	98.21	62.51	58.24	48.87	45.21	31.00	30.69
Tolai	107.04	101.54	66.05	62.76	48.46	46.59	32.29	32.24
Hawaii	104.35	100.20	68.61	63.76	53.31	49.39	35.06	34.12
Easter I	106.45	101.19	68.55	62.00	53.59	49.08	34.22	33.51
Moriori	103.07	98.71	74.19	68.47	55.95	52.61	36.70	35.78
Arikara	98.60	95.15	71.69	67.63	54.45	50.52	34.95	34.63
Santa Cruz	98.88	95.18	68.92	64.65	50.71	46.71	35.18	34.27
Peru	94.27	88.87	67.78	63.65	50.35	47.65	34.27	34.15
N Japan	98.45	92.66	70.96	66.16	52.80	50.28	34.56	34.41
S Japan	99.32	94.56	69.02	65.85	51.76	49.37	34.04	33.93
Hainan	96.56	93.42	69.69	65.39	52.36	49.32	33.60	32.84
Atayal	94.34	91.28	65.14	60.33	50.28	46.94	33.48	32.83
Philippines	97.88	–	66.78	–	51.46	–	33.22	–
Guam	101.50	96.44	69.93	66.59	54.33	51.04	35.50	34.74
Egypt	96.52	91.25	68.43	64.06	51.74	48.96	32.95	32.83
Bushman	93.66	90.61	57.51	56.12	43.76	42.86	30.83	30.96
Andaman Is	92.83	90.86	60.69	56.63	46.86	43.71	32.71	32.20
Ainu	104.56	97.42	67.50	64.00	50.96	48.18	34.15	34.24
Buriat	98.87	94.59	74.51	69.35	56.91	53.33	35.87	34.89
Eskimo	103.06	99.47	71.74	67.11	54.13	50.44	36.23	35.11
Anyang	97.50	–	69.43	–	52.48	–	32.79	–

TABLE B-1. Continued.
Means of Measurements

	Orbit Breadth OBB		Bijugal Breadth JUB		Nasal Breadth NLB		Palate Breadth MAB	
	Male	Female	Male	Female	Male	Female	Male	Female
Norse	40.38	39.20	117.13	110.02	25.42	24.18	63.62	60.11
Zalavár	39.96	38.67	115.53	109.58	25.36	24.67	64.15	60.71
Berg	40.14	38.38	117.14	111.06	25.46	24.89	63.88	60.60
Teita	39.55	37.86	117.21	112.60	27.82	27.26	62.76	59.28
Dogon	39.55	38.13	115.51	109.63	28.43	27.69	64.45	61.19
Zulu	40.44	39.20	116.89	111.85	28.65	27.98	65.35	62.65
Australia	41.87	39.96	120.88	111.71	27.88	26.24	66.88	62.63
Tasmania	40.78	39.52	118.00	110.48	28.87	27.55	67.09	63.71
Tolai	41.18	39.04	118.61	110.80	27.79	26.69	66.02	62.11
Hawaii	40.69	39.43	120.76	112.67	27.39	26.02	65.78	61.73
Easter I	39.86	37.97	119.73	111.84	28.45	26.70	64.90	59.46
Moriori	41.88	40.25	122.91	115.94	27.07	25.61	66.02	62.41
Arikara	40.55	39.22	122.33	115.00	27.10	25.81	66.88	62.07
Santa Cruz	40.25	38.27	118.84	110.61	24.80	23.63	67.43	62.63
Peru	38.25	36.82	116.11	108.56	25.24	23.96	64.60	61.09
N Japan	39.64	38.22	118.85	109.72	25.93	25.69	67.22	62.88
S Japan	39.30	37.71	117.52	110.68	26.10	25.41	66.32	62.34
Hainan	38.67	37.61	118.89	112.45	27.31	26.03	64.80	62.34
Atayal	38.28	37.00	116.72	108.56	26.59	25.89	63.76	60.28
Philippines	39.04	–	118.16	–	28.26	–	64.86	–
Guam	41.43	39.74	124.63	117.59	27.77	26.52	67.43	63.78
Egypt	39.50	37.87	111.88	106.13	24.83	24.02	62.81	59.68
Bushman	39.27	37.67	111.15	105.86	27.17	25.92	60.05	57.96
Andaman Is	37.57	36.40	111.83	106.31	24.71	24.14	60.80	58.11
Ainu	41.75	39.95	122.75	114.63	27.73	26.45	66.77	62.26
Buriat	41.53	39.74	124.89	115.00	28.38	26.89	68.87	64.69
Eskimo	41.98	40.47	121.15	113.20	23.68	23.33	65.94	61.85
Anyang	39.05	–	121.21	–	28.29	–	66.69	–

TABLE B-1. Continued.
Means of Measurements

	Mastoid Height MDH		Mastoid Breadth MDB		Bimaxillary Breadth ZMB		Zygomaxill Subtense SSS	
	Male	Female	Male	Female	Male	Female	Male	Female
Norse	29.55	26.02	13.13	11.73	94.02	90.15	22.96	22.05
Zalavár	29.51	26.31	13.55	11.76	94.75	90.09	23.55	21.69
Berg	28.34	25.58	13.11	11.55	93.29	89.53	22.70	21.92
Teita	29.18	24.22	13.06	10.30	99.42	93.62	22.21	20.38
Dogon	29.02	25.21	12.13	10.40	96.17	93.13	21.34	21.04
Zulu	28.42	25.61	11.78	10.98	95.87	91.13	23.91	21.96
Australia	29.87	24.73	12.71	10.76	98.35	91.63	24.13	23.22
Tasmania	26.58	22.48	13.16	11.12	94.67	88.88	27.13	25.83
Tolai	28.71	26.15	13.88	11.61	97.50	90.96	26.54	24.76
Hawaii	30.92	25.55	15.39	12.33	99.08	92.65	24.90	23.22
Easter I	30.08	24.30	15.37	12.76	98.22	90.92	26.06	23.35
Moriori	32.32	27.14	15.07	12.18	98.89	92.90	28.21	26.04
Arikara	28.24	24.89	12.86	11.11	101.19	94.81	25.86	23.63
Santa Cruz	28.92	25.14	13.82	12.22	100.24	92.65	24.94	23.65
Peru	29.96	26.31	12.60	10.73	96.91	91.80	22.60	21.82
N Japan	30.73	26.59	12.35	10.75	98.16	91.78	23.15	22.59
S Japan	30.08	25.22	12.46	10.61	97.96	92.00	23.42	21.73
Hainan	29.49	25.24	12.89	10.61	98.20	95.34	22.40	21.34
Atayal	26.72	23.78	12.14	10.28	95.72	88.83	21.03	20.44
Philippines	29.62	–	13.50	–	98.20	–	22.50	–
Guam	30.93	27.07	13.47	11.63	102.63	96.67	22.90	21.00
Egypt	30.19	25.23	13.12	10.83	93.83	89.38	24.26	22.92
Bushman	25.24	21.61	11.63	9.16	92.20	88.78	19.49	19.86
Andaman Is	25.54	22.80	11.31	10.31	93.20	90.00	24.03	22.54
Ainu	29.94	24.76	13.94	11.29	99.17	93.71	22.65	21.76
Buriat	29.87	25.57	13.31	11.26	104.33	96.54	19.55	18.74
Eskimo	27.57	23.02	13.57	11.55	99.83	92.76	20.42	19.09
Anyang	30.60	–	13.93	–	100.83	–	22.38	–

TABLE B-1. Continued.
Means of Measurements

	Bifrontal Breadth FMB		Nasio-Front Subtense NAS		Biorbital Breadth EKB		Dacryon Subtense DKS	
	Male	Female	Male	Female	Male	Female	Male	Female
Norse	99.02	94.60	18.80	17.62	98.89	94.85	10.98	11.02
Zalavár	98.06	94.78	18.36	16.49	97.70	95.22	9.98	9.51
Berg	99.59	95.04	18.25	16.77	98.70	95.19	10.41	9.94
Teita	100.00	95.56	18.70	17.22	99.82	96.06	11.55	10.42
Dogon	99.34	94.40	16.34	15.46	99.30	95.15	9.77	9.50
Zulu	101.98	97.74	17.84	16.48	100.95	97.67	10.45	10.13
Australia	102.42	97.65	17.54	17.24	101.98	97.53	10.27	10.27
Tasmania	101.80	96.60	17.16	16.88	100.71	96.17	10.02	10.02
Tolai	101.63	96.28	16.80	15.46	101.20	96.24	9.80	9.54
Hawaii	100.37	95.16	16.12	14.84	100.12	95.80	9.55	9.08
Easter I	99.59	94.43	17.94	15.89	99.84	95.46	10.53	9.68
Moriori	100.09	95.82	18.04	16.57	100.60	96.84	11.42	10.96
Arikara	99.05	94.78	17.50	16.30	99.17	95.96	10.36	10.26
Santa Cruz	99.67	94.20	16.96	16.12	99.43	94.61	10.14	10.31
Peru	96.13	91.11	15.95	14.33	95.45	90.78	8.89	8.45
N Japan	98.00	92.63	14.38	13.97	98.87	94.47	8.47	9.13
S Japan	96.86	91.68	15.42	13.93	97.46	93.68	9.48	8.88
Hainan	97.13	92.84	15.44	14.29	97.89	94.08	9.24	8.82
Atayal	95.83	91.33	14.07	14.22	96.93	92.39	8.24	8.89
Philippines	98.12	–	15.64	–	98.36	–	9.14	–
Guam	101.23	96.93	17.20	15.52	101.17	97.81	9.90	9.52
Egypt	96.05	91.70	18.76	17.19	95.81	92.08	11.57	11.32
Bushman	97.27	93.90	16.20	15.41	97.02	93.90	10.02	9.88
Andaman Is	92.40	89.23	15.74	14.89	93.17	90.54	10.31	9.69
Ainu	100.81	95.68	16.40	15.74	102.50	97.66	9.98	9.97
Buriat	101.56	95.56	15.15	14.30	102.44	96.63	7.89	7.91
Eskimo	98.98	94.98	14.83	14.33	100.38	96.53	8.87	8.15
Anyang	97.38	–	14.29	–	98.79	–	8.50	–

TABLE B-1. Continued.
Means of Measurements

	Interorbital Breadth DKB		Naso-Dacryal Subtense NDS		Simotic Chord WNB		Simotic Subtense SIS	
	Male	*Female*	*Male*	*Female*	*Male*	*Female*	*Male*	*Female*
Norse	22.35	20.64	12.29	10.98	9.07	9.01	4.32	3.87
Zalavár	21.42	20.67	11.83	10.82	9.25	9.35	4.44	3.85
Berg	22.88	22.08	11.52	10.66	9.41	9.10	4.67	3.90
Teita	24.24	23.98	10.82	9.50	9.24	9.86	2.07	1.70
Dogon	23.51	22.23	9.83	9.06	9.59	9.68	2.77	2.52
Zulu	23.53	22.26	9.76	8.87	9.08	9.11	2.89	2.48
Australia	21.69	20.90	11.54	10.16	10.33	10.18	4.07	3.47
Tasmania	22.38	20.55	10.82	10.07	8.26	8.12	3.40	3.00
Tolai	22.04	21.20	10.11	8.96	8.70	8.41	3.47	2.78
Hawaii	21.65	19.94	9.59	8.20	7.47	7.38	2.95	2.38
Easter I	23.43	22.16	10.51	9.00	7.95	8.20	3.32	2.64
Moriori	20.67	20.08	10.25	9.31	7.08	7.39	3.18	3.00
Arikara	21.12	20.15	10.62	9.48	8.56	8.56	4.25	3.47
Santa Cruz	22.00	20.78	10.69	9.06	7.57	6.93	3.45	2.80
Peru	21.13	19.44	10.40	9.55	9.05	8.65	4.41	3.73
N Japan	21.71	20.34	7.82	7.56	7.26	7.46	2.66	2.03
S Japan	21.50	20.68	7.94	7.24	6.71	7.22	2.39	1.99
Hainan	22.16	20.95	8.44	7.87	8.13	7.49	2.93	2.21
Atayal	22.41	20.56	8.55	8.06	7.71	7.87	2.85	2.43
Philippines	22.60	–	8.52	–	8.13	–	2.95	–
Guam	21.83	21.04	9.63	8.22	8.05	7.63	2.78	2.37
Egypt	20.86	20.04	11.86	10.89	9.94	10.09	4.65	3.94
Bushman	21.73	21.73	7.78	7.41	6.91	7.18	1.28	1.29
Andaman Is	21.29	20.83	9.66	8.89	8.21	8.94	2.33	2.17
Ainu	21.75	20.58	10.25	9.24	8.72	8.08	3.65	2.78
Buriat	21.75	19.87	8.93	8.17	8.11	8.10	2.78	2.41
Eskimo	18.58	17.27	9.51	8.42	6.04	5.62	2.58	1.90
Anyang	22.45	–	7.86	–	7.78	–	2.37	–

TABLE B-1. Continued.
Means of Measurements

	Infer Malar Length IML		Max Malar Length XML		Malar Subtense MLS		Cheek Height WMH	
	Male	Female	Male	Female	Male	Female	Male	Female
Norse	37.09	34.04	55.29	50.71	11.09	10.38	24.20	22.29
Zalavár	35.83	32.53	53.23	48.44	10.66	9.73	23.23	21.11
Berg	35.70	32.68	53.66	49.36	10.54	9.74	23.14	21.09
Teita	38.70	37.76	54.18	51.16	11.91	10.88	22.27	20.18
Dogon	37.62	34.29	53.32	48.81	12.11	11.12	21.21	19.94
Zulu	38.25	36.00	53.65	50.91	11.76	11.61	20.73	20.07
Australia	40.98	37.02	55.35	50.45	11.37	10.43	21.19	19.47
Tasmania	39.91	36.17	54.67	50.21	11.31	10.50	21.29	19.38
Tolai	41.27	38.26	56.45	52.59	11.52	10.93	22.95	20.96
Hawaii	39.22	36.06	55.22	51.69	11.92	11.31	25.43	23.47
Easter I	39.69	38.16	56.73	53.22	12.27	11.70	25.49	22.59
Moriori	38.53	35.84	55.84	52.73	11.18	10.45	25.12	23.08
Arikara	38.31	34.85	55.93	50.67	11.62	10.70	24.43	22.26
Santa Cruz	36.25	34.24	54.20	50.41	11.92	10.92	23.55	21.16
Peru	35.55	31.78	52.58	48.00	10.42	9.58	24.45	22.05
N Japan	35.31	31.22	54.42	49.16	12.45	10.28	23.47	22.13
S Japan	34.54	32.02	53.70	48.85	12.14	10.73	23.52	22.02
Hainan	35.80	33.68	54.71	51.26	12.24	11.76	24.91	24.55
Atayal	34.55	33.39	52.24	49.00	12.14	11.22	21.31	19.72
Philippines	36.06	–	52.84	–	12.22	–	23.00	–
Guam	40.27	36.30	59.50	54.67	12.87	12.26	25.53	24.59
Egypt	35.45	31.85	52.03	47.53	10.84	9.96	22.53	19.83
Bushman	34.22	31.14	50.02	46.33	11.51	10.59	20.93	19.84
Andaman Is	35.91	33.71	51.20	48.00	11.43	10.40	20.23	18.57
Ainu	35.60	32.24	53.79	48.50	11.96	10.45	23.90	22.18
Buriat	37.53	34.39	58.02	53.83	12.73	11.56	28.96	26.93
Eskimo	41.57	38.11	59.34	53.55	12.79	11.67	25.87	24.04
Anyang	36.07	–	54.88	–	12.67	–	26.45	–

TABLE B-1. Continued.
Means of Measurements

	Supraorbital Projection SOS		Glabella Projection GLS		Foramen Mag Length FOL		Frontal Chord FRC	
	Male	*Female*	*Male*	*Female*	*Male*	*Female*	*Male*	*Female*
Norse	6.29	5.29	3.25	1.96	36.53	34.80	113.13	107.98
Zalavár	6.72	5.44	3.28	2.16	37.21	35.18	112.70	107.47
Berg	6.73	5.26	3.59	2.38	38.98	36.23	111.05	106.23
Teita	6.45	4.96	1.55	0.90	36.06	34.46	108.85	105.72
Dogon	5.49	4.02	2.19	1.27	35.00	33.27	110.17	105.65
Zulu	6.18	5.24	2.16	1.43	37.33	36.04	111.69	109.39
Australia	7.40	6.18	5.37	3.96	36.65	35.20	111.90	105.86
Tasmania	7.53	6.52	5.60	4.33	36.47	34.71	110.29	105.86
Tolai	7.05	6.04	4.75	3.07	34.91	33.15	108.64	103.00
Hawaii	6.27	4.76	4.73	2.90	36.53	34.27	117.71	111.29
Easter I	7.45	5.68	4.94	3.41	37.53	34.86	116.29	109.59
Moriori	5.88	4.84	5.16	3.78	36.09	34.94	114.35	108.08
Arikara	6.45	4.74	3.48	2.07	37.86	35.44	109.29	105.63
Santa Cruz	6.76	5.00	4.53	2.96	36.43	34.61	109.78	104.86
Peru	5.91	4.55	3.09	2.04	35.16	33.85	109.73	105.07
N Japan	6.58	5.09	4.24	2.25	36.58	35.22	111.40	105.13
S Japan	6.30	4.73	2.76	1.73	36.40	34.61	110.98	106.37
Hainan	6.31	5.21	3.04	2.16	36.76	34.68	109.44	108.26
Atayal	5.69	4.78	3.03	2.17	37.31	35.33	109.28	104.56
Philippines	6.24	–	3.52	–	35.70	–	110.90	–
Guam	6.97	5.48	3.77	2.52	36.67	34.96	116.40	110.59
Egypt	6.00	4.77	3.03	1.34	35.67	33.91	111.91	108.13
Bushman	6.73	5.69	2.37	1.57	37.10	34.84	109.17	105.10
Andaman Is	5.83	4.86	2.46	1.63	33.66	32.11	106.66	101.57
Ainu	5.42	4.47	4.23	2.71	37.63	34.74	112.44	108.74
Buriat	6.04	4.80	2.85	1.46	37.18	36.09	113.44	109.98
Eskimo	5.70	4.44	3.30	2.16	38.40	37.62	112.79	109.62
Anyang	6.02	–	3.14	–	36.67	–	113.52	–

TABLE B-1. Continued.
Means of Measurements

	Frontal Subtense FRS		Nas-Subtense Fraction FRF		Parietal Chord PAC		Parietal Subtense PAS	
	Male	Female	Male	Female	Male	Female	Male	Female
Norse	25.11	25.55	51.67	48.31	114.44	109.53	24.69	23.13
Zalavár	26.79	26.53	50.00	46.98	115.28	110.64	25.13	23.67
Berg	27.05	26.51	50.21	46.85	110.09	105.21	24.09	23.32
Teita	26.64	27.00	48.97	47.30	114.27	109.68	23.36	23.74
Dogon	26.74	25.67	47.98	44.62	112.15	107.73	23.43	22.25
Zulu	27.71	27.70	47.16	46.04	115.31	112.00	24.11	23.24
Australia	25.23	25.33	50.23	46.49	116.63	110.27	23.90	22.63
Tasmania	25.04	25.17	49.20	45.24	115.80	111.24	24.71	23.45
Tolai	23.88	23.48	49.18	45.22	116.36	112.63	25.79	25.20
Hawaii	24.76	24.43	51.45	46.33	112.69	105.61	24.88	22.45
Easter I	26.47	26.49	51.12	47.08	116.51	109.65	24.71	23.22
Moriori	21.89	22.45	51.26	47.08	110.60	106.45	22.86	22.61
Arikara	21.31	23.37	50.71	46.78	108.93	104.07	24.10	22.59
Santa Cruz	23.06	23.06	52.39	48.61	105.02	101.80	21.24	21.27
Peru	22.95	23.31	48.47	45.11	108.98	104.07	23.89	22.58
N Japan	25.75	25.28	50.58	45.88	113.35	106.84	23.73	21.50
S Japan	26.06	25.59	50.50	45.22	113.84	109.56	24.32	23.49
Hainan	24.47	25.26	48.38	47.11	111.98	109.00	25.16	24.24
Atayal	26.59	25.78	46.66	45.17	112.31	108.83	24.34	24.11
Philippines	24.98	–	51.08	–	111.64	–	24.72	–
Guam	27.23	27.19	51.97	48.37	114.83	109.52	25.23	23.81
Egypt	25.59	25.98	51.71	48.89	115.72	110.49	25.57	23.81
Bushman	28.46	28.22	47.59	45.08	109.49	105.29	21.95	21.02
Andaman Is	24.83	23.71	48.71	46.00	107.54	102.34	24.83	22.91
Ainu	26.98	26.71	50.85	48.71	115.60	110.74	23.48	22.82
Buriat	25.51	25.70	53.15	49.67	109.67	102.69	22.65	21.04
Eskimo	26.43	26.65	53.13	50.71	114.91	111.58	23.96	23.67
Anyang	26.02	–	51.45	–	113.88	–	24.36	–

TABLE B-1. Continued.
Means of Measurements

	Breg-Subtense Fraction PAF		Occipital Chord OCC		Occipital Subtense OCS		Lam-Subtense Fraction OCF	
	Male	*Female*	*Male*	*Female*	*Male*	*Female*	*Male*	*Female*
Norse	61.02	58.20	97.25	95.33	30.82	29.84	47.40	45.16
Zalavár	58.64	56.60	96.17	94.20	29.64	28.69	47.51	45.16
Berg	58.50	54.66	94.00	91.43	28.50	27.91	48.34	45.94
Teita	61.82	60.46	93.70	89.90	28.79	26.28	47.79	42.28
Dogon	64.28	61.54	94.49	94.02	23.72	22.94	43.06	44.38
Zulu	60.69	59.13	96.53	95.02	26.85	27.24	47.13	45.43
Australia	58.40	55.00	92.12	91.41	29.13	28.98	43.52	40.39
Tasmania	57.56	54.45	93.18	92.02	28.64	27.69	44.69	42.98
Tolai	58.23	57.11	95.68	93.26	29.59	27.74	46.34	44.41
Hawaii	53.90	51.98	102.45	99.92	26.55	25.22	53.69	51.49
Easter I	57.69	54.05	100.12	96.46	29.92	28.97	49.41	46.92
Moriori	55.42	53.61	102.51	98.37	28.54	26.10	49.91	45.20
Arikara	54.71	53.37	95.14	91.04	27.55	26.56	45.50	44.15
Santa Cruz	53.08	50.96	97.55	95.24	30.73	30.33	45.90	44.61
Peru	54.36	51.76	98.11	95.53	30.16	29.47	47.31	45.84
N Japan	59.15	54.53	100.09	96.25	28.73	26.81	50.60	47.28
S Japan	61.82	58.00	100.38	95.83	28.22	27.61	50.62	46.83
Hainan	60.53	59.32	96.02	94.71	26.33	25.24	45.96	46.71
Atayal	59.38	58.06	93.31	91.44	26.52	25.56	43.34	42.94
Philippines	60.28	–	96.92	–	25.58	–	46.24	–
Guam	61.13	58.52	100.20	96.93	28.53	26.74	48.23	47.37
Egypt	63.74	59.36	97.48	94.57	26.97	26.40	46.17	45.08
Bushman	57.17	55.59	88.56	88.47	28.44	28.27	45.39	43.76
Andaman Is	57.74	55.43	91.69	89.60	24.29	22.51	43.77	42.23
Ainu	60.54	56.95	100.42	97.26	28.75	27.45	47.77	45.63
Buriat	55.64	53.13	94.62	94.65	30.60	28.72	48.44	48.81
Eskimo	57.75	56.45	98.23	96.05	29.49	27.76	50.94	48.31
Anyang	60.26	–	99.43	–	27.62	–	48.62	–

TABLE B-1. Continued.
Means of Measurements

	Vertex Radius VRR		Nasion Radius NAR		Subspinale Radius SSR		Prosthion Radius PRR	
	Male	*Female*	*Male*	*Female*	*Male*	*Female*	*Male*	*Female*
Norse	121.96	117.47	95.27	90.60	95.56	91.29	100.40	96.38
Zalavár	122.04	117.51	94.62	89.56	95.47	89.16	101.17	94.58
Berg	120.82	116.32	94.91	89.74	93.21	88.77	98.14	93.85
Teita	118.39	115.04	96.33	90.62	97.73	91.82	105.03	99.30
Dogon	121.64	117.77	89.72	86.58	91.43	87.98	101.19	96.87
Zulu	122.11	119.00	94.44	90.26	96.47	91.85	105.04	100.63
Australia	116.19	111.71	96.08	91.12	100.52	95.45	108.50	103.59
Tasmania	121.02	116.33	94.78	89.71	100.24	94.50	105.80	100.33
Tolai	122.66	117.15	95.52	90.46	102.70	96.85	110.32	104.70
Hawaii	131.80	125.10	98.82	93.35	101.22	95.55	106.98	101.59
Easter I	130.73	124.00	102.98	95.86	103.29	96.51	107.84	101.19
Moriori	126.95	122.00	98.07	93.92	100.88	96.18	105.91	101.02
Arikara	120.86	115.93	97.14	91.85	99.00	93.15	103.98	98.85
Santa Cruz	119.00	114.71	91.69	86.35	96.04	91.02	102.41	98.08
Peru	122.47	117.85	89.60	84.44	90.69	85.18	96.95	91.02
N Japan	125.15	117.59	93.71	87.94	94.69	89.09	101.87	95.69
S Japan	125.88	119.85	94.10	88.49	95.06	89.80	101.98	97.37
Hainan	124.11	122.13	92.16	88.05	93.04	89.21	100.18	96.58
Atayal	121.97	118.00	90.97	86.78	89.41	86.11	96.76	92.83
Philippines	122.66	–	92.22	–	94.08	–	101.86	–
Guam	127.10	122.11	96.67	90.67	98.97	91.85	106.33	99.37
Egypt	122.52	117.68	93.45	88.45	94.64	88.77	100.03	94.04
Bushman	112.56	109.51	90.17	86.35	89.85	86.63	96.46	93.47
Andaman Is	119.80	115.23	87.14	83.23	89.71	86.09	94.49	91.94
Ainu	125.85	121.55	96.27	91.21	97.33	91.16	104.42	97.97
Buriat	123.31	119.50	98.11	93.06	96.47	91.02	103.15	97.70
Eskimo	124.62	121.56	99.72	94.44	101.00	95.91	107.06	103.25
Anyang	126.38	–	93.31	–	94.21	–	101.14	–

TABLE B-1. Continued.
Means of Measurements

	Dacryon Radius DKR		Zygoorbitale Radius ZOR		Frontomalare Radius FMR		Ectoconchion Radius EKR	
	Male	*Female*	*Male*	*Female*	*Male*	*Female*	*Male*	*Female*
Norse	82.65	79.25	81.91	78.16	76.82	73.75	71.35	68.51
Zalavár	82.00	77.91	80.70	76.20	76.68	73.62	71.32	67.84
Berg	82.57	78.38	79.75	76.34	76.96	73.34	71.20	67.89
Teita	84.85	80.50	83.94	79.20	78.24	74.46	73.30	69.78
Dogon	79.00	76.37	78.34	75.69	73.53	71.54	68.89	66.98
Zulu	83.05	80.13	80.75	78.11	76.60	74.20	71.58	69.26
Australia	82.90	78.96	82.83	79.06	79.42	74.82	72.46	68.92
Tasmania	82.20	78.12	80.67	76.64	77.87	73.64	71.67	67.86
Tolai	84.36	80.24	83.75	79.89	79.38	75.85	74.20	70.61
Hawaii	87.57	83.12	84.55	80.80	83.39	79.49	77.80	73.90
Easter I	91.08	85.22	87.65	82.92	86.14	81.00	80.57	75.84
Moriori	86.32	83.18	82.84	80.25	81.16	78.43	74.95	72.41
Arikara	84.90	81.30	80.95	77.63	80.36	76.48	74.33	70.85
Santa Cruz	80.20	76.73	78.25	74.82	75.43	71.63	70.24	66.82
Peru	78.65	74.07	74.95	70.62	74.02	70.60	68.93	65.13
N Japan	84.09	79.19	81.33	76.91	79.65	74.50	74.87	69.84
S Japan	84.20	79.63	81.42	77.29	79.14	75.39	74.58	70.54
Hainan	81.87	78.79	79.62	77.08	77.13	74.82	72.09	70.08
Atayal	80.55	76.94	77.41	74.17	77.17	73.06	71.72	67.72
Philippines	81.56	–	79.46	–	77.20	–	72.04	–
Guam	85.77	81.15	83.67	79.15	80.50	76.41	75.63	71.44
Egypt	81.24	77.58	79.45	75.26	75.28	71.75	69.62	66.26
Bushman	80.88	77.22	79.59	75.84	74.66	70.94	70.37	67.00
Andaman Is	76.57	73.26	73.91	71.40	72.51	69.60	66.20	63.89
Ainu	85.19	81.18	83.23	78.63	80.58	76.32	74.33	70.87
Buriat	87.36	83.44	86.36	82.28	83.44	79.28	79.38	75.46
Eskimo	88.91	84.84	88.15	84.05	85.30	81.45	79.96	76.53
Anyang	83.40	–	81.10	–	79.24	–	74.50	–

TABLE B-1. Continued.
Means of Measurements

	Zygomaxill Radius ZMR		M1 Alveolus Radius AVR	
	Male	Female	Male	Female
Norse	73.04	69.58	80.75	76.69
Zalavár	72.87	67.84	81.28	75.27
Berg	71.11	67.96	78.48	74.83
Teita	76.27	72.16	83.82	78.04
Dogon	70.06	67.25	78.89	75.50
Zulu	72.71	70.00	82.75	79.50
Australia	77.29	73.08	88.04	82.35
Tasmania	73.47	68.83	85.02	79.12
Tolai	76.46	72.56	86.84	81.41
Hawaii	77.16	72.82	84.24	79.41
Easter I	78.51	74.59	85.98	80.14
Moriori	73.93	71.39	86.88	82.02
Arikara	74.07	70.37	83.64	78.37
Santa Cruz	71.90	68.39	83.02	78.43
Peru	68.44	63.56	76.98	70.80
N Japan	72.80	67.81	81.60	75.88
S Japan	72.90	69.37	80.80	76.37
Hainan	71.42	69.05	79.09	76.05
Atayal	69.28	67.22	76.59	72.94
Philippines	72.28	–	79.64	–
Guam	76.97	71.74	83.37	77.30
Egypt	70.91	66.49	79.64	74.06
Bushman	70.71	67.08	77.85	74.33
Andaman Is	66.54	64.14	74.40	71.66
Ainu	75.71	70.53	84.58	78.03
Buriat	78.35	73.78	82.91	77.76
Eskimo	82.55	79.45	88.15	84.36
Anyang	72.86	–	80.81	–

TABLE B-1. Continued.
Means of Measurements

	Number of Crania		Bregma Radius BRR		Lambda Radius LAR		Opisthion Radius OSR	
	Male	Female	Male	Female	Male	Female	Male	Female
Norse	–	–	–	–	–	–	–	–
Zalavár	53	45	119.08	114.58	105.66	102.96	42.21	40.93
Berg	56	53	118.71	113.96	102.61	99.49	41.63	38.60
Teita	–	–	–	–	–	–	–	–
Dogon	–	–	–	–	–	–	–	–
Zulu	55	46	117.95	114.74	109.87	107.76	41.96	40.76
Australia	52	49	114.21	109.35	103.15	100.02	41.38	39.47
Tasmania	42	34	118.62	113.59	103.93	101.53	39.67	39.15
Tolai	56	54	120.05	113.94	104.66	101.35	38.80	37.24
Hawaii	51	49	127.47	120.92	112.22	108.02	40.98	39.16
Easter I	48	37	128.65	121.92	110.31	105.11	42.81	41.49
Moriori	57	51	121.30	117.24	114.12	108.45	40.75	40.08
Arikara	42	27	118.05	113.59	102.02	98.89	41.21	38.63
Santa Cruz	51	51	115.37	110.10	106.25	103.16	41.65	40.08
Peru	55	55	117.22	112.69	107.51	104.27	39.98	38.58
N Japan	55	32	121.24	114.50	109.91	104.16	42.16	40.81
S Japan	50	41	122.50	116.49	109.92	104.95	41.88	40.15
Hainan	45	38	121.11	118.55	105.91	104.74	41.64	39.58
Atayal	29	18	119.21	115.33	105.31	100.67	42.76	41.22
Philippines	50	–	119.70	–	105.22	–	40.44	–
Guam	30	27	124.33	118.96	108.30	105.89	42.60	42.19
Egypt	–	–	–	–	–	–	–	–
Bushman	41	49	109.93	106.45	101.37	99.65	40.56	38.45
Andaman Is	24	16	115.96	112.69	104.08	100.81	38.92	36.31
Ainu	48	38	121.83	117.63	114.33	108.97	44.73	40.89
Buriat	–	–	–	–	–	–	–	–
Eskimo	–	–	–	–	–	–	–	–
Anyang	42	–	123.45	–	108.83	–	42.55	–

TABLE B-1. Continued.
Means of Measurements

	Basion Radius BAR	
	Male	Female
Norse	–	–
Zalavár	16.06	14.62
Berg	12.80	11.49
Teita	–	–
Dogon	–	–
Zulu	16.35	14.39
Australia	15.37	14.16
Tasmania	13.93	13.53
Tolai	15.73	13.83
Hawaii	16.84	15.69
Easter I	16.38	15.68
Moriori	15.33	14.96
Arikara	16.31	13.89
Santa Cruz	14.12	14.84
Peru	13.80	12.62
N Japan	16.76	15.78
S Japan	16.20	14.98
Hainan	17.24	15.32
Atayal	15.66	14.83
Philippines	15.88	–
Guam	20.30	19.00
Egypt	–	–
Bushman	13.10	13.49
Andaman Is	14.21	12.56
Ainu	17.65	15.58
Buriat	–	–
Eskimo	–	–
Anyang	17.79	–

TABLE B-2
Standard Deviations of Measurements

	Glab-Occip Length GOL		Nasio-Occip Length NOL		Bas-Nasion Length BNL		Bas-Bregma Height BBH	
	Male	*Female*	*Male*	*Female*	*Male*	*Female*	*Male*	*Female*
Norse	5.25	4.66	5.24	4.65	3.55	3.58	5.13	4.10
Zalavár	5.77	5.96	5.59	5.99	4.37	3.87	5.14	5.11
Berg	7.35	6.51	7.44	6.56	4.52	3.82	4.31	4.77
Teita	5.12	5.09	4.66	5.13	3.70	3.28	4.82	4.10
Dogon	5.21	6.24	4.86	5.93	3.20	3.96	4.76	4.33
Zulu	5.92	4.96	5.79	4.71	5.00	4.51	5.95	5.27
Australia	5.42	6.36	5.41	6.09	3.38	3.14	5.36	4.68
Tasmania	5.68	5.97	5.34	5.71	3.82	3.39	4.71	5.17
Tolai	5.24	5.19	4.98	4.92	3.62	3.78	4.03	3.70
Hawaii	6.22	5.97	5.97	5.66	4.08	3.57	5.26	4.48
Easter I	5.71	5.20	5.24	5.09	3.59	3.93	4.24	4.35
Moriori	5.32	4.93	5.23	4.77	4.35	3.26	4.40	4.31
Arikara	5.82	6.06	5.74	6.14	3.09	3.65	4.15	4.77
Santa Cruz	4.49	5.07	4.17	5.20	3.11	3.43	4.77	3.34
Peru	5.22	5.20	5.22	5.19	3.53	3.68	5.22	4.05
N Japan	6.13	6.55	6.13	6.45	4.60	3.86	6.06	5.49
S Japan	5.66	5.53	5.31	5.58	3.66	3.51	4.11	4.24
Hainan	6.14	5.67	5.86	5.19	4.00	3.44	4.47	3.69
Atayal	5.81	4.54	5.85	4.28	3.91	2.93	4.30	5.19
Philippines	6.91	–	6.74	–	3.87	–	5.09	–
Guam	6.23	4.50	6.05	4.32	4.50	2.92	4.03	4.21
Egypt	6.15	4.49	6.05	4.41	3.64	3.30	5.16	3.95
Bushman	6.23	5.67	6.16	5.83	4.84	3.72	4.71	5.04
Andaman Is	5.39	4.79	5.03	4.52	3.33	2.51	4.95	4.58
Ainu	5.03	5.35	4.98	5.34	4.12	4.28	3.49	4.97
Buriat	6.31	5.43	5.90	5.35	3.97	3.69	5.07	4.96
Eskimo	5.79	4.87	5.25	4.59	3.48	3.62	4.98	4.57
Anyang	4.27	–	4.59	–	4.07	–	5.33	–

TABLE B-2. Continued.
Standard Deviations of Measurements

	Max Cranial Breadth XCB		Max Frontal Breadth XFB		Bistephanic Breadth STB		Bizygomatic Breadth ZYB	
	Male	Female	Male	Female	Male	Female	Male	Female
Norse	4.72	4.31	5.59	4.35	7.20	5.36	3.87	3.76
Zalavár	4.03	4.44	4.61	4.12	5.13	5.45	3.54	4.10
Berg	5.52	4.63	5.17	4.70	6.11	4.91	4.89	3.97
Teita	4.32	4.33	5.16	4.95	7.77	6.58	4.17	3.95
Dogon	4.43	4.49	4.87	4.31	5.64	5.24	4.03	3.61
Zulu	5.09	5.07	5.30	5.23	5.92	5.80	4.08	3.95
Australia	5.10	4.68	4.25	3.50	6.26	5.20	4.17	4.67
Tasmania	5.67	5.17	4.69	4.04	6.49	6.30	4.87	4.91
Tolai	3.98	3.90	3.34	4.02	6.03	6.06	3.07	5.13
Hawaii	5.07	4.84	4.78	3.99	5.78	4.33	4.95	4.00
Easter I	4.66	3.40	3.51	4.26	4.30	4.74	3.83	3.80
Moriori	4.33	5.24	3.79	4.47	6.14	5.27	4.78	4.31
Arikara	5.33	4.97	4.67	4.24	7.28	4.97	5.39	4.44
Santa Cruz	5.09	4.13	4.75	3.62	5.02	4.25	5.14	3.68
Peru	3.98	4.48	4.37	4.25	5.03	5.02	4.28	4.09
N Japan	4.46	4.33	4.51	5.16	6.72	6.56	4.43	4.81
S Japan	4.58	4.08	3.88	4.38	5.03	5.46	3.92	4.44
Hainan	4.26	4.81	4.92	5.12	6.33	5.08	4.63	4.72
Atayal	3.63	5.32	3.83	4.32	5.93	5.39	5.70	3.47
Philippines	5.61	–	4.69	–	5.79	–	5.76	–
Guam	3.65	3.93	3.28	4.14	5.69	4.53	4.58	3.64
Egypt	4.97	4.36	4.72	4.50	5.29	5.28	4.22	3.39
Bushman	5.12	3.75	4.89	4.36	5.23	5.69	4.69	5.30
Andaman Is	3.89	4.42	4.72	4.56	5.49	5.39	3.78	4.24
Ainu	4.26	3.61	4.25	3.73	5.26	4.78	5.16	3.76
Buriat	6.59	5.21	5.70	5.07	8.91	5.43	5.32	4.80
Eskimo	4.85	4.12	3.85	4.04	7.33	5.89	4.62	3.87
Anyang	5.43	–	4.98	–	7.12	–	5.07	–

TABLE B-2. Continued.
Standard Deviations of Measurements

	Biauricular Breadth AUB		Min Cranial Breadth WCB		Biasterionic Breadth ASB		Bas-Prosth Length BPL	
	Male	Female	Male	Female	Male	Female	Male	Female
Norse	4.04	3.76	3.15	3.58	3.56	4.11	5.15	4.39
Zalavár	3.99	4.18	3.04	3.39	3.79	5.13	4.94	6.31
Berg	5.42	4.45	4.19	3.65	4.34	4.95	5.70	5.15
Teita	3.43	3.57	3.29	3.38	4.51	3.66	5.30	4.39
Dogon	3.69	3.55	4.00	3.16	4.53	4.36	3.93	4.66
Zulu	3.16	3.45	4.26	3.47	4.50	3.83	6.10	5.19
Australia	4.17	4.45	3.04	2.82	4.84	4.50	4.47	3.84
Tasmania	4.63	3.96	3.65	3.56	4.68	3.75	5.13	4.77
Tolai	3.75	4.22	3.56	2.94	3.56	3.46	4.76	3.87
Hawaii	4.62	4.19	2.90	3.32	4.51	3.61	5.41	4.10
Easter I	3.99	3.70	3.61	3.29	3.61	3.90	4.31	4.01
Moriori	4.47	4.64	3.60	3.20	4.79	4.29	3.84	3.32
Arikara	4.92	4.51	3.76	3.44	5.17	5.74	3.94	4.26
Santa Cruz	4.57	3.75	3.93	2.70	3.84	3.73	4.48	3.53
Peru	4.33	4.24	3.21	3.30	4.37	4.11	4.18	3.95
N Japan	3.91	4.97	4.13	3.10	4.81	3.87	5.95	4.04
S Japan	4.16	4.22	3.26	3.58	3.83	4.52	4.64	4.34
Hainan	3.84	4.35	3.20	3.40	3.95	3.46	5.72	4.69
Atayal	5.23	4.62	3.77	3.93	4.33	3.70	5.49	4.21
Philippines	5.29	–	4.18	–	4.47	–	4.71	–
Guam	4.19	3.99	3.37	3.36	4.56	2.72	5.37	3.50
Egypt	4.03	4.04	3.39	2.96	4.43	4.55	3.78	3.62
Bushman	4.80	4.79	3.07	3.89	5.00	4.98	5.28	4.42
Andaman Is	4.37	4.10	2.97	3.44	4.74	3.32	3.53	3.39
Ainu	4.58	3.53	3.61	3.39	3.84	4.52	4.47	4.87
Buriat	5.74	4.58	3.86	3.62	4.96	4.66	4.78	4.56
Eskimo	4.28	3.50	3.81	3.53	4.05	3.71	4.58	4.86
Anyang	4.85	–	3.30	–	4.36	–	4.28	–

TABLE B-2. Continued.
Standard Deviations of Measurements

	Nas-Prosth Height NPH		Nasal Height NLH		Orbit Height OBH		Orbit Breadth OBB	
	Male	*Female*	*Male*	*Female*	*Male*	*Female*	*Male*	*Female*
Norse	3.37	4.04	2.65	2.67	2.21	2.05	1.43	1.57
Zalavár	4.23	3.59	2.91	2.54	1.99	1.76	1.16	1.72
Berg	4.17	4.05	2.94	2.97	1.83	1.86	1.45	1.20
Teita	3.80	4.22	2.75	3.21	1.82	1.88	1.44	1.64
Dogon	4.14	3.67	2.80	2.32	1.95	1.66	1.70	1.62
Zulu	4.07	4.17	2.56	2.61	1.76	2.04	1.91	1.34
Australia	4.16	3.95	2.68	2.54	1.91	1.86	1.52	1.51
Tasmania	4.81	3.92	2.94	2.56	2.66	1.87	1.86	1.61
Tolai	3.97	3.69	2.78	2.38	2.00	1.70	1.69	1.64
Hawaii	3.73	3.59	2.77	2.35	1.65	1.56	1.35	1.34
Easter I	3.84	3.45	2.54	2.63	1.70	1.56	1.38	1.28
Moriori	3.65	4.00	3.27	2.45	1.53	1.50	1.65	1.21
Arikara	3.87	3.81	2.54	2.10	1.86	1.74	1.15	1.31
Santa Cruz	3.95	3.17	2.55	2.04	1.86	1.59	1.43	1.47
Peru	3.59	3.67	2.24	2.50	1.47	1.39	1.42	1.29
N Japan	3.85	3.52	2.88	2.64	1.42	1.92	1.52	1.81
S Japan	3.66	3.73	2.71	2.47	1.60	1.51	1.61	1.36
Hainan	3.76	3.89	2.53	2.78	2.13	1.81	1.64	1.50
Atayal	4.04	3.53	2.53	2.84	1.45	1.54	1.41	1.61
Philippines	3.28	–	2.17	–	1.53	–	1.41	–
Guam	3.45	2.83	2.68	2.53	1.68	1.23	1.52	1.16
Egypt	3.00	3.34	2.69	2.27	2.04	1.82	1.78	1.61
Bushman	5.32	4.26	2.94	2.93	2.41	2.12	1.86	1.72
Andaman Is	3.59	2.85	2.38	2.02	1.23	1.47	1.36	1.19
Ainu	3.94	4.57	2.81	2.89	1.89	1.72	1.82	1.83
Buriat	4.21	4.14	3.03	2.82	1.85	1.67	1.82	1.59
Eskimo	3.65	3.72	2.51	2.49	1.73	1.86	1.78	1.40
Anyang	3.09	–	2.25	–	1.60	–	1.34	–

TABLE B-2. Continued.
Standard Deviations of Measurements

	Bijugal Breadth JUB		Nasal Breadth NLB		Palate Breadth MAB		Mastoid Height MDH	
	Male	Female	Male	Female	Male	Female	Male	Female
Norse	3.61	3.49	1.45	1.90	3.21	2.22	3.49	2.51
Zalavár	3.07	3.41	1.52	1.65	2.81	3.30	2.87	2.78
Berg	3.81	3.59	1.98	1.72	3.25	2.98	2.79	2.59
Teita	4.04	3.58	1.74	1.94	3.62	2.51	3.21	3.17
Dogon	4.22	3.54	1.72	1.59	3.22	3.25	2.79	2.45
Zulu	3.97	3.87	1.94	1.77	3.03	3.33	2.82	3.36
Australia	3.97	4.18	1.73	1.51	3.31	2.74	3.17	2.59
Tasmania	4.31	4.17	2.27	1.67	2.96	3.72	3.85	3.12
Tolai	3.41	3.81	1.84	1.80	2.95	2.71	3.20	3.06
Hawaii	3.88	3.89	1.81	1.61	3.48	2.95	3.08	2.71
Easter I	3.92	4.36	1.65	1.73	3.49	3.15	3.43	2.67
Moriori	3.70	3.43	1.60	2.03	3.21	2.93	2.44	2.25
Arikara	4.59	3.37	1.74	1.62	2.88	2.85	2.72	2.47
Santa Cruz	4.14	3.28	1.70	1.59	3.61	2.85	3.08	2.62
Peru	3.75	3.57	1.78	1.60	3.34	3.01	3.14	2.91
N Japan	4.42	4.12	1.94	1.57	3.91	3.49	2.38	2.99
S Japan	4.53	4.10	1.67	1.69	3.69	3.10	3.81	2.72
Hainan	4.25	4.34	1.87	2.06	3.33	2.12	2.46	2.86
Atayal	4.70	3.63	2.18	1.57	3.67	3.14	3.02	2.84
Philippines	4.60	–	1.61	–	3.06	–	2.93	–
Guam	4.75	3.86	1.72	1.78	2.74	2.56	3.13	2.77
Egypt	3.24	3.35	1.69	1.56	3.05	2.84	3.09	2.27
Bushman	4.85	4.61	2.27	2.10	3.22	2.86	3.45	3.89
Andaman Is	3.78	3.22	1.58	1.67	2.10	2.30	2.64	2.81
Ainu	4.61	3.57	2.09	1.80	3.30	2.58	2.83	2.80
Buriat	4.86	3.38	2.16	1.84	3.83	3.26	2.51	3.21
Eskimo	4.59	3.60	1.88	1.33	2.82	2.91	2.96	2.58
Anyang	3.91	–	2.10	–	3.55	–	2.27	–

SKULL SHAPES AND THE MAP

TABLE B-2. Continued.
Standard Deviations of Measurements

	Mastoid Breadth MDB		Bimaxillary Breadth ZMB		Zygomaxill Subtense SSS		Bifrontal Breadth FMB	
	Male	Female	Male	Female	Male	Female	Male	Female
Norse	1.61	1.53	5.02	4.52	2.67	2.25	2.88	3.64
Zalavár	1.61	1.30	4.14	3.45	2.81	2.15	2.73	3.26
Berg	1.46	1.29	4.31	3.85	2.65	2.90	3.33	2.83
Teita	2.06	1.75	5.33	4.65	2.78	2.78	3.63	3.28
Dogon	1.95	1.39	4.04	4.25	3.00	2.61	3.46	3.04
Zulu	1.64	2.23	4.85	4.49	2.77	3.27	3.47	2.82
Australia	1.79	1.42	4.06	4.61	2.18	2.46	3.56	3.73
Tasmania	1.78	1.68	4.22	4.10	3.26	3.35	3.76	3.37
Tolai	1.91	1.53	4.12	3.64	2.40	2.15	3.10	3.16
Hawaii	2.06	1.66	4.63	3.41	2.48	2.51	3.03	3.60
Easter I	1.72	1.79	5.58	4.11	3.01	2.69	2.95	3.17
Moriori	1.70	1.42	3.74	3.98	2.60	2.69	3.53	2.65
Arikara	1.68	1.40	4.27	3.32	2.53	2.56	3.14	2.85
Santa Cruz	1.40	1.21	4.30	3.54	2.41	2.19	3.02	2.60
Peru	1.65	1.45	4.18	3.95	2.14	2.11	3.14	2.85
N Japan	1.38	1.55	5.19	4.23	2.61	1.97	3.81	3.75
S Japan	1.78	1.43	4.60	4.27	2.51	2.18	3.71	2.92
Hainan	1.37	1.24	4.04	3.86	2.99	3.31	2.97	3.44
Atayal	1.57	0.96	4.93	4.03	2.29	2.12	3.25	4.17
Philippines	1.73	–	4.33	–	2.54	–	3.26	–
Guam	1.43	1.28	4.53	4.31	1.88	1.75	3.37	2.84
Egypt	1.72	1.60	4.27	4.79	2.62	2.49	2.85	2.93
Bushman	2.42	1.45	4.84	4.39	2.55	2.39	4.51	3.63
Andaman Is	1.30	2.03	3.98	3.78	2.55	2.42	3.56	2.89
Ainu	1.60	1.25	4.80	4.29	2.96	2.44	4.12	3.32
Buriat	1.82	1.54	5.10	4.32	2.45	2.08	3.59	3.41
Eskimo	1.77	1.66	4.85	4.19	2.26	2.65	3.23	2.77
Anyang	1.57	–	4.50	–	2.39	–	3.00	–

TABLE B-2. Continued.
Standard Deviations of Measurements

	Nasio-Front Subtense NAS		Biorbital Breadth EKB		Dacryon Subtense DKS		Interorbital Breadth DKB	
	Male	*Female*	*Male*	*Female*	*Male*	*Female*	*Male*	*Female*
Norse	2.15	2.16	2.88	3.45	1.93	2.05	2.48	2.17
Zalavár	2.31	2.40	2.72	3.31	1.82	1.88	2.38	2.39
Berg	2.33	2.28	3.20	2.66	1.87	2.22	2.50	2.16
Teita	2.40	2.48	3.67	3.13	1.82	2.11	2.26	2.54
Dogon	2.41	1.88	3.60	2.86	2.05	1.82	2.04	2.39
Zulu	2.02	1.91	3.42	2.74	1.86	1.89	2.32	2.11
Australia	2.55	1.98	3.33	3.31	1.88	1.45	2.07	1.76
Tasmania	2.13	2.29	3.73	2.72	1.63	1.76	2.16	1.42
Tolai	1.92	1.96	2.95	3.25	1.79	2.06	2.31	1.90
Hawaii	2.21	2.01	3.08	3.41	1.74	1.79	2.17	2.14
Easter I	2.09	1.79	2.74	3.28	1.78	1.81	1.58	1.59
Moriori	2.38	1.99	3.46	2.53	1.89	1.68	1.93	1.68
Arikara	2.04	2.22	3.14	2.82	1.90	2.12	2.06	1.81
Santa Cruz	1.99	1.89	2.87	2.62	1.79	1.57	1.67	1.43
Peru	2.09	1.96	3.04	2.85	1.82	1.70	1.97	1.84
N Japan	2.40	2.29	3.47	3.75	2.16	1.76	2.41	2.32
S Japan	1.82	2.02	3.66	2.96	1.57	1.75	2.07	1.65
Hainan	2.12	2.14	2.96	3.17	1.77	1.98	1.65	2.07
Atayal	1.93	1.83	2.95	3.78	1.43	1.57	1.70	2.31
Philippines	2.14	–	3.32	–	1.73	–	1.71	–
Guam	1.69	1.55	3.71	2.76	1.81	1.74	2.29	1.83
Egypt	2.23	1.84	2.74	2.81	2.50	1.84	1.80	2.10
Bushman	2.45	2.22	4.66	3.47	2.21	2.02	2.43	1.98
Andaman Is	1.92	2.17	3.19	2.52	1.59	1.69	2.30	1.96
Ainu	2.24	2.11	3.92	3.37	1.97	1.81	2.05	2.33
Buriat	2.37	1.57	3.73	3.34	2.23	1.51	2.14	2.22
Eskimo	2.15	2.03	3.46	2.54	1.94	1.84	1.84	1.89
Anyang	2.40	–	2.96	–	2.11	–	1.84	–

SKULL SHAPES AND THE MAP

TABLE B-2. Continued.
Standard Deviations of Measurements

	Naso-Dacryal Subtense NDS		Simotic Chord WNB		Simotic Subtense SIS		Infer Malar Length IML	
	Male	Female	Male	Female	Male	Female	Male	Female
Norse	1.31	1.25	1.55	1.80	0.95	0.89	2.99	2.67
Zalavár	1.38	1.34	2.08	1.87	1.24	0.94	3.23	2.91
Berg	1.41	1.40	2.05	2.12	1.39	1.04	3.38	2.72
Teita	1.83	1.45	2.84	2.56	1.03	0.85	3.88	2.67
Dogon	1.45	1.51	2.92	1.98	1.13	0.80	3.37	3.44
Zulu	1.57	1.38	2.31	2.31	0.92	0.82	3.63	3.57
Australia	1.24	1.25	2.10	1.63	1.07	0.91	3.03	2.93
Tasmania	1.42	1.47	1.75	1.23	1.15	0.85	3.62	3.05
Tolai	1.52	1.06	1.85	1.98	0.86	0.76	3.49	3.36
Hawaii	1.19	1.08	1.67	1.76	0.97	0.95	2.47	2.73
Easter I	1.42	1.15	1.80	1.64	0.92	0.77	2.66	3.42
Moriori	1.44	1.24	1.54	1.51	0.96	0.88	2.67	2.96
Arikara	1.21	1.28	1.81	2.05	1.06	1.15	2.53	2.67
Santa Cruz	1.38	1.39	1.69	1.79	0.85	0.69	2.76	2.24
Peru	1.23	1.17	1.41	1.42	0.98	0.72	3.18	3.12
N Japan	1.25	1.29	1.77	2.10	0.94	0.92	2.81	3.58
S Japan	1.15	1.04	1.80	1.58	0.97	0.78	3.24	3.00
Hainan	1.27	1.21	2.07	1.85	0.96	0.91	3.11	3.21
Atayal	1.33	1.00	1.52	1.79	0.93	0.99	2.75	2.23
Philippines	1.33	–	2.15	–	1.04	–	3.43	–
Guam	1.27	1.22	1.92	1.31	0.87	0.74	2.95	2.40
Egypt	1.49	1.19	1.60	1.85	1.20	0.85	4.01	3.43
Bushman	1.29	1.27	2.44	2.31	0.85	0.83	3.47	3.34
Andaman Is	1.08	1.49	2.41	2.08	1.08	0.80	3.03	3.05
Ainu	1.56	1.42	1.97	1.89	1.11	0.98	3.52	3.07
Buriat	1.27	1.30	1.99	2.01	0.92	0.87	2.84	2.98
Eskimo	1.32	1.38	2.07	1.57	0.89	0.63	3.51	2.99
Anyang	1.46	–	2.54	–	1.01	–	2.72	–

TABLE B-2. Continued.
Standard Deviations of Measurements

	Max malar Length XML		Malar Subtense MLS		Cheek Height WMH		Supraorbital Projection SOS	
	Male	Female	Male	Female	Male	Female	Male	Female
Norse	2.99	2.85	1.76	1.42	2.02	1.98	1.33	0.98
Zalavár	2.98	3.39	1.43	1.37	2.31	1.99	1.18	0.94
Berg	3.29	2.70	1.50	1.13	2.46	2.01	1.17	1.00
Teita	2.90	2.44	1.74	1.62	2.57	1.62	1.33	0.88
Dogon	3.82	3.16	1.86	1.59	1.85	2.27	1.41	0.85
Zulu	3.63	3.30	1.50	1.57	1.98	2.68	1.26	1.16
Australia	3.15	3.19	1.41	1.41	2.13	2.07	1.05	1.35
Tasmania	3.88	3.79	1.65	1.50	1.67	1.96	1.24	1.29
Tolai	3.32	3.75	1.83	1.34	2.32	2.04	1.02	0.93
Hawaii	3.44	2.84	1.38	1.26	2.08	1.80	1.15	0.83
Easter I	2.78	3.63	1.50	1.76	2.20	2.10	1.17	1.08
Moriori	2.82	3.05	1.24	1.47	2.46	2.13	1.05	0.78
Arikara	2.84	3.19	1.36	1.07	1.98	1.95	1.09	0.90
Santa Cruz	3.09	2.38	1.16	1.15	2.27	1.63	1.16	0.69
Peru	3.15	3.23	1.51	1.42	2.00	2.20	0.99	0.98
N Japan	3.21	3.26	1.63	1.57	2.51	2.21	1.38	1.15
S Japan	3.51	3.17	1.65	1.48	2.79	2.63	1.05	0.84
Hainan	3.09	3.01	1.60	1.34	1.94	2.00	1.22	0.91
Atayal	3.14	2.89	1.55	1.26	2.29	1.90	1.00	0.94
Philippines	3.67	–	1.50	–	2.27	–	1.06	–
Guam	3.07	2.75	1.74	1.06	2.01	1.95	1.10	0.89
Egypt	3.43	3.23	1.42	1.40	1.89	2.08	1.23	0.91
Bushman	3.48	3.93	1.58	1.44	2.47	1.89	1.43	1.04
Andaman Is	3.41	3.05	1.31	1.58	1.75	1.48	1.25	0.85
Ainu	3.91	3.81	1.30	1.35	2.45	1.93	1.03	0.89
Buriat	3.43	3.39	1.78	1.51	2.43	2.12	1.10	0.92
Eskimo	3.81	3.66	1.96	1.93	2.14	2.30	0.95	0.92
Anyang	2.66	–	1.28	–	2.09	–	0.92	–

TABLE B-2. Continued.
Standard Deviations of Measurements

	Glabella Projection GLS		Foramen Mag Length FOL		Frontal Chord FRC		Frontal Subtense FRS	
	Male	Female	Male	Female	Male	Female	Male	Female
Norse	1.29	0.64	2.57	2.14	4.78	3.75	2.59	2.25
Zalavár	1.01	0.85	2.40	2.55	3.88	4.41	2.44	2.31
Berg	1.01	0.92	3.08	2.49	3.99	3.91	2.56	2.61
Teita	0.75	0.74	2.12	1.89	4.31	4.53	2.15	2.58
Dogon	1.15	0.63	2.38	2.61	4.22	4.13	2.70	2.41
Zulu	0.83	0.75	2.46	2.52	5.14	4.36	2.79	2.91
Australia	0.97	1.04	1.74	2.18	3.74	4.26	2.52	1.96
Tasmania	1.10	1.28	2.30	2.63	4.06	4.66	2.82	2.57
Tolai	1.37	0.93	2.10	2.28	4.03	4.00	2.20	2.33
Hawaii	1.10	0.74	2.39	2.17	4.10	4.78	2.47	2.31
Easter I	1.01	0.96	2.06	2.23	3.56	3.52	2.51	1.64
Moriori	1.18	0.92	2.37	1.88	4.39	4.37	2.45	2.33
Arikara	1.06	0.96	2.32	1.93	4.06	4.99	2.56	2.71
Santa Cruz	0.97	0.82	2.07	1.77	4.38	3.69	2.40	2.21
Peru	1.02	0.86	2.29	1.99	4.42	3.99	2.44	2.22
N Japan	1.05	0.92	2.14	2.07	4.79	4.39	2.78	2.58
S Japan	1.10	0.78	2.46	1.76	4.29	4.74	2.58	1.87
Hainan	0.77	0.86	2.21	2.24	4.31	4.10	2.67	2.34
Atayal	0.94	0.79	2.93	2.40	4.40	4.89	2.34	2.21
Philippines	1.03	–	2.22	–	4.57	–	2.21	–
Guam	0.97	0.85	1.88	1.91	3.41	5.31	2.18	2.15
Egypt	1.08	0.73	2.35	1.71	5.48	4.14	3.08	2.82
Bushman	0.94	0.71	2.75	2.66	5.15	4.87	2.64	2.55
Andaman Is	0.92	0.65	2.15	1.78	4.93	3.67	2.50	2.54
Ainu	1.04	0.69	2.11	1.81	4.33	4.03	2.72	2.12
Buriat	0.99	0.61	2.13	2.49	4.64	4.26	2.85	2.04
Eskimo	0.89	0.79	2.35	2.16	5.10	4.22	2.69	2.39
Anyang	0.93	–	2.46	–	4.70	–	2.95	–

TABLE B-2. Continued.
Standard Deviations of Measurements

	Nas-Subtense Fraction FRF		Parietal Chord PAC		Parietal Subtense PAS		Breg-Subtense Fraction PAF	
	Male	*Female*	*Male*	*Female*	*Male*	*Female*	*Male*	*Female*
Norse	3.97	2.96	5.35	5.18	2.76	2.37	3.17	3.26
Zalavár	3.03	3.53	4.79	5.55	2.28	2.45	3.26	4.36
Berg	3.23	3.31	4.71	5.66	2.85	2.93	4.49	4.07
Teita	3.27	3.03	6.79	4.99	3.12	2.62	4.46	4.23
Dogon	3.63	3.71	6.00	5.46	2.92	2.88	4.81	4.60
Zulu	3.69	3.11	5.41	5.61	2.67	2.50	4.88	4.46
Australia	3.46	3.07	4.76	6.05	2.30	2.31	3.94	3.48
Tasmania	3.65	3.44	5.11	5.39	2.51	2.56	4.45	4.42
Tolai	4.01	3.04	4.90	4.98	2.81	2.25	4.41	3.84
Hawaii	3.82	3.15	6.13	5.31	2.71	2.66	5.61	4.09
Easter I	5.23	4.02	5.80	6.75	3.08	3.05	4.50	4.96
Moriori	4.85	3.36	4.89	4.75	2.25	2.07	5.16	4.78
Arikara	4.58	4.31	3.88	3.93	2.23	2.63	4.50	4.24
Santa Cruz	3.55	4.05	5.57	4.95	2.98	2.79	5.23	3.81
Peru	3.60	2.84	6.01	6.08	3.31	3.17	5.55	4.24
N Japan	4.59	4.05	6.52	5.52	2.90	2.65	4.93	3.81
S Japan	4.32	3.95	5.91	4.63	2.91	2.48	4.00	3.94
Hainan	3.73	4.28	5.03	6.16	2.77	2.83	4.36	4.06
Atayal	3.12	4.82	5.71	5.18	2.61	2.14	4.94	4.18
Philippines	4.85	–	6.59	–	3.12	–	4.46	–
Guam	3.02	4.48	5.07	5.19	2.81	2.70	3.01	3.69
Egypt	4.24	3.75	6.19	4.71	2.56	2.63	5.27	3.46
Bushman	3.49	3.49	4.57	6.19	2.26	3.23	4.59	4.27
Andaman Is	3.37	2.66	5.43	4.78	2.22	2.47	5.35	4.51
Ainu	3.30	3.17	4.56	4.48	2.58	1.89	4.16	4.61
Buriat	4.15	3.40	4.78	5.63	2.53	3.01	3.99	4.00
Eskimo	3.87	3.36	5.34	5.71	2.17	2.52	5.28	4.80
Anyang	4.13	–	4.52	–	2.87	–	4.66	–

TABLE B-2. Continued.
Standard Deviations of Measurements

	Occipital Chord OCC		Occipital Subtense OCS		Lam-Subtense Fraction OCF		Vertex Radius VRR	
	Male	*Female*	*Male*	*Female*	*Male*	*Female*	*Male*	*Female*
Norse	3.96	4.64	3.26	2.85	5.44	5.19	4.19	3.47
Zalavár	5.11	4.16	3.03	2.73	5.10	4.27	3.63	3.82
Berg	5.22	4.95	3.38	3.55	6.27	5.86	3.56	3.00
Teita	5.03	4.51	3.94	2.50	5.70	4.34	4.38	3.56
Dogon	4.92	5.28	3.36	3.94	4.73	5.27	4.33	3.48
Zulu	5.79	4.43	3.85	2.87	5.74	4.66	4.50	4.36
Australia	4.46	4.44	2.77	2.80	4.73	3.64	4.00	3.77
Tasmania	4.51	4.70	3.27	2.89	4.58	4.58	3.85	4.06
Tolai	4.80	3.10	2.93	2.45	4.88	3.18	3.85	3.01
Hawaii	4.63	5.21	2.86	3.46	5.47	5.03	4.34	3.83
Easter I	5.40	5.05	2.77	2.35	5.81	5.35	3.62	3.11
Moriori	3.55	3.55	3.58	2.95	5.58	5.22	3.83	3.59
Arikara	5.86	5.90	3.81	4.17	5.26	5.61	3.89	3.60
Santa Cruz	5.03	4.84	3.26	3.17	5.56	4.67	4.18	3.35
Peru	6.25	6.18	3.87	3.52	6.46	4.63	3.99	3.61
N Japan	5.82	6.06	3.03	2.75	5.65	5.80	4.66	4.83
S Japan	5.51	4.22	3.24	2.67	5.05	4.68	3.33	3.20
Hainan	5.68	4.85	3.23	3.28	6.11	5.77	3.46	3.20
Atayal	3.97	4.26	3.04	2.04	5.11	4.89	2.96	3.91
Philippines	5.29	–	3.44	–	5.00	–	4.42	–
Guam	5.91	6.06	2.90	3.15	8.44	5.18	3.37	3.62
Egypt	4.61	3.88	2.51	2.71	6.61	4.67	3.84	3.83
Bushman	4.63	4.86	2.80	2.48	4.67	4.30	3.98	4.57
Andaman Is	4.16	3.86	2.42	2.55	4.72	4.48	4.11	3.20
Ainu	4.23	4.34	2.72	2.16	4.43	4.62	3.66	3.80
Buriat	6.09	6.06	3.24	3.25	6.49	6.79	3.72	4.15
Eskimo	5.94	5.15	3.05	3.14	6.07	5.57	4.13	3.35
Anyang	5.93	–	3.38	–	4.65	–	4.08	–

TABLE B-2. Continued.
Standard Deviations of Measurements

	Nasion Radius NAR		Subspinale Radius SSR		Prosthion Radius PRR		Dacryon Radius DKR	
	Male	Female	Male	Female	Male	Female	Male	Female
Norse	3.38	3.36	4.35	3.01	4.65	3.59	3.47	3.10
Zalavár	3.64	3.34	4.34	4.49	4.38	5.31	3.37	2.85
Berg	3.84	3.01	4.71	4.15	4.77	4.63	3.41	3.11
Teita	3.16	3.55	4.09	3.91	4.22	4.66	3.20	3.33
Dogon	3.34	3.36	3.67	3.81	4.39	4.59	3.29	3.49
Zulu	4.18	4.10	4.70	4.91	4.95	5.05	3.99	3.48
Australia	3.16	2.78	3.64	2.48	4.12	3.28	2.91	2.65
Tasmania	2.83	3.22	4.51	4.62	4.91	5.11	2.58	2.65
Tolai	3.16	3.76	3.64	3.55	4.76	4.17	3.39	3.46
Hawaii	3.53	3.15	3.97	3.30	4.74	3.50	3.42	2.75
Easter I	3.00	3.31	4.20	3.75	4.51	4.06	3.09	3.19
Moriori	4.01	3.15	3.86	3.15	3.49	2.99	3.54	2.96
Arikara	3.37	4.19	3.88	3.96	3.94	4.50	3.43	4.01
Santa Cruz	3.55	3.00	4.16	3.11	4.06	3.51	3.33	2.71
Peru	3.55	3.48	3.75	3.71	4.34	4.05	3.17	3.04
N Japan	4.40	3.37	5.01	3.68	5.74	3.90	3.95	2.68
S Japan	3.47	3.81	4.35	3.79	4.56	4.32	3.30	3.76
Hainan	3.27	2.90	4.27	3.26	4.96	4.10	3.07	2.69
Atayal	3.47	2.10	4.11	3.53	4.96	4.53	3.13	2.13
Philippines	3.67	–	3.85	–	4.42	–	3.40	–
Guam	3.40	3.36	3.65	3.16	4.28	3.61	3.24	2.96
Egypt	3.27	3.66	2.68	3.50	2.89	3.77	3.22	3.22
Bushman	4.06	3.63	4.19	3.94	4.80	4.70	3.86	3.34
Andaman Is	2.72	3.30	3.53	2.85	3.58	3.56	2.52	2.82
Ainu	3.45	3.31	3.57	4.30	3.81	4.56	3.15	2.94
Buriat	4.12	3.82	4.59	3.85	4.54	4.50	3.73	3.76
Eskimo	3.40	3.18	3.55	4.56	4.03	4.85	3.05	3.03
Anyang	3.22	–	3.34	–	4.01	–	2.96	–

TABLE B-2. Continued.
Standard Deviations of Measurements

	Zygoorbitale Radius ZOR		Frontomalare Radius FMR		Ectoconchion Radius EKR		Zygomaxill Radius ZMR	
	Male	Female	Male	Female	Male	Female	Male	Female
Norse	3.74	3.00	3.74	3.04	3.69	2.71	4.15	3.39
Zalavár	3.57	3.31	2.79	2.72	2.95	2.71	3.52	3.52
Berg	3.68	3.06	3.12	2.67	3.05	2.56	3.70	3.19
Teita	3.91	3.36	3.32	3.30	3.15	3.32	4.65	3.52
Dogon	3.34	3.63	3.38	3.16	3.11	3.23	3.02	3.62
Zulu	4.12	3.53	4.47	3.53	4.09	3.18	3.84	3.99
Australia	2.88	2.86	3.29	3.17	2.48	2.65	2.91	2.83
Tasmania	3.44	3.07	3.42	2.82	3.01	2.72	3.94	3.04
Tolai	3.42	3.46	3.42	3.33	3.08	2.88	3.31	3.54
Hawaii	3.41	2.63	3.03	2.71	3.02	2.29	3.07	3.19
Easter I	3.17	3.06	3.29	2.86	2.96	2.93	3.71	3.25
Moriori	3.22	2.82	3.09	3.10	2.94	2.65	3.48	3.19
Arikara	3.17	3.28	3.05	3.15	2.89	2.57	3.01	2.79
Santa Cruz	3.18	2.61	3.15	2.51	2.78	2.27	3.55	2.85
Peru	2.96	3.21	3.22	2.64	2.96	2.37	3.60	3.71
N Japan	4.00	2.67	3.77	2.51	3.62	2.40	4.12	3.18
S Japan	3.80	3.79	3.46	3.81	3.67	3.53	3.72	4.02
Hainan	3.17	2.61	2.84	3.37	2.91	2.73	3.14	3.56
Atayal	3.26	2.81	2.96	2.92	2.67	2.56	3.14	2.76
Philippines	3.72	–	3.34	–	3.30	–	3.77	–
Guam	3.26	2.74	2.99	3.43	2.57	3.06	3.20	3.30
Egypt	3.01	2.84	2.52	3.09	2.40	2.60	3.45	2.98
Bushman	4.05	3.24	3.55	3.19	3.50	2.84	3.61	3.72
Andaman Is	2.45	3.01	2.51	3.66	2.36	2.96	2.39	3.01
Ainu	3.52	3.54	2.58	3.08	2.65	2.83	2.68	3.49
Buriat	3.70	3.65	3.46	3.29	3.52	3.32	3.90	3.51
Eskimo	3.31	3.62	3.31	3.29	3.00	3.17	3.26	3.93
Anyang	3.05	–	2.69	–	2.62	–	2.97	–

TABLE B-2. Continued.
Standard Deviations of Measurements

	MI Alveolus Radius AVR	
	Male	*Female*
Norse	4.31	3.84
Zalavár	3.59	4.56
Berg	4.44	4.17
Teita	4.54	4.00
Dogon	3.86	4.08
Zulu	4.65	4.23
Australia	3.70	3.39
Tasmania	4.69	4.78
Tolai	4.10	3.77
Hawaii	4.35	3.18
Easter I	4.47	3.90
Moriori	3.06	3.36
Arikara	3.56	3.49
Santa Cruz	3.88	3.34
Peru	3.85	3.66
N Japan	4.88	3.49
S Japan	4.55	3.57
Hainan	4.07	3.60
Atayal	4.58	3.35
Philippines	3.82	—
Guam	3.77	3.22
Egypt	2.97	3.37
Bushman	3.82	3.82
Andaman Is	3.50	3.71
Ainu	3.34	4.68
Buriat	4.61	3.81
Eskimo	3.76	4.70
Anyang	3.47	—

TABLE B-2. Continued.
Standard Deviations of Measurements

	Bregma Radius BRR		Lambda Radius LAR		Opisthon Radius OSR		Basion Radius BAR	
	Male	*Female*	*Male*	*Female*	*Male*	*Female*	*Male*	*Female*
Norse	–	–	–	–	–	–	–	–
Zalavár	3.67	3.92	4.37	3.98	3.58	2.75	4.07	3.01
Berg	3.39	3.35	5.67	4.92	4.61	3.59	3.39	3.29
Teita	–	–	–	–	–	–	–	–
Dogon	–	–	–	–	–	–	–	–
Zulu	4.34	4.39	4.78	4.42	3.48	3.04	3.69	1.95
Australia	3.81	3.67	3.77	4.19	2.81	2.73	3.14	2.91
Tasmania	3.29	4.20	3.89	4.08	2.76	3.00	2.96	2.34
Tolai	3.80	3.01	4.64	3.54	2.67	3.17	2.74	2.42
Hawaii	4.29	4.17	4.76	4.59	2.87	2.90	2.60	2.21
Easter I	3.36	3.28	5.31	4.41	2.89	2.96	2.90	2.21
Moriori	3.66	4.21	3.86	4.30	2.77	2.61	3.01	2.51
Arikara	3.98	3.68	5.29	4.99	3.30	4.50	3.20	3.15
Santa Cruz	4.25	3.53	4.40	4.16	2.89	2.27	2.94	5.66
Peru	3.96	3.50	4.17	4.54	3.26	2.53	2.71	2.29
N Japan	5.24	4.36	4.64	4.88	3.01	2.90	3.07	2.99
S Japan	3.33	3.40	4.20	3.99	3.21	2.22	3.04	2.69
Hainan	3.15	3.14	4.98	4.22	3.32	2.93	2.87	2.82
Atayal	2.92	4.43	4.42	3.71	3.26	3.30	2.44	2.33
Philippines	4.68	–	5.22	–	2.96	–	2.79	–
Guam	3.19	4.13	5.28	4.44	2.72	2.62	2.85	2.18
Egypt	–	–	–	–	–	–	–	–
Bushman	3.84	4.07	4.31	4.37	3.12	2.89	2.77	2.57
Andaman Is	3.74	3.26	3.45	4.05	3.40	1.99	2.95	3.24
Ainu	3.31	3.69	3.93	3.98	2.59	2.84	2.67	2.62
Buriat	–	–	–	–	–	–	–	–
Eskimo	–	–	–	–	–	–	–	–
Anyang	4.21	–	4.14	–	3.20	–	2.72	–

Appendix C
Angles: Group Means

DEFINITIONS

Angles have not been considered in this study; however, group means and standard deviations are given here in tables C-1 and C-2. These are comparable to tables in my 1973 report, but with added populations and with a few differences due to changes in the composition of some samples.

Definitions and descriptions are given in appendix B of the 1973 report. A few new angles appear here, most of which are not available for some groups on which the requisite radial measurements were not taken. These angles are specified and defined herewith.

Bregma angle (basion-nasion)   BRA

The angle at bregma whose sides are basion-bregma height and nasion-bregma chord (the opposite side being basion-nasion).
This supplies the third angle in the triangle nasion-bregma-basion, complementing NBA and BBA, already defined.

Radio-frontal angle (nasion-bregma)   RFA

The angle at the transmeatal axis of which the opposite side is the frontal chord (FRC).
Computed from the radii to nasion and bregma and the frontal chord. It is meant as an angular measure of the sagittal span of the frontal bone as compared to that of the parietal and occipital bones.

Radio-parietal angle (bregma-lambda)   RPA

The angle at the transmeatal axis of which the opposite side is the parietal chord (PAC).
Computed from the radii to bregma and lambda and parietal chord, as a measure of the relative sagittal span of the parietal bones.

Radio-occipital angle (lambda-opisthion)   ROA

Thee angle at the transmeatal axis of which the opposite side is the occipital chord (OCC).
Computed from the radii to lambda and opisthion and the occipital chord, as a measure of the relative sagittal span of the occipital bone.

Basal angle (prosthion-opisthion)   BSA

The angle at the basion between the basion-prosthion and basion-opisthion (FOL) distances.
A measure of the flexion, not of the base itself but of the post-basion part. Computed as 360 degrees less the combined angles at basion involving radii and distances to prosthion, basion, and opisthion.

Sub-bregma angle   SBA

The angle at bregma of the triangle nasion-bregma-lambda.
Computed from the triangles used for RFA and RPA above.

Sub-lambda angle   SLA

The angle at lambda of the triangle bregma-lambda-opisthion.
Computed from the triangles used for RPA and ROA above.

Trans-basal angle   TBA

The angle at basion subtended by the transverse axis.
A measure of elevation of basion relative to the skull base. Computed from the basion radius and the auricular breadth (AUB), the latter as an approximation to the transmeatal axis in breadth and location.

TABLE C-1
Means of Angles

	Number of Crania		Nasion Angle (ba-pr) NAA		Prosth Angle (ba-na) PRA		Basion Angle (na-pr) BAA	
	Male	Female	Male	Female	Male	Female	Male	Female
Norse	55	55	66.09	67.69	73.53	73.18	40.56	39.20
Zalavár	53	45	66.47	66.71	73.25	74.20	40.36	39.11
Berg	56	53	65.61	67.09	73.11	72.21	41.25	40.62
Teita	33	50	71.33	71.44	71.06	71.78	37.67	36.84
Dogon	47	52	72.26	72.29	69.74	70.13	37.96	37.58
Zulu	55	46	71.13	72.35	70.40	69.91	38.53	37.70
Australia	52	49	74.77	75.84	68.90	68.08	36.33	36.08
Tasmania	45	42	75.20	75.69	69.09	69.33	35.78	34.95
Tolai	56	54	76.18	76.74	67.09	66.39	36.82	36.93
Hawaii	51	49	68.92	70.51	73.22	72.67	37.82	36.84
Easter I	49	37	67.88	69.70	75.55	75.41	36.55	35.00
Moriori	57	51	67.32	68.00	71.04	72.04	41.68	39.98
Arikara	42	27	65.98	67.63	72.33	71.44	41.62	41.00
Santa Cruz	51	51	70.78	71.98	68.12	67.88	41.08	40.20
Peru	55	55	67.78	67.82	70.53	70.73	41.67	41.44
N Japan	55	32	67.02	67.16	71.51	71.78	41.55	41.19
S Japan	50	41	67.88	68.80	72.06	70.66	40.08	40.49
Hainan	45	38	66.98	68.58	71.33	70.82	41.51	40.61
Atayal	29	18	67.24	68.72	73.24	73.28	39.52	37.94
Philippines	50	–	69.60	–	70.68	–	39.76	–
Guam	30	27	67.57	67.22	72.83	73.19	39.57	39.59
Egypt	58	53	65.90	66.11	73.71	73.92	40.29	39.96
Bushman	41	49	71.15	71.06	73.39	73.08	35.54	35.76
Andaman Is	35	35	70.09	73.06	72.00	70.43	37.83	36.51
Ainu	48	38	69.73	69.00	73.04	73.29	37.35	37.89
Buriat	55	54	66.09	67.09	70.35	70.39	43.56	42.50
Eskimo	53	55	67.43	69.76	72.58	71.02	40.08	39.25
Anyang	42	–	66.64	–	72.64	–	40.76	–

TABLE C-1. Continued.
Means of Angles

	Nasion Angle (ba-br) NBA		Basion Angle (na-br) BBA		Bregma Angle (ba-na) BRA		Zygomaxill Angle SSA	
	Male	Female	Male	Female	Male	Female	Male	Female
Norse	75.38	75.53	56.20	56.07	48.38	48.35	127.93	127.84
Zalavár	77.96	78.11	54.81	54.76	47.30	47.18	127.19	128.67
Berg	76.50	77.13	56.05	56.36	47.41	46.66	128.14	128.00
Teita	75.30	76.36	54.64	55.10	49.97	48.58	131.91	132.98
Dogon	78.28	79.21	54.79	54.13	47.00	46.63	132.13	131.44
Zulu	77.25	76.83	54.60	55.80	48.11	47.26	127.09	128.74
Australia	74.33	75.22	56.23	55.96	49.38	48.84	127.75	126.18
Tasmania	77.67	77.93	54.76	55.05	47.53	47.10	120.40	119.93
Tolai	79.79	79.61	52.48	52.76	47.77	47.63	122.89	122.93
Hawaii	79.55	79.76	53.53	53.27	47.00	46.98	126.65	126.67
Easter I	79.02	79.70	52.06	51.86	48.96	48.57	124.20	125.65
Moriori	76.26	77.78	54.82	53.41	49.00	48.78	120.65	121.53
Arikara	77.86	77.19	53.31	54.30	48.95	48.44	125.93	126.93
Santa Cruz	76.90	77.49	55.92	55.67	47.22	46.88	127.14	125.82
Peru	78.49	79.04	55.45	55.64	46.11	45.35	129.98	129.13
N Japan	79.84	80.28	53.29	53.13	46.96	46.66	129.51	127.50
S Japan	80.98	80.59	52.38	53.32	46.62	46.05	128.92	129.37
Hainan	81.60	80.89	52.33	54.03	46.02	45.16	131.04	131.84
Atayal	79.97	81.11	53.66	53.11	46.24	45.83	132.66	130.67
Philippines	79.86	–	54.12	–	45.96	–	130.74	–
Guam	80.70	81.07	53.07	52.89	46.10	46.22	132.00	132.96
Egypt	77.45	76.96	54.81	55.85	47.84	47.19	125.34	125.72
Bushman	73.51	74.45	58.61	57.92	47.78	47.73	134.22	131.86
Andaman Is	80.00	80.31	54.29	54.11	45.66	45.54	125.49	126.80
Ainu	78.38	78.66	52.67	53.58	48.96	47.74	130.98	130.16
Buriat	75.76	75.63	56.11	56.93	48.07	47.48	139.00	137.52
Eskimo	78.70	78.38	52.72	53.96	48.66	47.65	135.55	135.24
Anyang	81.19	–	53.14	–	45.60	–	132.14	–

TABLE C-1. Continued.
Means of Angles

	Nasio-Front Angle NFA		Dacryal Angle DKA		Naso-Dacryal Angle NDA		Simotic Angle SIA	
	Male	Female	Male	Female	Male	Female	Male	Female
Norse	138.45	139.20	148.38	147.33	84.55	86.56	93.24	98.98
Zalavár	139.02	141.67	150.96	151.49	84.36	87.49	93.34	101.20
Berg	139.82	141.17	149.89	149.92	89.73	92.21	92.04	99.13
Teita	139.06	140.34	145.88	148.00	96.94	103.36	133.06	142.28
Dogon	143.66	143.67	151.36	151.13	100.40	101.92	121.30	126.02
Zulu	141.51	142.70	149.96	149.87	100.91	103.09	115.55	122.28
Australia	142.15	141.06	151.62	150.20	86.56	91.84	104.19	112.04
Tasmania	142.76	141.52	151.56	150.60	92.13	91.55	102.62	107.88
Tolai	143.45	144.41	152.43	151.72	95.16	99.67	102.57	112.96
Hawaii	144.35	145.35	152.84	153.24	97.00	101.14	104.25	115.53
Easter I	140.41	142.78	149.27	150.41	96.45	101.92	100.90	115.05
Moriori	140.53	141.86	148.39	148.37	90.84	94.57	97.35	102.80
Arikara	141.05	142.11	150.40	149.59	89.79	93.74	91.05	103.63
Santa Cruz	142.41	142.18	150.82	148.63	91.94	98.24	95.47	102.47
Peru	143.36	145.15	153.09	153.47	91.04	91.27	92.25	98.51
N Japan	147.35	146.50	155.33	152.25	108.44	106.91	108.25	124.16
S Japan	144.62	146.27	151.98	152.73	107.16	110.07	110.82	123.05
Hainan	144.71	145.92	152.24	152.84	105.60	106.26	109.02	120.11
Atayal	147.28	145.39	155.07	152.22	105.48	103.67	108.14	117.61
Philippines	144.60	–	152.84	–	106.24	–	109.22	–
Guam	142.37	144.48	152.40	152.22	97.23	104.15	111.10	117.22
Egypt	137.41	138.98	146.00	145.19	83.02	85.40	95.10	104.09
Bushman	143.20	143.65	150.46	149.53	108.90	111.65	140.93	141.55
Andaman Is	142.43	143.17	148.06	149.14	95.49	99.51	123.86	129.14
Ainu	144.04	143.63	152.44	151.05	93.69	96.45	101.42	111.79
Buriat	146.78	146.69	158.13	157.00	101.35	101.46	111.76	119.44
Eskimo	146.62	146.45	155.57	156.69	89.06	91.91	98.57	112.09
Anyang	147.43	–	154.83	–	110.45	–	118.10	–

TABLE C-1. Continued.
Means of Angles

	Frontal Angle FRA		Parietal Angle PAA		Occipital Angle OCA	
	Male	Female	Male	Female	Male	Female
Norse	131.78	128.93	133.16	134.07	114.93	115.55
Zalavár	128.70	126.80	132.83	133.62	116.36	117.00
Berg	127.68	126.40	132.59	132.15	117.16	116.96
Teita	127.45	125.44	135.33	132.84	116.73	119.10
Dogon	127.55	127.23	133.74	134.37	126.17	127.65
Zulu	126.33	125.33	134.47	134.85	121.69	120.02
Australia	131.12	128.33	135.37	135.41	115.06	114.65
Tasmania	130.76	128.43	133.71	134.19	116.58	117.67
Tolai	132.14	130.43	132.14	131.76	116.29	118.33
Hawaii	133.80	131.53	132.06	133.96	124.90	126.35
Easter I	130.35	127.46	133.88	134.14	118.00	117.78
Moriori	137.56	134.24	134.89	133.76	121.60	123.69
Arikara	137.12	131.78	132.02	133.00	119.79	119.41
Santa Cruz	134.33	132.18	135.92	134.61	115.18	114.84
Peru	134.20	131.35	132.60	133.13	116.53	116.56
N Japan	129.98	127.97	134.45	136.09	120.15	121.47
S Japan	129.28	127.68	133.54	133.46	121.10	119.90
Hainan	131.36	129.32	131.33	131.76	122.04	123.58
Atayal	127.34	126.67	132.86	132.00	120.48	121.17
Philippines	131.14	—	132.10	—	124.08	—
Guam	129.33	126.93	132.33	132.85	120.03	122.07
Egypt	130.59	128.30	131.91	133.11	121.38	121.36
Bushman	124.29	122.73	136.10	136.39	114.37	114.71
Andaman Is	129.80	129.51	130.06	131.49	123.83	126.26
Ainu	128.35	127.21	135.71	135.05	120.13	120.71
Buriat	131.40	129.52	135.05	135.37	113.84	117.04
Eskimo	129.58	127.93	134.47	133.82	117.74	119.75
Anyang	130.48	—	133.43	—	121.79	—

TABLE C-1. Continued.
Means of Angles

	Number of Crania		Radio-Front Angle RFA		Radio-Pariet Angle RPA		Radio-Occip Angle ROA	
	Male	Female	Male	Female	Male	Female	Male	Female
Norse	–	–	–	–	–	–	–	–
Zalavár	53	45	62.40	62.07	61.38	60.80	65.49	66.09
Berg	56	53	61.46	61.43	59.14	58.60	66.29	66.57
Teita	–	–	–	–	–	–	–	–
Dogon	–	–	–	–	–	–	–	–
Zulu	55	46	62.27	63.24	60.65	60.39	60.55	61.00
Australia	52	49	63.60	62.94	64.65	63.41	62.94	65.88
Tasmania	42	34	60.88	61.38	62.14	62.38	62.76	64.03
Tolai	56	54	59.20	59.22	61.93	62.83	65.89	66.78
Hawaii	51	49	61.10	60.98	55.75	54.59	65.69	67.55
Easter I	48	37	58.98	58.97	57.60	57.22	65.15	66.57
Moriori	57	51	61.84	60.39	55.96	56.14	63.25	64.78
Arikara	42	27	60.07	60.70	58.81	58.07	68.45	66.74
Santa Cruz	51	51	62.78	63.14	56.37	56.90	66.57	67.29
Peru	55	55	62.35	62.49	57.85	57.18	65.71	66.24
N Japan	55	32	60.80	60.91	58.45	58.34	65.40	67.41
S Japan	50	41	59.90	60.63	58.30	59.00	65.70	65.80
Hainan	45	38	59.93	61.08	58.73	58.03	64.82	64.53
Atayal	29	18	60.93	60.39	59.66	60.06	62.24	65.22
Philippines	50	–	61.42	–	59.06	–	67.06	–
Guam	30	27	62.07	61.93	58.70	57.85	67.60	66.19
Egypt	–	–	–	–	–	–	–	–
Bushman	41	49	65.27	65.10	62.29	61.35	60.15	62.16
Andaman Is	24	16	61.92	60.94	58.08	57.50	62.08	63.44
Ainu	48	38	60.73	61.24	58.52	58.42	60.65	62.66
Buriat	–	–	–	–	–	–	–	–
Eskimo	–	–	–	–	–	–	–	–
Anyang	42	–	61.29	–	58.40	–	65.86	–

TABLE C-1. Continued.
Means of Angles

	Basal Angle (pr-os) BSA		Sub-Bregma Angle SBA		Sub-Lambda Angle SLA		Trans-Basal Angle TBA	
	Male	Female	Male	Female	Male	Female	Male	Female
Norse	–	–	–	–	–	–	–	–
Zalavár	162.19	160.60	101.60	101.82	88.51	88.24	150.92	152.36
Berg	159.91	159.15	101.79	101.70	91.61	90.36	157.30	158.36
Teita	–	–	–	–	–	–	–	–
Dogon	–	–	–	–	–	–	–	–
Zulu	170.05	167.24	104.67	104.15	85.29	84.83	148.75	151.43
Australia	165.79	164.14	103.40	104.22	85.81	85.55	151.40	151.90
Tasmania	168.02	167.15	101.40	101.53	87.48	86.62	154.50	153.82
Tolai	169.79	163.76	101.66	102.11	87.18	85.57	150.71	153.02
Hawaii	172.49	172.96	102.67	103.69	90.39	90.16	150.61	150.51
Easter I	172.46	170.35	102.54	102.24	91.92	92.24	150.42	149.76
Moriori	166.68	164.84	107.81	106.86	86.00	87.71	153.28	152.65
Arikara	165.10	164.74	103.62	103.22	91.71	90.89	152.17	154.67
Santa Cruz	157.06	160.43	105.47	105.49	89.08	87.78	154.84	152.33
Peru	162.25	161.27	102.98	102.80	87.25	87.09	154.84	155.80
N Japan	165.29	164.00	103.05	102.97	88.25	88.72	149.98	149.88
S Japan	166.56	162.39	102.52	101.66	88.56	88.10	150.52	151.41
Hainan	168.96	165.03	100.69	100.03	90.56	89.42	148.89	150.84
Atayal	165.76	165.33	100.76	99.39	90.14	90.78	151.48	151.39
Philippines	163.94	–	100.98	–	89.42	–	151.08	–
Guam	168.90	167.85	100.87	101.33	90.80	90.37	145.47	145.52
Egypt	–	–	–	–	–	–	–	–
Bushman	164.88	166.22	103.61	104.31	86.05	85.06	153.98	151.90
Andaman Is	169.17	167.44	101.38	101.25	88.25	88.06	152.08	154.06
Ainu	172.85	170.39	105.77	104.26	86.81	86.61	148.69	150.58
Buriat	–	–	–	–	–	–	–	–
Eskimo	–	–	–	–	–	–	–	–
Anyang	166.14	–	100.60	–	90.17	–	148.31	–

TABLE C-2
Standard Deviations of Angles

	Nasion Angle (ba-pr) NAA		Prosth Angle (ba-na) PRA		Basion Angle (na-pr) BAA		Nasion Angle (ba-br) NBA	
	Male	*Female*	*Male*	*Female*	*Male*	*Female*	*Male*	*Female*
Norse	3.50	3.57	2.55	3.68	2.63	3.02	3.06	2.57
Zalavár	3.50	4.16	3.66	3.49	2.96	2.29	3.07	3.28
Berg, Austria	4.18	4.24	2.85	3.72	2.93	3.06	3.28	3.78
Teita, E Africa	3.94	3.52	3.61	3.48	2.26	2.56	2.99	2.45
Dogon, W Africa	3.36	3.36	3.31	3.02	2.22	1.99	2.53	2.27
Zulu, S Africa	4.05	3.69	3.20	3.45	2.78	2.22	3.03	2.56
S. Australia	3.24	3.90	3.06	3.50	2.26	2.41	3.19	2.38
Tasmania	4.45	4.02	3.86	3.78	2.81	2.39	2.77	3.26
Tolai, N Britain	3.34	3.04	2.94	2.88	1.97	2.01	2.40	2.26
Mokapu, Hawaii	3.17	2.48	2.91	2.38	2.14	2.52	2.85	2.04
Easter I	3.23	2.48	3.25	2.69	2.19	1.93	2.43	2.09
Moriori, Chatham	2.68	2.77	2.71	2.37	2.48	2.31	2.66	2.61
Arikara	2.90	3.05	2.78	3.81	2.16	2.50	2.15	3.44
Santa Cruz I	3.85	3.07	2.67	2.76	2.70	1.93	2.73	1.92
Peru, Yauyos	2.71	3.10	2.31	2.98	2.27	2.27	3.35	2.45
N Japan	3.27	3.55	2.71	3.03	2.52	2.36	3.38	2.79
S Japan	2.78	2.81	2.51	2.92	2.04	2.56	2.66	2.69
Hainan Chinese	4.15	3.58	3.40	3.54	2.52	2.55	2.66	2.58
Atayal, Taiwan	4.30	3.53	3.89	2.97	2.56	1.98	2.20	1.97
Philippines	2.85	–	2.94	–	2.46	–	2.93	–
Guam, Marianas	3.58	2.93	2.96	2.92	2.33	2.04	2.23	2.59
Egypt	3.10	3.31	2.75	3.05	2.18	2.17	2.88	2.83
Bushman, S Afr	3.04	4.10	3.69	3.50	2.80	2.55	2.37	2.72
Andaman Is	2.93	4.01	3.03	3.93	2.38	1.62	2.51	2.67
Ainu	3.23	3.65	3.23	3.35	1.99	2.57	2.58	2.34
Buriat, Siberia	3.62	3.12	3.35	3.05	2.90	2.79	3.46	3.09
Eskimo, G'nland	3.52	2.99	3.15	2.71	2.43	2.14	2.93	2.24
Anyang, Shang Dy	3.10	–	3.63	–	2.39	–	2.74	–

TABLE C-2. Continued.
Standard Deviations of Angles

	Basion Angle (na-br) BBA		Bregma Angle (ba-na) BRA		Zygomaxill Angle SSA		Nasio-Front Angle NFA	
	Male	*Female*	*Male*	*Female*	*Male*	*Female*	*Male*	*Female*
Norse	2.68	2.59	2.42	2.02	4.86	4.71	4.04	4.20
Zalavár	2.73	2.53	2.10	2.40	5.37	4.27	4.41	4.57
Berg, Austria	3.08	3.30	2.27	2.11	5.31	5.63	4.41	4.79
Teita, E Africa	2.57	2.18	2.24	2.07	5.54	5.89	4.42	5.05
Dogon, W Africa	2.25	2.17	2.15	1.94	6.21	5.48	4.84	3.95
Zulu, S Africa	2.64	2.37	2.54	2.08	4.66	6.05	3.89	4.07
S. Australia	2.01	2.27	2.61	1.60	4.29	5.18	4.78	3.87
Tasmania	2.83	2.80	1.93	1.83	6.61	5.69	4.30	4.48
Tolai, N Britain	1.99	1.99	1.78	1.77	4.28	4.37	3.61	3.70
Mokapu, Hawaii	2.23	2.05	1.83	2.08	4.14	5.31	4.34	4.01
Easter I	2.00	2.12	1.59	1.34	4.71	5.50	4.07	3.61
Moriori, Chatham	2.53	2.11	2.15	1.60	4.49	4.93	4.31	4.04
Arikara	1.94	3.35	1.77	1.87	4.38	5.28	3.94	4.69
Santa Cruz I	2.26	1.95	1.96	1.56	4.41	4.34	4.18	3.87
Peru, Yauyos	2.54	2.18	1.79	1.66	4.26	4.27	4.13	4.14
N Japan	2.45	2.99	2.67	1.70	5.21	3.84	4.68	4.52
S Japan	2.46	2.47	1.63	1.53	4.96	4.91	3.62	4.35
Hainan Chinese	1.92	2.44	2.08	1.91	5.82	6.56	4.37	4.43
Atayal, Taiwan	2.14	2.25	1.84	1.98	4.75	4.52	3.74	3.40
Philippines	2.29	–	2.03	–	5.11	–	4.09	–
Guam, Marianas	1.98	2.47	1.81	1.55	4.01	3.94	3.16	3.29
Egypt	2.86	2.50	2.04	2.13	5.10	4.30	4.12	3.65
Bushman, S Afr	2.63	2.77	2.47	1.62	5.18	4.81	4.46	4.68
Andaman Is	1.95	2.10	2.24	1.70	5.28	4.89	3.56	4.62
Ainu	2.55	2.10	2.01	1.94	6.01	4.92	3.93	4.06
Buriat, Siberia	3.28	2.38	1.94	2.18	4.70	4.24	4.76	3.24
Eskimo, G'nland	2.50	1.97	1.99	1.54	4.29	5.81	4.24	4.36
Anyang, Shang Dy	2.56	–	2.06	–	4.03	–	4.81	–

TABLE C-2. Continued.
Standard Deviations of Angles

	Dacryal Angle DKA		Naso-Dacryal Angle NDA		Simotic Angle SIA		Frontal Angle FRA	
	Male	Female	Male	Female	Male	Female	Male	Female
Norse	5.36	5.56	7.69	8.22	12.39	12.63	3.73	3.81
Zalavár	5.18	5.42	7.28	7.76	11.60	10.93	3.57	3.43
Berg, Austria	5.25	6.72	8.92	8.98	18.40	11.63	3.77	4.10
Teita, E Africa	5.54	6.03	10.44	8.79	14.77	14.57	3.05	3.43
Dogon, W Africa	5.66	5.26	10.33	9.22	16.36	11.57	4.02	3.57
Zulu, S Africa	5.21	5.72	10.03	9.43	13.32	15.93	4.34	3.88
S. Australia	4.88	4.26	8.52	8.20	12.88	12.56	3.64	3.24
Tasmania	4.46	4.89	10.90	9.59	17.88	13.79	4.53	3.70
Tolai, N Britain	4.82	5.65	11.00	7.75	16.49	14.30	3.37	3.49
Mokapu, Hawaii	4.75	5.14	7.73	7.66	12.77	17.93	3.59	3.10
Easter I	5.11	5.23	8.54	7.62	12.87	13.53	3.93	2.48
Moriori, Chatham	4.89	4.69	8.80	7.23	16.24	14.73	3.50	3.70
Arikara	5.14	5.97	7.50	9.80	15.19	14.46	4.04	3.34
Santa Cruz I	5.11	4.48	8.63	9.31	11.07	14.53	3.70	3.65
Peru, Yauyos	5.40	5.18	7.94	8.26	11.18	11.97	3.73	3.55
N Japan	5.96	5.14	10.44	10.34	20.38	15.14	4.08	3.81
S Japan	4.30	4.96	9.22	8.74	18.62	18.37	3.96	3.25
Hainan Chinese	5.22	5.89	9.45	8.58	14.95	17.66	4.03	3.17
Atayal, Taiwan	3.95	4.44	8.79	8.50	18.96	16.37	2.86	2.85
Philippines	4.82	–	8.86	–	17.71	–	3.44	–
Guam, Marianas	4.80	5.05	9.29	8.75	16.67	15.48	3.15	2.37
Egypt	6.71	5.20	7.68	7.52	12.57	11.17	4.22	3.72
Bushman, S Afr	5.95	6.00	10.43	9.02	18.60	19.24	4.00	3.58
Andaman Is	4.65	5.06	7.82	10.63	18.82	12.99	3.29	4.14
Ainu	5.13	4.78	9.29	9.06	17.01	16.44	4.18	3.21
Buriat, Siberia	6.00	4.17	7.72	10.39	13.27	16.88	3.79	2.83
Eskimo, G'nland	5.00	5.20	9.61	10.83	16.40	18.48	3.62	3.53
Anyang, Shang Dy	6.12	–	10.30	–	17.34	–	4.21	–

TABLE C-2. Continued.
Standard Deviations of Angles

	Parietal Angle PAA		Occipital Angle OCA	
	Male	Female	Male	Female
Norse	3.61	3.28	5.05	4.62
Zalavár	3.18	3.34	4.61	3.88
Berg, Austria	4.21	4.19	5.54	5.56
Teita, E Africa	3.61	3.93	5.26	4.12
Dogon, W Africa	4.33	4.46	5.55	6.98
Zulu, S Africa	3.87	3.24	6.33	5.25
S. Australia	3.16	2.99	4.22	4.06
Tasmania	3.29	3.37	5.04	4.78
Tolai, N Britain	3.89	3.06	4.13	4.20
Mokapu, Hawaii	3.56	3.76	4.30	5.36
Easter I	4.00	3.74	4.39	3.40
Moriori, Chatham	3.70	3.42	5.82	4.79
Arikara	3.82	4.07	5.63	5.49
Santa Cruz I	3.97	4.32	4.55	4.41
Peru, Yauyos	4.25	4.45	5.19	4.01
N Japan	3.82	3.77	4.36	4.32
S Japan	3.58	3.74	4.79	4.20
Hainan Chinese	3.98	3.69	4.75	5.09
Atayal, Taiwan	3.48	2.85	4.63	3.50
Philippines	3.82	–	5.42	–
Guam, Marianas	3.84	3.11	4.14	3.96
Egypt	3.38	3.69	4.15	4.69
Bushman, S Afr	3.61	4.65	4.38	4.52
Andaman Is	3.00	3.48	4.54	4.75
Ainu	3.86	3.36	4.20	3.63
Buriat, Siberia	4.11	4.50	5.29	4.61
Eskimo, G'nland	2.98	3.78	4.51	4.23
Anyang, Shang Dy	4.45	–	4.87	–

TABLE C-2. Continued.
Standard Deviations of Angles

	Radio-Front Angle RFA		Radio-Pariet Angle RPA		Radio-Occip Angle ROA		Basal Angle (pr-os) BSA	
	Male	*Female*	*Male*	*Female*	*Male*	*Female*	*Male*	*Female*
Norse	–	–	–	–	–	–	–	–
Zalavár	2.41	2.27	2.71	2.56	5.33	4.40	7.74	11.49
Berg, Austria	2.64	2.71	3.01	3.52	4.71	5.50	8.02	6.70
Teita, E Africa	–	–	–	–	–	–	–	–
Dogon, W Africa	–	–	–	–	–	–	–	–
Zulu, S Africa	2.58	2.41	2.74	3.38	5.11	5.12	6.78	6.63
S. Australia	2.05	2.14	2.74	3.27	4.22	4.90	6.53	7.63
Tasmania	2.48	2.45	2.32	2.40	3.82	5.47	10.22	8.96
Tolai, N Britain	1.99	1.90	2.74	2.59	4.50	4.19	4.82	6.97
Mokapu, Hawaii	2.12	2.15	3.03	3.10	3.99	4.44	6.22	6.06
Easter I	2.04	1.82	3.17	4.19	5.53	4.19	6.78	5.00
Moriori, Chatham	2.19	1.91	2.64	2.63	5.54	4.02	7.26	12.48
Arikara	1.83	2.30	2.44	2.81	4.61	5.89	6.26	9.15
Santa Cruz I	2.09	1.76	3.08	2.39	6.01	4.54	7.52	13.01
Peru, Yauyos	2.21	2.04	3.48	3.72	5.74	6.41	8.24	7.00
N Japan	2.39	2.66	3.23	2.92	5.11	4.61	6.24	8.25
S Japan	2.08	2.23	3.28	2.60	5.45	4.73	6.39	7.34
Hainan Chinese	1.88	2.19	2.78	3.48	4.17	4.93	5.83	7.18
Atayal, Taiwan	2.20	2.30	3.32	2.80	4.18	3.49	7.12	7.41
Philippines	1.98	–	3.34	–	4.78	–	7.35	–
Guam, Marianas	1.89	2.74	3.41	3.32	4.70	5.06	7.52	8.01
Egypt	–	–	–	–	–	–	–	–
Bushman, S Afr	2.62	2.57	2.81	3.45	6.12	4.41	9.55	7.39
Andaman Is	2.12	2.17	2.72	2.50	5.02	4.05	7.07	14.50
Ainu	2.23	2.01	2.48	2.20	4.26	5.33	6.99	6.56
Buriat, Siberia	–	–	–	–	–	–	–	–
Eskimo, G'nland	–	–	–	–	–	–	–	–
Anyang, Shang Dy	2.12	–	3.00	–	5.88	–	8.09	–

TABLE C-2. Continued.
Standard Deviations of Angles

	Sub-Bregma Angle SBA		Sub-Lambda Angle SLA		Trans-Basal Angle TBA	
	Male	Female	Male	Female	Male	Female
Norse	–	–	–	–	–	–
Zalavár	2.86	3.24	2.76	3.16	7.35	5.54
Berg, Austria	3.75	3.32	3.98	4.40	6.07	6.22
Teita, E Africa	–	–	–	–	–	–
Dogon, W Africa	–	–	–	–	–	–
Zulu, S Africa	2.99	3.30	3.09	3.13	6.61	3.83
S. Australia	2.84	2.43	3.38	2.83	5.54	5.55
Tasmania	2.84	3.18	2.90	2.90	5.64	4.78
Tolai, N Britain	3.25	2.55	2.52	3.08	4.74	4.56
Mokapu, Hawaii	2.72	3.58	3.11	2.43	4.43	3.96
Easter I	2.94	2.98	3.08	3.20	4.96	4.21
Moriori, Chatham	2.99	2.63	3.09	2.91	5.12	4.54
Arikara	3.15	3.66	3.10	4.81	5.30	5.87
Santa Cruz I	3.69	3.86	3.55	2.97	4.95	8.79
Peru, Yauyos	3.44	3.37	3.06	3.04	4.71	4.44
N Japan	4.12	2.63	3.61	3.06	5.10	5.40
S Japan	3.37	2.46	3.18	3.34	5.15	5.04
Hainan Chinese	3.67	3.38	2.73	2.96	5.03	5.25
Atayal, Taiwan	2.63	3.33	2.96	1.90	4.25	4.42
Philippines	3.92	–	3.07	–	4.92	–
Guam, Marianas	3.32	3.01	3.62	2.87	4.30	3.71
Egypt	–	–	–	–	–	–
Bushman, S Afr	3.31	2.44	3.99	3.08	5.51	4.97
Andaman Is	3.39	2.89	3.04	2.24	5.38	6.31
Ainu	2.42	2.11	2.28	2.87	4.42	4.76
Buriat, Siberia	–	–	–	–	–	–
Eskimo, G'nland	–	–	–	–	–	–
Anyang, Shang Dy	2.71	–	2.59	–	4.89	–

Appendix D
Q-Mode Factor Analysis on 18 Populations

TABLE D-1
Factor Pattern of 18 Populations

	Factor 1		Factor 2		Factor 3	
	Male	*Female*	*Male*	*Female*	*Male*	*Female*
Norse	0.48	0.41	0.57	-0.59	-0.15	-0.03
Zalavár	0.56	0.67	0.56	-0.56	-0.03	0.07
Berg	0.74	0.73	0.45	-0.49	-0.15	-0.05
Teita	-0.60	-0.58	0.34	-0.23	0.39	0.53
Dogon	-0.02	-0.08	0.56	-0.20	0.60	0.78
Zulu	-0.36	-0.32	0.50	-0.26	0.63	0.75
Australia	-0.76	-0.71	0.33	-0.49	-0.37	-0.30
Tasmania	-0.58	-0.54	0.29	-0.47	-0.37	-0.30
Tolai	-0.87	-0.82	-0.06	-0.00	-0.14	-0.16
Hawaii	-0.02	-0.15	-0.82	0.81	0.09	-0.10
Easter I	-0.54	-0.64	-0.55	0.49	0.18	-0.01
Moriori	-0.06	-0.14	-0.67	0.58	-0.45	-0.64
Arikara	0.25	0.33	-0.37	0.22	-0.58	-0.52
Santa Cruz	0.38	0.33	0.04	-0.21	-0.65	-0.59
Peru	0.77	0.83	0.22	-0.23	-0.19	-0.09
N Japan	0.49	0.60	-0.58	0.53	0.33	0.13
S Japan	0.36	0.40	-0.51	0.68	0.68	0.41
Hainan	0.56	0.44	-0.26	0.55	0.47	0.46

	Factor 4		Factor 5		Factor 6	
	Male	*Female*	*Male*	*Female*	*Male*	*Female*
Norse	-0.55	-0.54	-0.11	-0.04	0.13	0.26
Zalavár	-0.48	-0.30	0.22	-0.21	-0.03	0.01
Berg	-0.17	-0.15	0.14	0.08	-0.24	-0.18
Teita	-0.08	-0.07	-0.49	0.44	0.05	0.11
Dogon	0.34	0.19	-0.10	0.19	-0.02	-0.30
Zulu	0.04	-0.04	-0.08	0.04	0.05	0.15
Australia	0.12	0.17	0.07	0.02	0.14	0.21
Tasmania	0.20	0.26	0.54	-0.38	-0.17	-0.23
Tolai	0.22	0.30	0.14	-0.06	-0.03	0.01
Hawaii	-0.33	-0.34	0.17	-0.18	-0.09	-0.21
Easter I	-0.51	-0.43	0.02	-0.22	-0.09	0.06
Moriori	-0.16	-0.21	-0.29	0.15	0.23	-0.02
Arikara	0.19	-0.02	-0.39	0.68	-0.43	-0.09
Santa Cruz	0.45	0.49	-0.05	0.02	0.33	0.17
Peru	0.19	0.17	-0.06	-0.14	0.12	-0.12
N Japan	0.21	0.32	0.29	-0.09	0.24	0.30
S Japan	0.05	0.15	0.10	-0.10	0.17	0.30
Hainan	0.45	0.24	-0.06	-0.05	-0.30	-0.20

TABLE D-1. Continued.
Factor Pattern of 18 Populations

| | Factor 7 | | Factor 8 | | Factor 9 | |
	Male	Female	Male	Female	Male	Female
Norse	0.01	-0.22	0.07	-0.02	0.15	0.12
Zalavár	0.06	0.18	0.11	-0.06	0.04	0.09
Berg	0.13	0.26	-0.20	-0.07	-0.13	-0.17
Teita	0.21	-0.09	0.14	-0.23	-0.18	-0.12
Dogon	-0.35	-0.25	-0.17	0.24	0.01	0.16
Zulu	0.03	0.19	-0.33	0.37	0.05	-0.13
Australia	0.15	0.09	0.05	0.03	0.16	0.10
Tasmania	-0.02	0.24	-0.08	0.03	0.03	0.03
Tolai	-0.06	0.00	0.27	-0.22	0.02	0.15
Hawaii	-0.25	0.00	-0.16	0.20	-0.18	-0.17
Easter I	-0.03	-0.10	0.19	-0.18	-0.10	-0.13
Moriori	-0.21	-0.10	-0.23	0.24	0.21	0.23
Arikara	0.22	0.24	-0.08	-0.04	0.09	0.03
Santa Cruz	0.08	-0.29	-0.06	0.12	-0.30	-0.33
Peru	-0.33	-0.31	0.32	-0.06	0.01	0.09
N Japan	0.27	0.21	-0.06	0.13	0.11	0.08
S Japan	0.22	0.07	0.07	-0.10	0.03	0.08
Hainan	-0.05	-0.00	0.20	-0.27	0.09	-0.01

| | Factor 10 | | Factor 11 | | Factor 12 | |
	Male	Female	Male	Female	Male	Female
Norse	-0.15	0.20	0.08	-0.06	0.06	0.07
Zalavár	0.16	0.01	0.01	0.05	0.09	0.01
Berg	-0.08	-0.07	-0.02	0.09	-0.01	0.14
Teita	-0.07	-0.08	0.06	-0.08	0.00	0.05
Dogon	-0.15	-0.08	-0.04	0.04	0.08	0.10
Zulu	0.28	0.14	-0.01	0.02	-0.09	-0.15
Australia	-0.08	-0.08	-0.28	-0.06	0.01	-0.04
Tasmania	-0.06	0.02	0.20	-0.18	-0.11	-0.02
Tolai	0.12	0.17	0.08	0.30	0.19	0.06
Hawaii	0.02	0.08	-0.13	0.12	0.14	0.01
Easter I	-0.05	-0.21	-0.03	-0.02	-0.20	-0.04
Moriori	-0.02	0.04	0.15	-0.11	-0.02	0.06
Arikara	0.10	0.03	-0.03	0.02	0.03	-0.13
Santa Cruz	0.01	0.09	0.05	-0.01	0.00	0.06
Peru	0.15	-0.14	-0.08	0.07	-0.13	-0.22
N Japan	-0.07	-0.19	-0.11	-0.00	-0.02	0.13
S Japan	0.06	0.06	0.15	0.04	0.06	-0.07
Hainan	-0.10	0.22	0.04	-0.21	-0.02	0.02

TABLE D-2
Factor Scores of Measurements, 18 Populations

		Factor 1		Factor 2		Factor 3	
		Male	Female	Male	Female	Male	Female
Glab-Occip Length	(GOL)	-0.87	-0.84	0.49	-0.91	-0.22	-0.05
Nasio-Occip Length	(NOL)	-0.58	-0.56	0.51	-0.79	0.07	0.21
Bas-Nasion Length	(BNL)	-0.74	-0.71	1.02	0.90	0.82	-0.01
Bas-Bregma Height	(BBH)	0.24	0.10	-1.69	2.03	1.66	1.03
Max Cranial Breadth	(XCB)	2.40	2.13	-0.13	0.09	-0.64	-0.67
Max Frontal Breadth	(XFB)	1.97	1.94	1.03	-0.74	0.44	0.77
Bistephanic Breadth	(STB)	2.09	2.10	1.07	-0.61	1.27	1.37
Bizygomatic Breadth	(ZYB)	0.36	0.45	-0.95	0.38	-1.68	-1.49
Biauricular Breadth	(AUB)	1.68	1.57	-1.27	0.62	-2.09	-2.18
Min Cranial Breadth	(WCB)	1.54	1.75	-0.06	0.05	-0.13	-0.14
Biasterionic Breadth	(ASB)	1.13	1.16	0.54	-1.09	-1.20	-0.87
Bas-Prosth Length	(BPL)	-1.85	-1.88	-0.16	0.26	0.28	-0.01
Nas-Prosth Height	(NPH)	1.38	1.37	-0.84	1.11	0.08	-0.26
Nasal Height	(NLH)	1.15	1.27	-1.21	1.40	-0.20	-0.36
Orbit Height	(OBH)	0.97	0.99	-0.72	1.16	0.01	-0.61
Orbit Breadth	(OBB)	-0.75	-0.45	0.47	-0.54	-0.94	-0.74
Bijugal Breadth	(JUB)	-0.08	-0.10	-0.76	0.51	-0.61	-0.31
Nasal Breadth	(NLB)	-1.47	-1.26	0.44	-0.01	1.16	1.86
Palate Breadth	(MAB)	0.13	0.27	-0.19	0.17	-0.18	0.05
Mastoid Height	(MDH)	0.60	0.82	-0.23	0.03	0.58	0.31
Mastoid Breadth	(MDB)	-0.04	0.20	-0.41	-0.17	-0.61	-0.77
Bimaxillary Breadth	(ZMB)	0.10	0.42	-0.58	0.60	0.09	0.50
Zygomaxill Subtense	(SSS)	-0.67	-0.36	-0.43	0.05	-1.27	-1.47
Bifrontal Breadth	(FMB)	-1.03	-0.90	0.95	-1.13	-0.23	0.05
Nasio-Front Subtense	(NAS)	-0.16	-0.28	1.67	-1.72	-0.55	-0.31
Biorbital Breadth	(EKB)	-0.88	-0.68	0.53	-0.51	-0.02	0.21
Dacryon Subtense	(DKS)	-0.19	-0.03	0.99	-0.85	-0.14	-0.25
Interorbital Breadth	(DKB)	-0.21	-0.36	1.22	-0.75	1.19	1.59
Naso-Dacryal Subtense	(NDS)	-0.04	0.25	2.71	-2.85	-2.02	-0.84
Simotic Chord	(WNB)	0.04	-0.08	1.97	-1.57	0.14	0.99
Simotic Subtense	(SIS)	1.06	1.00	1.62	-2.05	-1.65	-1.34
Infer Malar Length	(IML)	-1.43	-1.69	0.60	-0.48	-0.47	-0.07
Max Malar Length	(XML)	-0.19	-0.58	-0.03	0.23	-0.14	-0.17
Malar Subtense	(MLS)	0.07	-0.32	-0.19	0.43	1.20	1.03
Cheek Height	(WMH)	1.25	1.20	-0.95	1.43	-0.15	-0.03
Supraorbital Projection	(SOS)	-0.28	-0.50	0.56	-0.95	-0.30	-0.36
Glabella Projection	(GLS)	-0.68	-0.85	-0.91	-0.09	-2.42	-2.76
Foramen Mag Length	(FOL)	0.63	0.62	0.53	-0.37	0.19	0.25
Frontal Chord	(FRC)	0.25	0.28	-0.10	0.18	0.37	0.75
Frontal Subtense	(FRS)	0.08	0.19	1.58	-0.87	2.32	2.25
Nas-Subtense Fraction	(FRF)	0.55	0.51	0.04	-0.44	-0.41	-0.15
Parietal Chord	(PAC)	-0.62	-0.52	0.88	-0.61	1.27	1.45
Parietal Subtense	(PAS)	0.22	-0.01	0.55	-0.34	0.77	0.74
Breg-Subtense Fraction	(PAF)	0.16	-0.05	1.40	-0.63	2.42	2.86
Occipital Chord	(OCC)	0.82	0.61	-0.92	0.83	0.71	0.31
Occipital Subtense	(OCS)	0.45	0.60	0.75	-1.16	-0.79	-0.76
Lam-Subtense Fraction	(OCF)	0.65	0.84	-0.51	0.81	0.83	0.62
Vertex Radius	(VRR)	0.60	0.39	-1.79	1.92	1.51	1.07
Nasion Radius	(NAR)	-0.86	-0.85	-0.67	0.40	-0.25	-0.56
Subspinale Radius	(SSR)	-1.65	-1.68	-0.55	0.29	-0.93	-1.26
Prosthion Radius	(PRR)	-1.75	-1.77	-0.22	0.23	-0.11	-0.28
Dacryon Radius	(DKR)	-0.68	-0.71	-1.27	1.24	0.50	-0.16
Zygoorbitale Radius	(ZOR)	-1.04	-1.15	-0.47	0.73	0.59	0.16
Frontomalare Radius	(FMR)	-0.68	-0.63	-1.64	1.61	0.14	-0.39
Ectoconchion Radius	(EKR)	-0.54	-0.66	-1.79	1.90	0.68	0.00
Zygomaxill Radius	(ZMR)	-1.18	-1.27	-0.28	0.43	0.04	-0.13
Ml Alveolus Radius	(AVR)	-1.45	-1.37	-0.16	0.10	-0.77	-0.65

TABLE D-2. Continued.
Factor Scores of Measurements, 18 Populations

		Factor 4		Factor 5		Factor 6	
		Male	*Female*	*Male*	*Female*	*Male*	*Female*
Glab-Occip Length	(GOL)	-2.00	-1.35	0.62	-1.36	1.97	1.87
Nasio-Occip Length	(NOL)	-2.02	-1.43	-0.29	-0.77	2.07	2.03
Bas-Nasion Length	(BNL)	-1.75	-2.19	-0.69	0.10	-0.46	0.33
Bas-Bregma Height	(BBH)	-0.54	-0.62	1.34	-1.76	-1.02	-1.08
Max Cranial Breadth	(XCB)	-0.34	-0.57	1.10	-0.23	-0.74	-1.99
Max Frontal Breadth	(XFB)	-0.70	-1.15	0.60	0.39	-1.04	-0.51
Bistephanic Breadth	(STB)	-1.12	-1.20	0.85	-0.33	-0.69	-0.61
Bizygomatic Breadth	(ZYB)	0.79	0.54	-0.17	1.22	-0.68	-0.73
Biauricular Breadth	(AUB)	-0.02	-0.16	-0.14	0.98	-1.61	-0.47
Min Cranial Breadth	(WCB)	1.76	2.00	1.44	-0.27	-0.01	0.98
Biasterionic Breadth	(ASB)	-0.45	0.27	1.12	-0.48	1.05	0.82
Bas-Prosth Length	(BPL)	0.64	0.64	0.25	-0.22	0.66	-0.19
Nas-Prosth Height	(NPH)	0.43	0.80	-1.93	1.54	0.75	1.50
Nasal Height	(NLH)	-0.44	-0.63	-1.59	0.87	-0.44	1.14
Orbit Height	(OBH)	0.87	0.81	-2.40	1.44	1.84	1.53
Orbit Breadth	(OBB)	0.16	-0.16	0.06	0.32	0.66	-0.10
Bijugal Breadth	(JUB)	1.19	0.28	-1.03	1.93	-0.49	-0.86
Nasal Breadth	(NLB)	1.60	1.37	-0.24	0.55	-2.22	-1.96
Palate Breadth	(MAB)	2.07	2.49	0.88	-0.54	0.75	0.06
Mastoid Height	(MDH)	0.34	0.54	-0.66	-0.07	1.79	0.79
Mastoid Breadth	(MDB)	-0.54	-0.34	-0.06	-0.88	0.09	-0.18
Bimaxillary Breadth	(ZMB)	2.00	1.59	-1.68	1.75	0.30	-0.79
Zygomaxill Subtense	(SSS)	0.65	1.31	0.49	-0.61	-0.10	-0.70
Bifrontal Breadth	(FMB)	0.78	0.19	0.20	0.46	0.04	-0.68
Nasio-Front Subtense	(NAS)	-1.01	-0.71	-1.52	0.95	-0.32	-0.11
Biorbital Breadth	(EKB)	0.91	0.32	-0.05	0.77	0.22	-0.05
Dacryon Subtense	(DKS)	-0.15	0.02	-1.73	0.99	0.17	0.61
Interorbital Breadth	(DKB)	0.85	0.69	-0.59	0.90	-0.24	-0.12
Naso-Dacryal Subtense	(NDS)	-1.76	-1.66	-1.01	0.36	-0.44	-1.48
Simotic Chord	(WNB)	0.62	-0.08	-0.68	0.94	-0.89	-0.70
Simotic Subtense	(SIS)	-0.36	-1.06	0.29	-0.09	-1.27	-1.40
Infer Malar Length	(IML)	0.64	0.21	-0.30	0.75	-0.90	-1.24
Max Malar Length	(XML)	0.65	0.23	-0.45	0.32	-0.48	-0.35
Malar Subtense	(MLS)	1.79	1.18	-0.28	0.20	0.31	-0.50
Cheek Height	(WMH)	0.00	0.02	-1.04	-0.23	-0.48	-0.42
Supraorbital Projection	(SOS)	0.74	0.99	1.43	-1.91	-0.35	0.52
Glabella Projection	(GLS)	0.79	1.46	3.52	-2.97	0.87	-1.45
Foramen Mag Length	(FOL)	0.24	0.33	-0.03	0.27	-1.31	0.80
Frontal Chord	(FRC)	-1.24	-0.93	0.54	-0.75	0.81	-0.54
Frontal Subtense	(FRS)	-0.25	-0.22	1.44	-0.77	0.58	0.84
Nas-Subtense Fraction	(FRF)	0.21	0.20	-0.06	0.34	1.10	0.70
Parietal Chord	(PAC)	-0.31	0.36	1.33	-1.40	-0.12	0.76
Parietal Subtense	(PAS)	0.30	0.55	0.79	-0.41	-1.53	-0.65
Breg-Subtense Fraction	(PAF)	0.84	0.59	-0.24	0.55	0.15	0.17
Occipital Chord	(OCC)	0.09	0.31	-0.03	-1.75	2.17	0.53
Occipital Subtense	(OCS)	-0.09	0.53	0.30	-1.38	2.12	2.82
Lam-Subtense Fraction	(OCF)	-0.25	0.33	0.29	-1.13	1.17	-0.37
Vertex Radius	(VRR)	-0.74	-0.97	1.06	-1.97	-0.11	-1.97
Nasion Radius	(NAR)	-1.89	-2.06	-0.59	0.61	-1.23	-0.13
Subspinale Radius	(SSR)	-0.40	-0.18	0.21	0.09	-0.49	-0.04
Prosthion Radius	(PRR)	0.63	1.04	0.13	0.33	0.07	0.24
Dacryon Radius	(DKR)	-1.23	-1.36	-0.54	0.76	-0.77	0.65
Zygoorbitale Radius	(ZOR)	-1.21	-1.16	-0.20	0.25	-0.23	0.83
Frontomalare Radius	(FMR)	-0.85	-1.21	0.13	0.06	-0.93	-0.03
Ectoconchion Radius	(EKR)	-0.75	-0.99	0.09	0.17	-0.62	0.37
Zygomaxill Radius	(ZMR)	-0.53	-0.45	-0.18	0.61	-0.23	0.79
MI Alveolus Radius	(AVR)	0.40	0.68	-0.07	0.48	0.72	0.71

TABLE D-2. Continued.
Factor Scores of Measurements, 18 Populations

		Factor 7		Factor 8		Factor 9	
		Male	Female	Male	Female	Male	Female
Glab-Occip Length	(GOL)	0.28	-0.31	-0.31	0.81	1.52	0.51
Nasio-Occip Length	(NOL)	0.24	-0.74	-0.49	1.18	1.59	0.48
Bas-Nasion Length	(BNL)	0.10	-0.04	0.46	0.91	0.51	0.57
Bas-Bregma Height	(BBH)	-1.30	-0.04	0.70	0.07	0.08	0.20
Max Cranial Breadth	(XCB)	-0.68	0.22	-2.57	1.41	0.24	-0.48
Max Frontal Breadth	(XFB)	0.41	1.32	-1.33	0.44	-0.19	-0.67
Bistephanic Breadth	(STB)	-0.07	1.35	-1.52	0.82	-1.37	-1.19
Bizygomatic Breadth	(ZYB)	-0.03	0.25	0.30	-1.05	0.27	0.23
Biauricular Breadth	(AUB)	0.65	1.00	-0.07	-1.29	-0.06	-0.52
Min Cranial Breadth	(WCB)	2.21	2.70	-0.25	-0.18	-0.12	-0.65
Biasterionic Breadth	(ASB)	1.17	0.43	0.05	-0.07	-0.37	-0.11
Bas-Prosth Length	(BPL)	-0.84	-0.64	-0.30	1.13	-0.68	-0.15
Nas-Prosth Height	(NPH)	0.60	-0.30	-0.06	0.31	1.85	1.24
Nasal Height	(NLH)	0.76	0.37	-0.38	0.04	1.73	2.30
Orbit Height	(OBH)	-0.91	-1.84	-1.28	1.59	-0.31	0.42
Orbit Breadth	(OBB)	0.03	0.90	-1.99	2.13	1.22	1.33
Bijugal Breadth	(JUB)	0.17	0.26	-0.48	-0.05	0.96	-0.16
Nasal Breadth	(NLB)	-1.59	1.42	-1.08	1.06	0.94	0.75
Palate Breadth	(MAB)	0.56	0.77	-0.41	1.15	0.26	0.42
Mastoid Height	(MDH)	-0.93	-1.03	0.78	0.51	0.86	1.53
Mastoid Breadth	(MDB)	-1.96	-1.27	0.83	0.20	-2.35	-1.46
Bimaxillary Breadth	(ZMB)	0.36	-1.33	0.81	-0.72	-1.34	-0.14
Zygomaxill Subtense	(SSS)	-0.64	0.10	-0.67	0.68	0.56	0.97
Bifrontal Breadth	(FMB)	-0.33	0.73	-1.76	1.50	-0.61	-0.63
Nasio-Front Subtense	(NAS)	-0.12	-0.63	-0.20	0.25	-0.49	-0.54
Biorbital Breadth	(EKB)	0.02	1.10	-1.48	1.35	-0.03	-0.23
Dacryon Subtense	(DKS)	-0.07	-0.91	-0.45	0.63	-0.36	-0.08
Interorbital Breadth	(DKB)	-0.18	-0.71	-0.04	-0.79	-2.11	-1.80
Naso-Dacryal Subtense	(NDS)	-1.12	-1.06	0.77	-0.68	-1.00	0.73
Simotic Chord	(WNB)	-0.84	-0.39	0.98	-0.38	0.46	1.21
Simotic Subtense	(SIS)	-0.90	-0.59	1.61	-0.52	1.36	1.70
Infer Malar Length	(IML)	-1.41	-1.23	-0.02	-0.68	0.00	-1.14
Max Malar Length	(XML)	-0.06	-1.04	0.70	-0.70	0.63	-0.70
Malar Subtense	(MLS)	0.52	-1.05	0.14	0.00	-0.77	-1.59
Cheek Height	(WMH)	-1.29	-1.40	2.51	-1.95	-0.40	0.34
Supraorbital Projection	(SOS)	1.37	1.46	1.40	-1.90	-0.91	-0.02
Glabella Projection	(GLS)	-1.05	0.33	0.07	-0.15	0.49	0.54
Foramen Mag Length	(FOL)	1.55	1.44	-0.74	0.46	-0.40	-1.16
Frontal Chord	(FRC)	-1.56	-0.41	-0.82	0.96	-0.19	-1.15
Frontal Subtense	(FRS)	0.86	1.27	-0.40	-0.25	-1.26	-1.23
Nas-Subtense Fraction	(FRF)	0.49	-1.25	0.42	-0.65	-0.94	-1.50
Parietal Chord	(PAC)	0.35	0.82	1.33	-1.22	2.40	2.28
Parietal Subtense	(PAS)	-0.52	0.05	1.81	-2.42	1.51	0.96
Breg-Subtense Fraction	(PAF)	0.65	-0.68	0.72	-1.17	2.25	2.60
Occipital Chord	(OCC)	-1.26	-1.93	0.09	1.72	-0.15	0.26
Occipital Subtense	(OCS)	1.06	-1.17	2.64	-1.42	-0.66	-1.47
Lam-Subtense Fraction	(OCF)	0.03	-0.49	0.17	0.30	-1.00	-0.92
Vertex Radius	(VRR)	-2.86	-1.26	0.21	0.17	-0.26	-0.01
Nasion Radius	(NAR)	1.13	1.10	-0.35	-0.36	-0.28	0.07
Subspinale Radius	(SSR)	0.34	0.38	-0.13	-0.14	-0.51	-0.07
Prosthion Radius	(PRR)	0.03	0.16	-0.34	0.45	-0.36	-0.19
Dacryon Radius	(DKR)	1.20	1.03	-0.10	-0.37	-0.43	-0.42
Zygoorbitale Radius	(ZOR)	1.26	0.60	0.37	-0.69	-0.26	0.05
Frontomalare Radius	(FMR)	1.09	1.05	0.24	-0.99	-0.13	0.16
Ectoconchion Radius	(EKR)	1.18	0.82	0.54	-1.10	-0.66	-0.30
Zygomaxill Radius	(ZMR)	1.16	0.10	0.77	-1.21	-1.00	-0.90
MI Alveolus Radius	(AVR)	0.67	0.25	-0.48	0.89	0.24	-0.27

TABLE D-2. Continued.
Factor Scores of Measurements, 18 Populations

		Factor 10		Factor 11		Factor 12	
		Male	*Female*	*Male*	*Female*	*Male*	*Female*
Glab-Occip Length	(GOL)	-0.38	0.70	-0.54	-1.67	-1.28	-1.24
Nasio-Occip Length	(NOL)	0.10	1.25	-0.43	-1.43	-1.14	-1.52
Bas-Nasion Length	(BNL)	0.10	-1.08	-0.66	-0.47	-0.43	-0.07
Bas-Bregma Height	(BBH)	1.09	-0.83	-0.26	-0.12	0.54	-0.30
Max Cranial Breadth	(XCB)	-2.02	1.28	0.75	-0.28	1.06	1.46
Max Frontal Breadth	(XFB)	0.51	1.15	-0.33	1.37	0.89	-0.26
Bistephanic Breadth	(STB)	1.00	0.61	-0.09	0.87	0.38	0.01
Bizygomatic Breadth	(ZYB)	-0.45	-0.32	-0.76	-0.06	0.23	-1.15
Biauricular Breadth	(AUB)	-0.66	0.88	1.02	-0.49	0.23	-1.12
Min Cranial Breadth	(WCB)	1.87	0.95	-0.49	0.24	0.67	0.57
Biasterionic Breadth	(ASB)	-0.77	-0.33	0.13	0.92	-0.20	0.25
Bas-Prosth Length	(BPL)	0.67	0.79	-0.02	1.49	0.74	-0.84
Nas-Prosth Height	(NPH)	1.03	0.59	0.49	0.33	0.18	-0.16
Nasal Height	(NLH)	-0.22	0.77	0.21	-1.09	-1.42	0.64
Orbit Height	(OBH)	0.09	-2.17	-1.87	0.55	-0.61	-0.73
Orbit Breadth	(OBB)	0.24	1.08	0.15	-0.12	2.35	0.84
Bijugal Breadth	(JUB)	-0.74	0.32	-0.79	-1.53	-0.26	-1.15
Nasal Breadth	(NLB)	-0.28	-1.76	0.35	-0.38	-2.56	-1.24
Palate Breadth	(MAB)	0.94	0.05	-0.09	-0.52	-0.50	-0.92
Mastoid Height	(MDH)	-0.44	-0.67	-1.16	2.17	0.61	1.34
Mastoid Breadth	(MDB)	-0.74	-0.17	0.98	1.49	0.86	1.27
Bimaxillary Breadth	(ZMB)	0.51	-0.36	-1.09	-1.18	0.16	-0.81
Zygomaxill Subtense	(SSS)	2.18	-0.39	3.32	0.22	-1.17	0.20
Bifrontal Breadth	(FMB)	0.44	0.53	-0.25	0.42	0.10	0.04
Nasio-Front Subtense	(NAS)	0.65	0.08	1.65	-1.33	-0.41	0.70
Biorbital Breadth	(EKB)	-0.54	0.13	-0.17	0.02	0.53	0.81
Dacryon Subtense	(DKS)	-0.51	0.09	2.13	-1.15	-0.36	1.27
Interorbital Breadth	(DKB)	-1.27	-1.84	0.46	0.15	-1.83	1.81
Naso-Dacryal Subtense	(NDS)	-0.27	-0.71	-0.12	-0.26	0.34	0.68
Simotic Chord	(WNB)	0.20	-2.33	-2.51	0.94	0.01	-0.77
Simotic Subtense	(SIS)	1.73	-0.33	-1.93	1.51	-0.10	-1.74
Infer Malar Length	(IML)	-0.05	0.40	-0.75	0.72	0.36	-0.95
Max Malar Length	(XML)	-1.07	0.95	0.45	-0.22	0.45	0.68
Malar Subtense	(MLS)	-1.35	1.13	0.09	-0.79	-0.14	-0.82
Cheek Height	(WMH)	-0.93	1.18	0.51	-1.33	0.13	0.54
TSupraorbital Projection	(SOS)	-0.21	-0.06	0.18	-0.68	-1.48	0.34
Glabella Projection	(GLS)	-2.51	-1.87	-0.71	-2.03	-1.47	1.64
Foramen Mag Length	(FOL)	0.64	-1.20	-0.45	-1.28	-1.85	-0.83
Frontal Chord	(FRC)	-0.22	0.44	-1.50	-1.62	-0.30	-1.43
Frontal Subtense	(FRS)	-0.09	-1.90	-0.61	-0.74	-0.79	0.07
Nas-Subtense Fraction	(FRF)	-1.30	0.23	0.36	-1.40	1.12	1.32
Parietal Chord	(PAC)	0.28	0.84	0.36	0.27	0.44	-0.61
Parietal Subtense	(PAS)	0.86	1.16	0.51	1.02	1.23	-0.74
Breg-Subtense Fraction	(PAF)	-2.64	1.57	1.90	-0.88	1.25	1.72
Occipital Chord	(OCC)	1.23	-0.30	0.77	0.69	-0.05	0.48
Occipital Subtense	(OCS)	0.90	-0.60	1.24	0.87	-1.36	-2.09
Lam-Subtense Fraction	(OCF)	1.05	-0.57	0.27	1.72	0.51	0.50
Vertex Radius	(VRR)	0.62	0.87	0.87	-0.20	-0.42	-0.83
Nasion Radius	(NAR)	0.04	-0.58	-0.07	-0.04	-0.77	-0.11
Subspinale Radius	(SSR)	1.11	1.06	1.01	1.04	1.01	0.13
Prosthion Radius	(PRR)	1.34	1.49	-0.12	1.61	1.74	-0.43
Dacryon Radius	(DKR)	0.04	-0.47	0.11	0.20	-0.65	0.19
Zygoorbitale Radius	(ZOR)	-1.43	0.20	0.26	0.46	1.70	2.52
Frontomalare Radius	(FMR)	-0.46	-0.94	-1.10	0.60	-0.62	-0.54
Ectoconchion Radius	(EKR)	-0.15	-0.96	-0.68	0.61	-0.21	0.13
Zygomaxill Radius	(ZMR)	-0.37	0.33	-1.20	0.72	1.86	0.68
MI Alveolus Radius	(AVR)	0.63	1.14	0.25	0.05	0.68	0.54

Appendix E
Q-Mode Factor Analysis on 28 Populations

TABLE E-1
Factor Pattern of 28 Populations

	Factor 1		Factor 2		Factor 3	
	Male	*Female*	*Male*	*Female*	*Male*	*Female*
Norse	-0.06	0.16	0.61	0.59	-0.46	-0.31
Zalavár	0.05	0.44	0.71	0.69	-0.34	-0.19
Berg	0.30	0.52	0.68	0.63	-0.43	-0.29
Teita	-0.56	-0.57	0.00	0.10	0.52	0.53
Dogon	-0.09	-0.11	0.58	0.41	0.59	0.69
Zulu	-0.38	-0.33	0.31	0.24	0.65	0.66
Australia	-0.80	-0.84	-0.22	0.08	0.01	-0.27
Tasmania	-0.62	-0.68	-0.05	0.20	0.02	-0.24
Tolai	-0.65	-0.79	-0.47	-0.29	0.26	-0.01
Hawaii	0.39	0.16	-0.67	-0.80	0.03	0.08
Easter I	-0.17	-0.43	-0.67	-0.63	0.27	0.19
Moriori	0.10	0.04	-0.65	-0.73	-0.46	-0.48
Arikara	0.29	0.40	-0.32	-0.29	-0.59	-0.51
Santa Cruz	0.15	0.16	0.13	0.18	-0.60	-0.60
Peru	0.42	0.64	0.58	0.53	-0.43	-0.26
N Japan	0.81	0.72	-0.17	-0.19	0.17	0.19
S Japan	0.71	0.62	-0.09	-0.34	0.47	0.50
Hainan	0.79	0.64	0.20	-0.19	0.32	0.55
Atayal	0.63	0.46	0.42	0.34	0.35	0.44
Philippines	0.65	—	0.31	—	0.42	—
Guam	0.53	0.52	-0.54	-0.54	0.19	0.33
Egypt	-0.17	0.18	0.68	0.73	-0.10	0.03
Bushman	-0.24	-0.30	0.44	0.47	0.49	0.43
Andaman Is	0.04	-0.01	0.73	0.62	0.26	0.26
Ainu	0.27	0.45	-0.22	-0.22	0.04	0.15
Buriat	0.68	0.71	-0.22	-0.35	-0.23	-0.09
Eskimo	0.13	-0.02	-0.73	-0.77	0.06	0.05
Anyang	0.80	—	-0.17	—	0.42	—

TABLE E-1. Continued.
Factor Pattern of 28 Populations

	Factor 4		Factor 5		Factor 6	
	Male	*Female*	*Male*	*Female*	*Male*	*Female*
Norse	0.52	0.59	0.12	-0.14	0.13	-0.05
Zalavár	0.46	0.38	0.10	0.02	-0.14	0.18
Berg	0.11	0.13	0.32	0.21	-0.04	-0.09
Teita	0.16	0.15	0.04	0.19	0.55	-0.46
Dogon	-0.12	-0.09	-0.03	-0.17	0.12	-0.33
Zulu	0.16	0.34	0.15	0.24	0.13	-0.03
Australia	-0.25	-0.00	0.28	0.28	-0.01	0.09
Tasmania	-0.45	-0.21	0.21	0.13	-0.49	0.41
Tolai	-0.32	-0.32	-0.12	0.01	-0.11	0.03
Hawaii	0.30	0.15	-0.17	-0.32	-0.32	0.10
Easter I	0.44	0.22	-0.23	-0.33	-0.13	0.14
Moriori	0.07	0.03	-0.32	-0.28	-0.00	-0.10
Arikara	-0.34	-0.07	0.00	0.27	0.35	-0.52
Santa Cruz	-0.55	-0.45	0.11	0.23	0.05	0.09
Peru	-0.16	-0.23	-0.26	-0.19	0.02	0.05
N Japan	0.01	-0.23	0.10	0.12	-0.20	0.26
S Japan	0.26	-0.07	-0.12	-0.01	-0.04	0.20
Hainan	-0.25	-0.29	-0.20	-0.05	0.14	-0.00
Atayal	-0.16	-0.30	0.19	0.07	-0.09	0.22
Philippines	-0.38	–	-0.01	–	-0.13	–
Guam	-0.01	-0.10	0.09	0.15	0.19	-0.10
Egypt	0.50	0.34	-0.36	-0.44	-0.03	-0.03
Bushman	-0.01	0.09	0.43	0.46	0.01	0.22
Andaman Is	-0.22	-0.52	-0.40	-0.29	-0.03	-0.17
Ainu	0.37	0.53	0.59	0.13	-0.33	0.24
Buriat	-0.05	0.12	0.49	0.42	0.26	-0.20
Eskimo	0.27	0.30	0.17	0.15	0.29	0.05
Anyang	-0.06	–	-0.04	–	-0.03	–

TABLE E-1. Continued.
Factor Pattern of 28 Populations

	Factor 7		Factor 8		Factor 9	
	Male	*Female*	*Male*	*Female*	*Male*	*Female*
Norse	0.02	0.27	0.00	-0.02	0.14	0.07
Zalavár	0.13	-0.07	0.13	0.19	0.13	0.11
Berg	0.03	-0.10	0.24	0.26	-0.17	-0.21
Teita	0.07	0.18	-0.00	0.08	-0.09	0.04
Dogon	-0.44	-0.28	-0.06	-0.23	0.04	0.05
Zulu	-0.29	-0.17	-0.11	-0.25	-0.16	-0.04
Australia	0.03	0.01	-0.10	-0.08	0.29	0.20
Tasmania	0.05	-0.32	0.21	0.18	0.05	0.04
Tolai	0.10	0.08	0.03	0.07	0.20	0.17
Hawaii	-0.10	-0.17	0.16	0.06	-0.20	-0.33
Easter I	0.19	0.18	0.24	0.26	-0.06	-0.18
Moriori	-0.20	-0.10	-0.23	-0.17	-0.19	0.05
Arikara	-0.08	-0.06	0.29	0.07	-0.04	0.09
Santa Cruz	0.13	0.16	-0.41	-0.31	-0.10	-0.08
Peru	0.01	0.05	-0.15	-0.07	0.21	0.04
N Japan	0.20	0.15	-0.31	-0.32	-0.03	-0.05
S Japan	0.20	0.26	-0.23	-0.16	-0.06	0.11
Hainan	-0.01	0.03	0.16	0.13	0.11	0.05
Atayal	0.14	0.01	0.11	0.39	0.19	0.24
Philippines	-0.09	–	0.11	–	-0.08	–
Guam	-0.16	-0.14	0.09	0.09	0.31	0.18
Egypt	-0.01	0.17	-0.05	-0.09	0.16	0.13
Bushman	0.39	0.22	-0.05	-0.04	-0.24	-0.31
Andaman Is	0.11	-0.02	0.03	0.10	-0.06	-0.15
Ainu	-0.38	-0.44	-0.18	-0.14	0.12	0.12
Buriat	-0.03	0.01	0.14	0.14	-0.13	-0.18
Eskimo	0.29	0.34	-0.08	0.10	0.22	0.18
Anyang	0.03	–	0.02	–	0.14	–

TABLE E-1. Continued.
Factor Pattern of 28 Populations

	Factor 10		Factor 11		Factor 12	
	Male	*Female*	*Male*	*Female*	*Male*	*Female*
Norse	0.14	0.15	-0.05	-0.10	0.08	-0.02
Zalavár	-0.04	-0.05	0.03	-0.10	0.09	0.00
Berg	-0.01	-0.11	0.11	-0.01	-0.04	0.04
Teita	0.05	0.06	-0.16	0.11	0.01	-0.10
Dogon	0.14	0.03	0.08	0.01	-0.00	0.08
Zulu	-0.23	-0.06	0.10	-0.17	-0.09	0.04
Australia	-0.02	0.01	-0.02	0.08	0.02	0.00
Tasmania	0.01	0.00	0.05	-0.00	0.09	-0.01
Tolai	-0.03	-0.14	-0.00	-0.22	0.16	0.16
Hawaii	0.22	0.07	0.09	0.04	-0.06	0.16
Easter I	0.04	0.03	-0.13	0.13	-0.18	-0.14
Moriori	0.04	-0.04	-0.02	0.17	0.02	-0.11
Arikara	-0.26	-0.18	0.06	0.20	0.02	0.04
Santa Cruz	0.16	0.37	0.04	0.04	-0.06	0.10
Peru	0.08	0.09	-0.20	-0.12	-0.17	-0.12
N Japan	-0.19	-0.27	0.07	0.11	0.07	-0.08
S Japan	-0.16	-0.18	0.08	0.01	0.11	0.07
Hainan	-0.09	0.11	-0.08	-0.17	0.07	-0.00
Atayal	-0.16	-0.03	0.01	0.22	-0.32	0.04
Philippines	0.07	–	-0.06	–	0.20	–
Guam	0.27	0.33	0.24	-0.09	-0.05	-0.24
Egypt	-0.03	-0.02	0.04	0.12	0.18	0.08
Bushman	0.22	0.08	-0.05	0.17	-0.01	-0.08
Andaman Is	0.14	0.15	0.29	0.17	-0.03	0.18
Ainu	-0.02	0.16	-0.06	0.23	-0.02	0.10
Buriat	0.08	-0.03	-0.04	-0.12	0.15	0.11
Eskimo	0.02	0.18	0.23	0.03	0.02	0.26
Anyang	0.13	–	-0.25	–	0.07	–

TABLE E-2
Factor Scores of Measurements, 28 Populations

		Factor 1		Factor 2		Factor 3	
		Male	Female	Male	Female	Male	Female
Glab-Occip Length	(GOL)	-1.25	-1.05	-0.45	0.06	-0.38	-0.39
Nasio-Occip Length	(NOL)	-1.03	0.78	-0.22	0.15	-0.30	-0.20
Bas-Nasion Length	(BNL)	-0.22	-0.17	-1.23	-1.15	0.27	0.26
Bas-Bregma Height	(BBH)	1.48	0.98	-0.90	-1.27	1.34	1.60
Max Cranial Breadth	(XCB)	1.77	2.08	1.09	0.61	-1.54	-0.96
Max Frontal Breadth	(XFB)	1.07	1.68	1.56	1.12	-0.76	-0.08
Bistephanic Breadth	(STB)	1.22	1.85	2.05	1.42	0.00	0.57
Bizygomatic Breadth	(ZYB)	0.82	0.80	-1.37	-1.04	-1.46	-1.27
Biauricular Breadth	(AUB)	1.86	1.80	-0.86	-0.90	-2.24	-2.04
Min Cranial Breadth	(WCB)	1.74	1.84	0.69	0.31	-0.03	0.00
Biasterionic Breadth	(ASB)	0.51	0.88	0.59	0.85	-1.31	-1.08
Bas-Prosth Length	(BPL)	-1.32	-1.62	-0.97	-0.86	0.85	0.25
Nas-Prosth Height	(NPH)	1.19	1.42	-0.16	-0.60	-0.98	-0.56
Nasal Height	(NLH)	1.41	1.56	-0.48	-0.81	-0.93	-0.48
Orbit Height	(OBH)	0.84	1.17	-0.08	-0.54	-0.53	-0.31
Orbit Breadth	(OBB)	-0.92	-0.44	-0.50	-0.29	-0.53	-0.71
Bijugal Breadth	(JUB)	0.78	0.31	-1.09	-0.95	-0.12	-0.07
Nasal Breadth	(NLB)	-0.36	-0.92	0.13	0.20	2.21	2.01
Palate Breadth	(MAB)	0.41	0.31	-0.18	-0.08	0.04	0.07
Mastoid Height	(MDH)	0.49	0.54	0.37	0.51	0.13	-0.04
Mastoid Breadth	(MDB)	0.02	-0.06	-0.08	0.20	-0.28	-0.84
Bimaxillary Breadth	(ZMB)	0.84	0.60	-0.38	-0.23	0.50	0.63
Zygomaxill Subtense	(SSS)	-1.18	-0.86	0.04	0.44	-0.80	-1.27
Bifrontal Breadth	(FMB)	-1.13	-1.08	-0.16	0.19	0.18	-0.13
Nasio-Front Subtense	(NAS)	-1.56	-0.94	1.27	1.46	-0.75	-0.68
Biorbital Breadth	(EKB)	-0.60	-0.63	-0.35	-0.19	0.45	0.18
Dacryon Subtense	(DKS)	-1.13	-0.51	1.14	1.24	-0.09	-0.25
Interorbital Breadth	(DKB)	-0.34	-0.73	1.35	1.28	1.35	1.39
Naso-Dacryal Subtense	(NDS)	-2.24	-0.80	1.65	2.27	-2.28	-1.81
Simotic Chord	(WNB)	-0.82	-0.61	1.79	1.91	0.15	0.40
Simotic Subtense	(SIS)	-0.66	0.05	1.67	1.92	-2.09	-2.17
Infer Malar Length	(IML)	-1.33	-1.67	-0.37	-0.22	0.32	0.14
Max Malar Length	(XML)	0.04	-0.37	-0.49	-0.57	0.03	0.06
Malar Subtense	(MLS)	0.83	-0.05	0.36	0.02	1.65	1.52
Cheek Height	(WMH)	1.49	1.51	-0.34	-0.96	-0.56	0.08
Supraorbital Projection	(SOS)	-0.72	-1.01	0.63	0.93	0.20	-0.14
Glabella Projection	(GLS)	-0.68	-1.04	-0.73	-0.38	-1.20	-1.94
Foramen Mag Length	(FOL)	0.26	0.35	0.74	0.54	0.16	0.23
Frontal Chord	(FRC)	0.33	0.39	0.12	0.09	0.25	0.70
Frontal Subtense	(FRS)	0.13	0.10	1.57	1.25	2.31	2.23
Nas-Subtense Fraction	(FRF)	0.40	0.41	0.47	0.61	-0.24	-0.07
Parietal Chord	(PAC)	-0.52	-0.56	0.64	0.72	1.35	1.37
Parietal Subtense	(PAS)	0.12	-0.14	1.12	0.84	0.86	0.85
Breg-Subtense Fraction	(PAF)	0.22	-0.05	1.71	1.36	2.19	2.65
Occipital Chord	(OCC)	0.91	0.66	-0.01	-0.17	0.18	0.30
Occipital Subtense	(OCS)	-0.41	-0.11	0.60	0.97	-0.83	-1.02
Lam-Subtense Fraction	(OCF)	0.49	0.77	0.27	0.08	0.36	0.65
Vertex Radius	(VRR)	1.44	1.11	-0.60	-1.03	0.79	1.27
Nasion Radius	(NAR)	-0.66	-0.60	-1.17	-0.92	-0.37	-0.50
Subspinale Radius	(SSR)	-1.43	-1.63	-1.38	-1.08	-0.38	-1.04
Prosthion Radius	(PRR)	-1.24	-1.63	-1.16	-0.97	0.49	-0.09
Dacryon Radius	(DKR)	-0.00	-0.20	-1.32	-1.39	0.40	0.16
Zygoorbitale Radius	(ZOR)	-0.48	-0.74	-1.11	-1.25	0.62	0.33
Frontomalare Radius	(FMR)	0.34	-0.01	-1.55	-1.72	0.36	0.06
Ectoconchion Radius	(EKR)	0.64	0.08	-1.64	-1.98	0.72	0.47
Zygomaxill Radius	(ZMR)	-0.58	-0.88	-1.22	-1.21	0.42	0.18
MI Alveolus Radius	(AVR)	-1.28	-1.38	-1.10	-0.84	-0.16	-0.50

TABLE E-2. Continued.
Factor Scores of Measurements, 28 Populations

		Factor 4		Factor 5		Factor 6	
		Male	Female	Male	Female	Male	Female
Glab-Occip Length	(GOL)	2.11	2.34	0.97	0.03	-0.90	1.53
Nasio-Occip Length	(NOL)	2.30	2.47	0.73	-0.08	-0.26	0.93
Bas-Nasion Length	(BNL)	2.02	1.76	-0.18	-1.13	-0.18	0.04
Bas-Bregma Height	(BBH)	1.03	-0.07	-1.56	-2.13	-1.56	1.34
Max Cranial Breadth	(XCB)	0.18	0.22	0.90	-0.26	-1.20	-0.20
Max Frontal Breadth	(XFB)	0.91	1.42	1.36	0.72	-0.27	-0.57
Bistephanic Breadth	(STB)	1.26	1.24	0.73	0.24	-0.70	-0.10
Bizygomatic Breadth	(ZYB)	-1.07	-0.67	0.87	1.05	0.23	-0.80
Biauricular Breadth	(AUB)	-0.78	-0.53	0.75	1.03	0.21	-0.50
Min Cranial Breadth	(WCB)	-1.45	-1.06	1.81	2.45	-0.77	1.49
Biasterionic Breadth	(ASB)	0.17	0.43	1.95	1.48	-0.78	1.25
Bas-Prosth Length	(BPL)	-0.39	-0.34	-0.00	-0.29	-0.71	0.06
Nas Prosth Height	(NPH)	0.26	-0.33	-1.30	-0.15	1.88	-1.22
Nasal Height	(NLH)	0.39	0.18	-1.19	-0.85	1.48	-0.91
Orbit Height	(OBH)	-0.31	-0.87	-0.87	-0.41	1.90	-0.73
Orbit Breadth	(OBB)	-0.02	0.94	1.53	0.96	0.02	0.10
Bijugal Breadth	(JUB)	-1.22	-0.28	0.86	0.94	0.63	-1.50
Nasal Breadth	(NLB)	-1.89	-0.95	0.53	1.00	-0.43	-0.36
Palate Breadth	(MAB)	-1.54	-1.52	0.32	0.86	-0.44	0.78
Mastoid Height	(MDH)	0.13	-0.75	-1.26	-0.90	0.16	-0.38
Mastoid Breadth	(MDB)	-0.09	-0.40	-0.93	-1.11	-0.91	0.31
Bimaxillary Breadth	(ZMB)	-1.54	-1.27	-0.16	0.46	1.57	-1.68
Zygomaxill Subtense	(SSS)	-1.34	-1.94	-2.52	-1.59	-1.43	0.59
Bifrontal Breadth	(FMB)	-0.86	0.46	1.35	1.48	0.11	-0.39
Nasio-Front Subtense	(NAS)	0.51	0.51	-0.72	-0.16	1.23	-1.05
Biorbital Breadth	(EKB)	-0.71	0.49	1.61	1.50	0.04	-0.28
Dacryon Subtense	(DKS)	0.11	-0.18	-1.05	-0.50	1.02	-0.62
Interorbital Breadth	(DKB)	-1.02	-0.99	-0.13	0.33	0.46	-1.02
Naso-Dacryal Subtense	(NDS)	0.82	1.17	-0.46	-1.35	0.73	-1.26
Simotic Chord	(WNB)	-0.50	-0.18	-0.30	-0.75	0.59	-1.53
Simotic Subtense	(SIS)	0.04	0.45	-0.65	-1.56	-0.63	-0.54
Infer Malar Length	(IML)	-1.20	-1.20	-0.69	-0.29	1.01	-1.61
Max Malar Length	(XML)	-0.66	-1.11	-0.27	-0.06	1.46	-1.14
Malar Subtense	(MLS)	-1.19	-1.46	0.04	0.31	0.63	-0.31
Cheek Height	(WMH)	0.10	-0.37	-0.79	-0.08	1.16	-0.34
Supraorbital Projection	(SOS)	-1.35	-1.38	-0.41	0.67	-0.28	1.65
Glabella Projection	(GLS)	-1.83	-2.05	-0.24	-0.52	-4.04	3.29
Foramen Mag Length	(FOL)	-0.05	-0.08	1.20	1.41	0.32	0.61
Frontal Chord	(FRC)	0.93	0.95	-0.30	-0.44	-0.61	0.38
Frontal Subtense	(FRS)	0.94	1.00	1.66	1.35	-0.34	1.18
Nas-Subtense Fraction	(FRF)	-0.24	0.13	-0.33	0.11	0.19	-0.19
Parietal Chord	(PAC)	0.74	0.40	0.07	-0.30	-0.83	1.51
Parietal Subtense	(PAS)	-0.35	-0.99	-1.28	-0.78	-0.38	0.20
Breg-Subtense Fraction	(PAF)	0.43	-0.03	-0.20	-0.41	0.65	-0.68
Occipital Chord	(OCC)	0.57	-0.14	-1.44	-1.61	-0.80	1.36
Occipital Subtense	(OCS)	-0.07	0.02	0.49	1.09	0.32	1.77
Lam-Subtense Fraction	(OCF)	0.52	-0.52	-0.78	-0.73	-0.17	0.74
Vertex Radius	(VRR)	1.13	0.11	-2.17	-2.90	-1.85	0.92
Nasion Radius	(NAR)	1.31	1.54	0.18	-0.16	0.48	-0.52
Subspinale Radius	(SSR)	-0.19	-0.10	-0.57	-0.38	-0.24	-0.28
Prosthion Radius	(PRR)	-0.67	-0.56	-0.15	0.35	0.00	-0.36
Dacryon Radius	(DKR)	1.14	1.15	0.18	0.20	0.49	-0.30
Zygoorbitale Radius	(ZOR)	1.20	1.23	0.83	0.43	0.73	-0.27
Frontomalare Radius	(FMR)	0.57	0.58	0.29	-0.27	-0.18	0.12
Ectoconchion Radius	(EKR)	0.67	0.64	0.33	0.21	0.26	0.05
Zygomaxill Radius	(ZMR)	0.46	0.57	0.99	0.83	0.89	-0.44
Ml Alveolus Radius	(AVR)	-0.42	-0.11	0.38	0.63	0.03	-0.10

TABLE E-2. Continued.
Factor Scores of Measurements, 28 Populations

		Factor 7		Factor 8		Factor 9	
		Male	Female	Male	Female	Male	Female
Glab-Occip Length	(GOL)	-0.23	0.28	-1.37	-1.06	0.94	0.97
Nasio-Occip Length	(NOL)	-0.59	0.46	-1.63	-1.63	0.56	0.86
Bas-Nasion Length	(BNL)	-1.03	-0.74	0.31	0.03	0.05	0.28
Bas-Bregma Height	(BBH)	-0.80	-1.26	0.99	0.84	1.82	1.01
Max Cranial Breadth	(XCB)	-1.23	-1.49	0.60	0.18	-2.02	-1.95
Max Frontal Breadth	(XFB)	-1.01	-1.03	0.76	0.29	-1.10	-1.10
Bistephanic Breadth	(STB)	-0.86	-1.17	0.81	0.22	-1.70	-1.80
Bizygomatic Breadth	(ZYB)	-0.94	-0.90	0.45	1.02	1.72	1.72
Biauricular Breadth	(AUB)	-0.00	-0.14	1.68	1.79	0.61	0.90
Min Cranial Breadth	(WCB)	0.97	-0.40	-0.63	0.25	0.19	1.08
Biasterionic Breadth	(ASB)	1.09	0.30	-0.62	0.43	0.33	0.89
Bas-Prosth Length	(BPL)	-1.13	-0.95	-0.95	-1.00	-0.29	-0.01
Nas-Prosth Height	(NPH)	-0.32	1.36	-1.22	-2.11	-0.18	1.15
Nasal Height	(NLH)	-0.24	1.24	0.63	-0.51	-0.04	0.95
Orbit Height	(OBH)	-0.67	0.89	-2.20	-2.24	-0.81	0.30
Orbit Breadth	(OBB)	-1.15	-1.56	-1.06	-1.09	0.16	0.55
Bijugal Breadth	(JUB)	-1.54	-1.73	-0.01	-0.05	0.88	0.87
Nasal Breadth	(NLB)	-2.26	-2.57	1.92	-0.06	-1.23	-0.62
Palate Breadth	(MAB)	-0.28	-0.82	-1.35	-1.50	0.49	0.73
Mastoid Height	(MDH)	-0.56	0.56	-1.66	-1.43	0.11	0.25
Mastoid Breadth	(MDB)	0.27	0.28	0.36	0.13	-0.66	-1.09
Bimaxillary Breadth	(ZMB)	-0.26	-0.21	-0.83	-1.02	0.39	0.15
Zygomaxill Subtense	(SSS)	0.29	-0.37	-0.16	-1.04	-1.79	-0.92
Bifrontal Breadth	(FMB)	-1.39	-1.60	-0.20	-0.55	-0.77	-0.39
Nasio-Front Subtense	(NAS)	-0.23	0.08	0.55	-0.04	-1.07	-0.41
Biorbital Breadth	(EKB)	-1.42	-1.66	-0.62	-0.90	-0.27	0.05
Dacryon Subtense	(DKS)	0.06	0.53	-0.44	-1.01	-1.38	-0.45
Interorbital Breadth	(DKB)	-0.09	0.24	0.46	-0.08	-1.46	-1.83
Naso-Dacryal Subtense	(NDS)	-0.52	-0.43	1.05	1.21	1.17	0.58
Simotic Chord	(WNB)	-0.86	-0.20	0.66	0.29	1.08	0.10
Simotic Subtense	(SIS)	-0.33	-0.38	0.98	0.99	1.96	1.15
Infer Malar Length	(IML)	-0.02	0.44	1.18	1.57	0.68	-0.04
Max Malar Length	(XML)	0.35	0.83	0.57	1.05	1.39	-0.09
Malar Subtense	(MLS)	0.76	0.59	-0.67	0.45	0.11	-0.30
Cheek Height	(WMH)	0.76	1.25	0.48	0.26	0.58	-0.86
Supraorbital Projection	(SOS)	2.61	1.15	0.78	1.37	-0.41	-0.89
Glabella Projection	(GLS)	1.07	-1.56	-0.52	0.92	0.35	-0.20
Foramen Mag Length	(FOL)	1.18	1.03	0.57	0.42	-0.56	-0.31
Frontal Chord	(FRC)	-0.21	-0.24	0.08	-0.05	0.04	-0.90
Frontal Subtense	(FRS)	1.06	0.44	-0.27	0.63	0.50	-0.49
Nas-Subtense Fraction	(FRF)	1.03	1.10	-0.86	-0.12	-0.00	0.02
Parietal Chord	(PAC)	0.44	0.26	0.31	0.44	2.06	2.62
Parietal Subtense	(PAS)	0.85	0.74	1.56	1.77	1.46	1.60
Breg-Subtense Fraction	(PAF)	-0.43	0.61	-0.51	0.09	1.78	2.66
Occipital Chord	(OCC)	-0.49	0.01	-2.30	-2.06	-0.21	-0.51
Occipital Subtense	(OCS)	2.67	2.58	-1.58	-0.58	0.50	-0.58
Lam-Subtense Fraction	(OCF)	1.36	0.86	-1.14	-0.47	-1.52	-2.03
Vertex Radius	(VRR)	-1.06	-1.31	0.25	0.71	0.12	0.03
Nasion Radius	(NAR)	0.46	0.01	1.58	1.21	-1.04	-0.61
Subspinale Radius	(SSR)	0.14	0.13	0.60	-0.03	-0.60	-0.44
Prosthion Radius	(PRR)	-0.67	-0.09	-0.20	-0.99	-0.12	0.23
Dacryon Radius	(DKR)	0.87	0.59	0.84	0.48	-1.31	-0.86
Zygoorbitale Radius	(ZOR)	0.90	0.96	0.58	0.44	-0.41	-0.77
Frontomalare Radius	(FMR)	1.21	0.44	1.07	1.36	-0.54	-0.52
Ectoconchion Radius	(EKR)	1.57	0.99	0.87	1.03	-0.81	-1.00
Zygomaxill Radius	(ZMR)	0.79	1.30	0.46	0.92	0.54	0.21
Ml Alveolus Radius	(AVR)	0.07	0.28	-1.01	-1.17	-0.25	0.03

TABLE E-2. Continued.
Factor Scores of Measurements, 28 Populations

		Factor 10		Factor 11		Factor 12	
		Male	Female	Male	Female	Male	Female
Glab-Occip Length	(GOL)	-0.07	0.65	-1.03	-0.77	-0.35	-1.21
Nasio-Occip Length	(NOL)	-0.11	0.81	-1.22	-0.72	-0.35	-0.99
Bas-Nasion Length	(BNL)	-0.81	0.05	0.02	1.70	-0.86	-1.31
Bas-Bregma Height	(BBH)	0.19	0.63	1.24	0.39	-0.58	-0.82
Max Cranial Breadth	(XCB)	1.23	0.48	1.29	0.10	2.01	1.70
Max Frontal Breadth	(XFB)	-0.79	-0.86	0.23	-1.34	0.82	1.17
Bistephanic Breadth	(STB)	0.15	-0.71	0.74	-1.37	0.01	0.11
Bizygomatic Breadth	(ZYB)	0.16	0.60	-0.12	0.00	-1.04	-0.96
Biauricular Breadth	(AUB)	0.31	0.00	-0.09	-0.02	-0.30	-0.81
Min Cranial Breadth	(WCB)	-1.72	-0.47	0.69	0.43	0.49	2.08
Biasterionic Breadth	(ASB)	0.30	-0.23	-0.72	0.35	-0.26	0.31
Bas-Prosth Length	(BPL)	-0.27	0.20	-0.01	-0.53	-0.03	1.73
Nas-Prosth Height	(NPH)	-2.34	-1.49	-0.59	-0.70	1.10	-0.20
Nasal Height	(NLH)	-1.41	-1.99	0.02	0.06	0.65	-1.71
Orbit Height	(OBH)	0.04	0.40	1.94	2.63	-2.92	0.17
Orbit Breadth	(OBB)	0.57	0.64	2.00	0.28	0.94	0.90
Bijugal Breadth	(JUB)	0.26	1.17	-0.40	0.55	-0.78	-1.58
Nasal Breadth	(NLB)	0.06	-2.15	-2.79	0.25	0.00	-1.26
Palate Breadth	(MAB)	-1.23	-0.62	0.24	-1.00	0.32	0.37
Mastoid Height	(MDH)	0.42	-1.08	-1.67	-1.54	0.99	-1.33
Mastoid Breadth	(MDB)	2.14	0.90	-1.78	-0.39	0.04	0.57
Bimaxillary Breadth	(ZMB)	0.56	1.47	-0.67	0.44	-0.25	-0.36
Zygomaxill Subtense	(SSS)	-1.71	-1.84	0.73	1.04	0.09	0.17
Bifrontal Breadth	(FMB)	0.20	0.56	0.06	-1.37	-0.16	-0.85
Nasio-Front Subtense	(NAS)	0.51	0.77	0.30	1.03	0.16	-0.63
Biorbital Breadth	(EKB)	0.03	0.28	-0.21	-0.06	-0.03	-0.34
Dacryon Subtense	(DKS)	0.46	0.41	0.62	2.44	0.02	-0.20
Interorbital Breadth	(DKB)	-0.01	-0.47	-1.78	0.56	-1.75	-1.65
Naso-Dacryal Subtense	(NDS)	0.97	0.66	0.40	0.08	-1.11	0.48
Simotic Chord	(WNB)	-0.35	-1.27	-1.00	0.56	-0.30	0.15
Simotic Subtense	(SIS)	-1.87	-0.78	-0.80	-0.60	-0.36	0.37
Infer Malar Length	(IML)	1.31	1.16	1.77	-1.13	-0.62	0.42
Max Malar Length	(XML)	0.94	1.30	1.48	-1.73	-0.05	-1.01
Malar Subtense	(MLS)	0.39	1.68	0.73	0.15	-0.38	0.50
Cheek Height	(WMH)	2.27	1.41	-2.50	-1.78	1.09	-1.26
Supraorbital Projection	(SOS)	0.08	-0.57	0.27	-1.12	0.17	-1.72
Glabella Projection	(GLS)	0.60	0.54	0.10	1.44	-0.31	-1.09
Foramen Mag Length	(FOL)	-1.83	-0.81	0.13	1.28	-2.08	0.10
Frontal Chord	(FRC)	2.36	1.41	0.39	-0.32	-0.90	-0.51
Frontal Subtense	(FRS)	0.83	0.56	1.46	1.27	-1.49	-0.66
Nas-Subtense Fraction	(FRF)	1.71	2.51	0.57	1.70	2.01	1.42
Parietal Chord	(PAC)	-1.25	-1.06	-0.32	-0.59	1.00	0.48
Parietal Subtense	(PAS)	-0.63	-0.45	0.76	-0.19	0.74	1.04
Breg-Subtense Fraction	(PAF)	-0.75	-0.12	0.35	0.18	2.20	0.69
Occipital Chord	(OCC)	0.25	0.70	-0.31	-0.47	-0.18	0.29
Occipital Subtense	(OCS)	0.32	0.58	-1.74	-0.73	-0.89	-1.01
Lam-Subtense Fraction	(OCF)	0.21	-0.17	0.12	-0.53	0.05	0.98
Vertex Radius	(VRR)	0.34	0.78	0.29	-0.88	-1.28	0.63
Nasion Radius	(NAR)	-0.82	-1.16	-0.13	0.78	-0.26	-0.30
Subspinale Radius	(SSR)	-0.20	-0.66	0.72	-0.72	1.33	0.84
Prosthion Radius	(PRR)	-0.45	-0.39	0.50	-1.39	1.25	1.51
Dacryon Radius	(DKR)	-0.70	-1.16	-0.22	1.18	-0.27	-0.16
Zygoorbitale Radius	(ZOR)	0.38	-0.63	-0.16	-0.23	1.53	0.51
Frontomalare Radius	(FMR)	-0.84	-1.28	-0.07	0.93	-0.74	0.62
Ectoconchion Radius	(EKR)	-0.58	-1.19	-0.39	0.56	-0.35	0.46
Zygomaxill Radius	(ZMR)	0.84	0.57	0.51	0.05	1.22	1.59
MI Alveolus Radius	(AVR)	-0.67	-0.23	0.03	-0.19	0.98	1.60

Appendix F
Mahalanobis D Distances

TABLE F-1
Mahalanobis D Distances (Based on Discriminant Scores)
28 Male Groups Plus 2 Neanderthals

	Nor	Zal	Ber	Tei	Dog	Zul	Aus	Tas	Tol	Haw	Eas	Mor	Ari	SCr
Norse	—	2.9	3.9	5.5	6.9	5.9	6.4	6.6	6.7	7.0	7.3	6.5	5.7	5.3
Zalavár	2.9	—	3.3	5.7	7.1	5.4	6.1	6.0	6.1	6.7	7.0	7.0	5.4	5.0
Berg	3.9	3.3	—	7.1	7.9	6.6	7.3	6.5	7.2	7.4	7.9	7.6	5.6	5.3
Teita	5.5	5.7	7.1	—	5.4	4.5	6.6	7.3	6.2	7.7	7.1	7.9	7.3	7.0
Dogon	6.9	7.1	7.9	5.4	—	4.3	7.6	7.7	6.9	8.0	8.4	8.3	8.6	8.0
Zulu	5.9	5.4	6.6	4.5	4.3	—	6.4	6.4	5.8	7.0	7.2	7.6	7.2	6.9
Australia	6.4	6.1	7.3	6.6	7.6	6.4	—	4.7	5.1	8.4	8.5	8.1	7.5	6.4
Tasmania	6.6	6.0	6.5	7.3	7.7	6.4	4.7	—	4.1	7.0	7.2	7.2	6.5	6.1
Tolai	6.7	6.1	7.2	6.2	6.9	5.8	5.1	4.1	—	6.4	6.3	7.0	6.5	6.0
Hawaii	7.0	6.7	7.4	7.7	8.0	7.0	8.4	7.0	6.4	—	4.3	4.9	6.1	6.9
Easter I	7.3	7.0	7.9	7.1	8.4	7.2	8.5	7.2	6.3	4.3	—	5.8	7.0	7.8
Moriori	6.5	7.0	7.6	7.9	8.3	7.6	8.1	7.2	7.0	4.9	5.8	—	5.6	6.4
Arikara	5.7	5.4	5.6	7.3	8.6	7.2	7.5	6.5	6.5	6.1	7.0	5.6	—	4.7
Santa Cruz	5.3	5.0	5.3	7.0	8.0	6.9	6.4	6.1	6.0	6.9	7.8	6.4	4.7	—
Peru	5.2	4.9	5.5	6.9	7.4	6.4	7.1	6.7	5.9	6.4	7.2	6.5	4.3	4.2
N Japan	6.1	5.5	6.2	6.7	6.7	5.7	7.8	7.3	6.5	5.7	6.3	6.0	5.8	5.6
S Japan	5.9	5.4	6.3	5.8	6.4	5.3	8.2	7.7	6.6	5.7	5.8	6.4	5.7	6.0
Hainan	5.9	5.2	6.0	6.1	6.2	5.5	8.1	7.3	6.4	5.8	6.1	6.4	5.1	5.9
Atayal	6.0	5.4	5.8	6.0	6.2	5.2	7.6	6.9	6.4	6.5	6.3	7.2	5.8	5.9
Philippines	5.8	5.1	5.7	5.9	5.7	4.9	7.2	6.5	6.0	5.4	6.5	6.6	5.3	5.5
Guam	6.3	5.8	6.8	6.4	7.1	6.3	7.4	7.2	6.2	5.1	5.6	6.5	5.8	6.2
Egypt	3.4	3.7	5.4	5.3	5.8	5.3	6.6	6.8	6.6	7.0	7.4	6.8	6.6	6.1
Bushman	6.8	6.5	7.0	5.7	6.8	5.7	7.6	7.7	7.9	9.2	9.1	9.6	8.7	7.7
Andaman Is	6.3	6.0	6.7	6.0	5.7	5.7	7.5	6.9	6.6	6.9	7.6	7.3	6.5	5.9
Ainu	5.1	4.9	5.9	6.4	6.4	5.6	6.6	6.7	6.5	6.3	6.5	6.2	6.6	6.2
Buriat	7.3	7.1	6.5	8.5	9.4	8.9	9.9	9.4	9.1	7.9	9.0	8.5	6.5	7.5
Eskimo	7.0	6.7	7.9	6.9	9.2	8.0	7.8	8.6	7.1	7.5	7.4	7.9	7.1	7.1
Anyang	6.5	6.0	7.0	6.4	6.7	6.0	8.5	7.7	6.8	5.6	5.7	6.3	5.8	6.6
Neanderthal	17.1	16.8	16.6	17.9	18.1	17.1	16.6	15.7	16.9	17.6	17.5	16.6	16.2	16.1

TABLE F-1. Continued.
Mahalanobis D Distances (Based on Discriminant Scores)
28 Male Groups Plus 2 Neanderthals

	Per	NJa	SJa	Hai	Ata	Phi	Gua	Egy	Bus	And	Ain	Bur	Esk	Any	Nea
Norse	5.2	6.1	5.9	5.9	6.0	5.8	6.3	3.4	6.8	6.3	5.1	7.3	7.0	6.5	17.1
Zalavár	4.9	5.5	5.4	5.2	5.4	5.1	5.8	3.7	6.5	6.0	4.9	7.1	6.7	6.0	16.8
Berg	5.5	6.2	6.3	6.0	5.8	5.7	6.8	5.4	7.0	6.7	5.9	6.5	7.9	7.0	16.6
Teita	6.9	6.7	5.8	6.1	6.0	5.9	6.4	5.3	5.7	6.0	6.4	8.5	6.9	6.4	17.9
Dogon	7.4	6.7	6.4	6.2	6.2	5.7	7.1	5.8	6.8	5.7	6.4	9.4	9.2	6.7	18.1
Zulu	6.4	5.7	5.3	5.5	5.2	4.9	6.3	5.3	5.7	5.7	5.6	8.9	8.0	6.0	17.1
Australia	7.1	7.8	8.2	8.1	7.6	7.2	7.4	6.6	7.6	7.5	6.6	9.9	7.8	8.5	16.6
Tasmania	6.7	7.3	7.7	7.3	6.9	6.5	7.2	6.8	7.7	6.9	6.7	9.4	8.6	7.7	15.7
Tolai	5.9	6.5	6.6	6.4	6.4	6.0	6.2	6.6	7.9	6.6	6.5	9.1	7.1	6.8	16.9
Hawaii	6.4	5.7	5.7	5.8	6.5	5.4	5.1	7.0	9.2	6.9	6.3	7.9	7.5	5.6	17.6
Easter I	7.2	6.3	5.8	6.1	6.3	6.5	5.6	7.4	9.1	7.6	6.5	9.0	7.4	5.7	17.5
Moriori	6.5	6.0	6.4	6.4	7.2	6.6	6.5	6.8	9.6	7.3	6.2	8.5	7.9	6.3	16.6
Arikara	4.3	5.8	5.7	5.1	5.8	5.3	5.8	6.6	8.7	6.5	6.6	6.5	7.1	5.8	16.2
Santa Cruz	4.2	5.6	6.0	5.9	5.9	5.5	6.2	6.1	7.7	5.9	6.2	7.5	7.1	6.6	16.1
Peru	–	5.4	5.4	4.8	5.1	5.1	6.0	5.8	8.0	5.7	6.3	7.4	7.4	5.6	17.3
N Japan	5.4	–	2.6	3.5	4.0	4.0	5.0	6.1	7.3	6.1	4.9	6.5	6.6	3.7	16.6
S Japan	5.4	2.6	–	2.9	3.6	3.6	4.5	5.8	7.0	5.6	5.1	6.8	6.3	3.1	17.6
Hainan	4.8	3.5	2.9	–	3.2	2.7	4.4	5.9	7.2	5.1	5.3	6.6	7.1	2.4	17.4
Atayal	5.1	4.0	3.6	3.2	–	3.6	5.2	6.2	6.5	5.3	5.4	7.5	7.2	3.8	17.7
Philippines	5.1	4.0	3.6	2.7	3.6	–	4.5	5.5	6.6	4.7	5.4	6.9	7.7	3.6	17.4
Guam	6.0	5.0	4.5	4.4	5.2	4.5	–	6.5	8.3	6.6	5.6	7.0	6.3	4.5	17.4
Egypt	5.8	6.1	5.8	5.9	6.2	5.5	6.5	–	7.1	5.4	5.3	8.6	7.6	6.6	17.4
Bushman	8.0	7.3	7.0	7.2	6.5	6.6	8.3	7.1	–	6.8	7.4	8.8	8.7	7.3	17.6
Andaman Is	5.7	6.1	5.6	5.1	5.3	4.7	6.6	5.4	6.8	–	6.6	9.0	8.5	6.0	18.2
Ainu	6.3	4.9	5.1	5.3	5.4	5.4	5.6	5.3	7.4	6.6	–	7.8	6.9	5.4	16.6
Buriat	7.4	6.5	6.8	6.6	7.5	6.9	7.0	8.6	8.8	9.0	7.8	–	7.4	6.9	17.4
Eskimo	7.4	6.6	6.3	7.1	7.2	7.7	6.3	7.6	8.7	8.5	6.9	7.4	–	7.0	18.6
Anyang	5.6	3.7	3.1	2.4	3.8	3.6	4.5	6.6	7.3	6.0	5.4	6.9	7.0	–	17.7
Neanderthal	17.3	16.6	17.6	17.4	17.7	17.4	17.4	17.4	17.6	18.2	16.6	17.4	18.6	17.7	–